EMPRYNTED
in thys manere:

EARLY PRINTED TREASURES FROM
CAMBRIDGE UNIVERSITY LIBRARY

The Crucifixion from *Horae ad usum Romanum* [French and Latin] (Paris: Pierre Le Rouge, for Vincent Commin, 9 May 1491); Inc.5.D.1.19[2530].

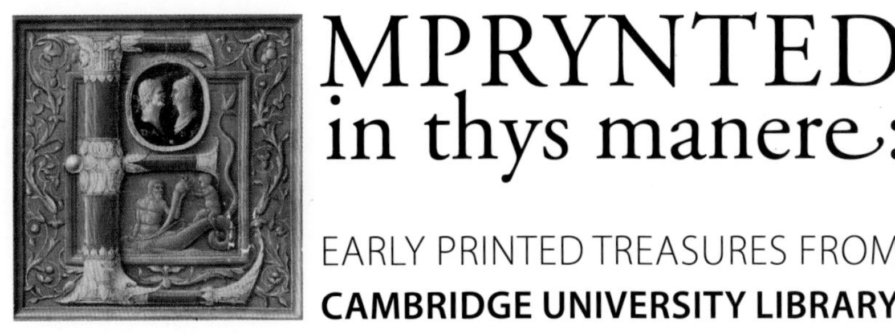

IMPRYNTED in thys manere:

EARLY PRINTED TREASURES FROM CAMBRIDGE UNIVERSITY LIBRARY

Edited by Ed Potten and Emily Dourish

MMXIV

Ipse dixit et fa
sūt ipse mādauit
creata sūt
Ps 32.

The hand-coloured woodcut of God the Father, from Hartmann Schedel (1440–1514) *Liber chronicarum* (Nuremberg: Anton Koberger, for Sebald Schreyer and Sebastian Kammermeister, 12 July 1493); Inc.0.A.7.2[888].

Acknowledgements:

The editors wish gratefully to acknowledge the following for permission to reproduce images from their collections: the British Library, the John Rylands Library (University of Manchester), Biblioteca Nazionale Marciana and Country Life. In addition, our thanks to staff in Cambridge University Library's Conservation Department and Digital Content Unit, to Andy Harvey and Binney Hare at H2 Associates and to Laura Nuvoloni, William Hale and Liam Sims in the Department of Rare Books.

The publication of this book was generously supported by Bernard Quaritch Ltd.

Bernard Quaritch Ltd

Rare books & manuscripts since 1847

ISBN: 978-0-902205-71-0 Paperback
ISBN: 978-0-902205-70-3 Hardback

Bibliographical details: for the sake of clarity and consistency across catalogue entries the editors have in almost all cases standardized authors' names, but have taken titles, uniform titles and imprint details directly from the Incunabula Short-Title Catalogue (www.istc.bl.uk). The use of square brackets in imprints indicates information not contained within the printed book, but which has been assigned through comparison with other early printed books or obtained from external historical evidence.

The front cover features details from:

János Thuróczy (born about 1435) *Chronica Hungarorum* [Latin] (Augsburg: Erhard Ratdolt, for Theobaldus Feger, 3 June 1488); Inc.5.A.6.18[829].

Hartmann Schedel (1440–1514) *Liber chronicarum* (Nuremberg: Anton Koberger, for Sebald Schreyer and Sebastian Kammermeister, 12 July 1493); Inc.0.A.7.2[888].

Hortus sanitatis (Mainz: Jacob Meydenbach, 23 June 1491); Inc.3.A.1.8[37].

Horae ad usum Romanum [French and Latin] (Paris: Pierre Le Rouge, for Vincent Commin, 9 May 1491); Inc.5.D.1.19[2530].

The illuminated initial "E" used on the titlepage is taken from Pliny the Elder *Historia naturalis* [Italian] (Venice: Nicolaus Jenson, 1476); Inc.1.B.3.2[1360].

Contributors

Professor Lilian Armstrong	Wellesley College
Sir David Attenborough	
Nicolas Barker	
Professor Richard Beadle	University of Cambridge
Professor Mary Beard	University of Cambridge
Sir Quentin Blake	
Professor Sir Leszek Borysiewicz	University of Cambridge
Dr Abigail Brundin	University of Cambridge
Dr Rodrigo Cacho	University of Cambridge
Professor James Carley	University of Kent
Sebastian Carter	
Dr Helen Castor	University of Cambridge
Dr Matthew Champion	St Catharine's College, Cambridge
Dr Alan Coates	Bodleian Libraries
Professor Helen Cooper	University of Cambridge
Dr Alexandra da Costa	University of Cambridge
Dr Martin Davies	
Dr Christopher de Hamel	Corpus Christi College, Cambridge
Dr Cristina Dondi	University of Oxford
Dr Emily Dourish	Cambridge University Library
Carol Ann Duffy	Poet Laureate
Professor Eamon Duffy	University of Cambridge
Dr Falk Eisermann	Staatsbibliothek zu Berlin
Professor Richard Field	Yale University
Margaret Lane Ford	Christie's
Professor Mirjam Foot	University College London
Bamber Gascoigne	
Roger Gaskell	Roger Gaskell Rare Books
John Goldfinch	Eton College
Professor Anthony Grafton	Princeton University
William Hale	Cambridge University Library
Robert Harding	Maggs Bros. Ltd.
Dr Lotte Hellinga	
Anne Jarvis	Cambridge University Library
Dr Kristian Jensen	British Library
Dr Peter Jones	King's College, Cambridge
Dr Sachiko Kusukawa	Trinity College, Cambridge
Professor David McKitterick	Trinity College, Cambridge
Dr Piers D. Mitchell	University of Cambridge
Professor Nigel Morgan	University of Cambridge
Paul Needham	Princeton University
Dottoressa Laura Nuvoloni	Cambridge University Library
Professor Christopher Page	University of Cambridge
Professor Nigel Palmer	University of Oxford
Dr Stella Panayotova	Fitzwilliam Museum
David Pearson	City of London Corporation
Professor Nicholas Pickwoad	University of the Arts London
Nicholas Poole-Wilson	Bernard Quaritch Ltd.
Ed Potten	Cambridge University Library
Mark Purcell	The National Trust
Professor Michael Reeve	University of Cambridge
Professor Miri Rubin	Queen Mary, University of London
Dr Ulinka Rublack	University of Cambridge
Dr Jason Scott-Warren	University of Cambridge
Professor William Sherman	University of York
Julianne Simpson	The John Rylands Library
Professor Toshiyuki Takamiya	Keio University
Dr Satoko Tokunaga	Keio University
Dr Bettina Wagner	Bayerische Staatsbibliothek
Professor Alexandra Walsham	University of Cambridge
Dr Jill Whitelock	Cambridge University Library

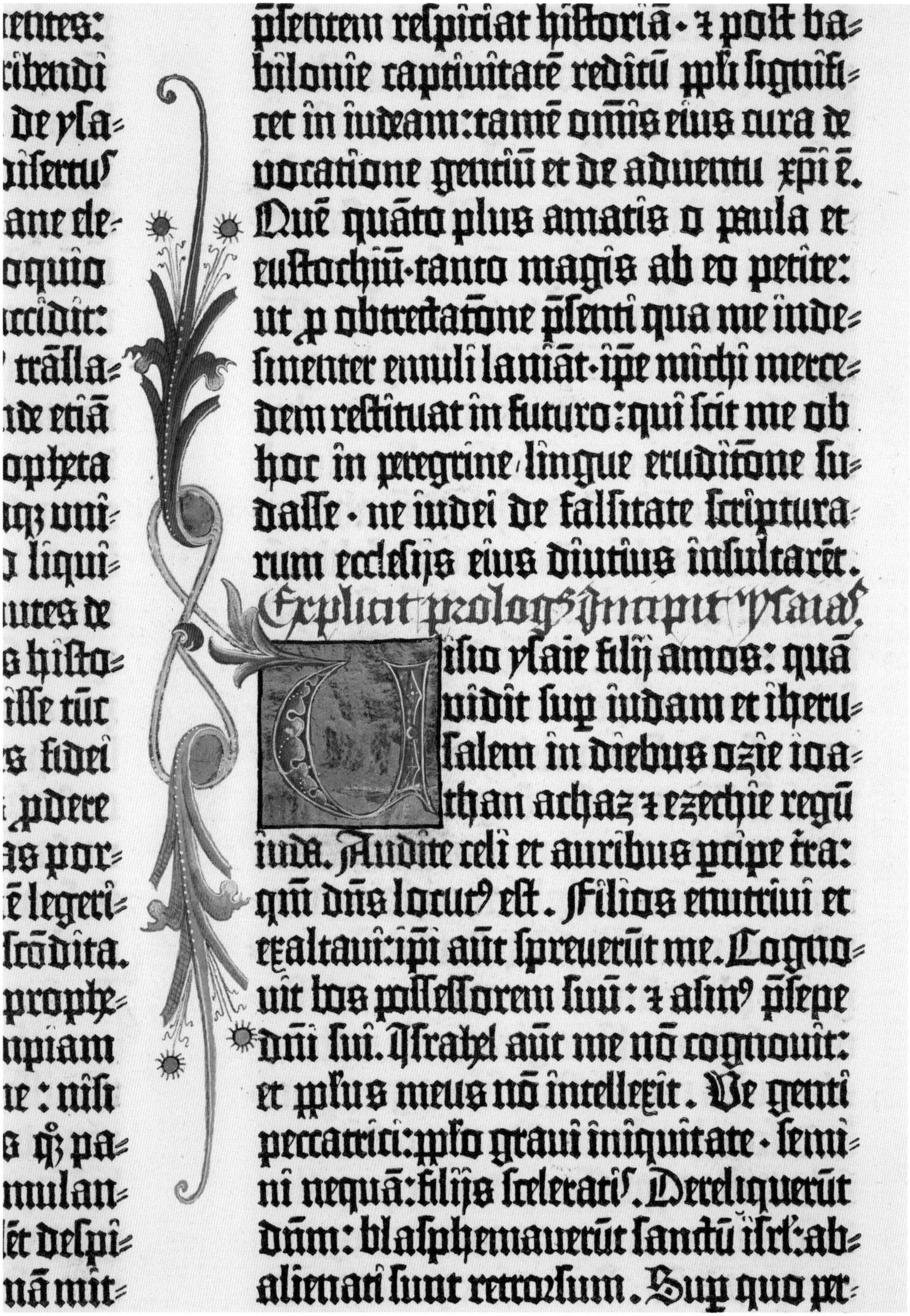

cetites:
cribendi
de ysa-
diserius
ane ele-
oquio
accidit:
trāsla-
de etiā
propheta
iuz uni-
liqui-
itures de
s histo-
ille tūc
s fidei
pdere
s por-
ē legeri-
scōdita.
prophe-
mpiam
ne: nisi
s q̄ pa-
mulan-
ēt despi-
nā mit-

p̄sentem respiciat historiā · ⁊ post ba-
bilonie captiuitatē reditū p̄p̄li signifi-
cet in iudeam: tamē oīs eius cura de
vocatione gentiū et de aduentu xp̄i ē.
Que quāto plus amatis o paula et
eustochiū · tanto magis ab eo petite:
ut p obtrectatione p̄senti qua me inde-
sinenter emuli laniāt · ipe michi merce-
dem restituat in futuro: qui scit me ob
hoc in peregrine lingue eruditōne su-
dasse · ne iudei de falsitate scriptura-
rum ecclesijs eius diutius insultarēt.
Explicit prologus Incipit ysaias.
Visio ysaie filij amos: quā
vidit sup iudam et iheru-
salem in diebus ozie ioa-
than achaz ⁊ ezechie regū
iuda. Audite celi et auribus pcipe tra:
quī dn̄s locutus est. Filios enutriui et
exaltaui: ipi aūt spreuerūt me. Cognouit bos possessorem suū: ⁊ asinus p̄sepe
dn̄i sui. Israhel aūt me nō cognouit:
et p̄p̄lus meus nō intellexit. Ve genti
peccatrici: p̄p̄lo graui iniquitate · semi-
ni nequā: filijs sceleratis. Dereliquerūt
dn̄m: blasphemauerūt sanctū isrl̄: ab-
alienati sunt retrorsum. Sup quo per-

1

Introduction

Over the past twenty-five years the study of incunabula – books printed between the invention of the printing press and the end of the fifteenth century – has been reinvigorated. Traditional study had at its heart enumerative bibliography; researchers endeavoured to chart the output of every press in Europe and thereby demonstrate a linear progression from Mainz in the 1450s to the end of the century, describing en route the development of printing in individual towns and cities. The modern incunabulist adopts a different approach. Research has shifted from the typographic to the copy specific, and researchers are now keenly interested in the material book – the individual history of individual copies. Today readers requesting incunabula at Cambridge University Library are as likely to be studying a book's binding, its provenance, annotation or decoration as its text. This increase in research activity has been matched by a growing public fascination with the birth of printing and the earliest outputs of western presses.

Recognising this changing research agenda, in 2009 Cambridge University Library successfully applied to the Andrew W. Mellon Foundation for funding for a five-year project to re-catalogue its world-class collection of fifteenth-century books. Its aim was two-fold: to produce detailed, on-line descriptions of all of the Library's incunabula, and to focus attention on those features which match current research interests. The Library was fortunate in securing the services of Dottoressa Laura Nuvoloni as Research Associate. She has treated each book in the collection as a miniature bibliographical project and her painstaking research has unearthed a treasure trove of previously unknown and unrecorded detail. Much of Dott. Nuvoloni's work underpins the sixty essays which make up this book.

The first substantive printed book which survives from the fifteenth century is the Latin Bible printed around 1455 in Mainz by Johann Gutenberg (**Figure 1** and see also pp. 2–5). We know, however, that printing took place earlier; a fragment of a *Sibyllenbuch*, for example, has been dated to 1452–1453 and a series of indulgences printed in Gutenberg's type is dated 1454 and 1455. The debate still rages over the precise dating of a series of printed fragments of the *Ars minor*, a Latin grammar by Aelius Donatus, but some fragments certainly predate the printing of the Bible (see pp. 12–13). Although Gutenberg's name does not appear on any extant contemporary printed document or book, all of these documents share typographic characteristics linking them to Mainz and to Gutenberg's printing house and identify him as the instigator of printing.

1. The illuminated initial 'V' from the opening of the Book of Isaiah in *Biblia latina* ([Mainz: Johann Gutenberg and Johann Fust, about 1455]); Inc.1.A.1.1[3761].

2. *Danse macabre* ([Lyons: Mathias Huss], 18 February 1499 [/1500?]). © The British Library Board IB.41735 G.1.

2

3

4

5

The nature of Gutenberg's innovation is more complex than it initially appears. Central to it was the printing press, although this was more of an adaptation than an invention; oil and wine presses had existed for centuries and the basic technology was well-established. We know relatively little about the printing press used by Gutenberg, and what we do know is inferred solely from its surviving output. Lotte Hellinga has suggested that the first presses were fixed, like those used for oil and wine, but by the date of the first extant image the technology had advanced considerably (**Figure 2**). This woodcut from a *danse macabre* printed in Lyons in 1499 shows skeletal figures summoning printing house workers to the grave. It gives the best idea of both the mechanics of the press and the nature of the printing house at the end of the incunable period. By this time the press consisted in essence of two moveable parts. The first was designed to hold the inked type and paper in place, and to carry both of these in and out of the press. The second pressed the paper down onto the inked type. Both processes are clearly visible in the 1499 woodcut. The carriage can be seen half in, half out of the press, and the pressman's arm has been pulled from the handle or bar which will work the spindle, pressing the heavy flat hardwood plate, or *platen*, down onto the inked type and paper to take an impression. The whole press has been braced to the ceiling; without bracing the constant and vigorous activity of the pressmen could cause the press to jump and move across the floor.

Equally critical to the development of the press was Gutenberg's invention of separately cast metal letters – *moveable type*. Prior to this, printing from wood blocks had been practised for many years in the west to produce single-sheet devotional images and patterns on fabrics. The production of 'block books', where text and images were carved together into a single wood block from which impressions were taken, developed in parallel to printing with moveable type (**Figure 3**). The earliest known block book is dated 1450–1452 and they continued to be produced throughout the fifteenth century (see pp. 62–65). Although wood blocks could be used to reproduce multiple copies of the same text they had several drawbacks: they damaged easily, wore down rapidly and could only be used to reproduce one combination of text and images.

Arguably, the invention of moveable type was the most significant innovation of the fifteenth century. A piece of printing type is essentially a three-dimensional representation of a letter form, reversed and cast in metal on a stem of a standard size (**Figure 4**). The production of multiple copies of each letter of the alphabet in upper and lower case with an attendant set of numbers, punctuation and symbols allowed printers to build up words, then lines, then pages set in type, pages which could be inked and used to print multiple identical copies. Crucially, these type-set pages could then be washed

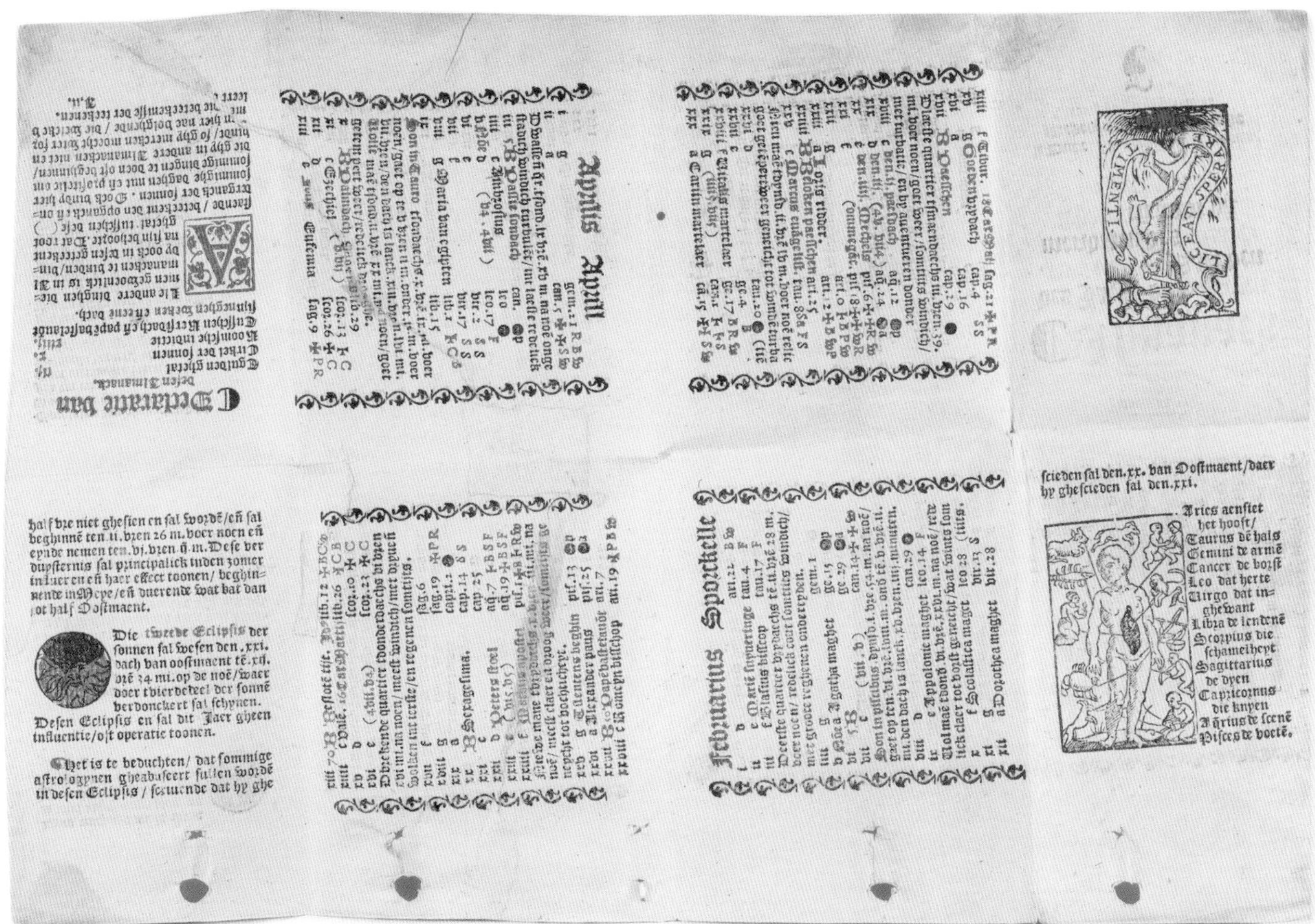

6

3. The fifteenth-century woodblock from which the second leaf of an edition of the block-book *Apocalypsis S. Johannis* was printed. © The University of Manchester 17252.

4. Examples of William Morris's Troy type, cast in the late-nineteenth century based on fifteenth-century gothic precursors (see pp. 32–33).

5. Modern examples of a punch, a matrix, and a mould, from the University Library's Historical Printing collection.

6. An incorrectly imposed sixteenth-century almanac. Sel.7.10.

of ink, broken up and redistributed, the individual pieces of type then being used to make other words, lines and pages. As with the printing press, Gutenberg's input into the development of moveable type is shrouded in uncertainty. By the 1470s type was produced in a standard manner. A relief pattern of each letter was cut by hand on the end of a piece of steel, called a punch. The engraving of the punch was a highly-skilled task, usually undertaken by a trained die-sinker or goldsmith, and required considerable artistic input. The punch was then hammered into a small block of copper called a *matrix*. In turn the matrix was locked into a mould, a steel box which slotted together to form a central chamber, clad in wood to protect the workman's hands from the hot steel. The type founder would hold the mould in his left hand and pour a liquid alloy of lead, antimony and tin (hard wearing when set, yet with a low melting point) into the mould, simultaneously shaking it to let the molten metal settle. The mould was then opened and a piece of type was removed; a good type-founder could produce a piece of type every 12 seconds (**Figure 5**).

Using a master copy of the text being printed, or the *exemplar*, teams of men called compositors would select letters and spaces from a carefully arranged type case to build up words and lines in a composing stick. When the stick was full, these lines were transferred to a flat tray called a *galley*, where they were built up into pages. The compositor at work can be clearly seen in the 1499 *Danse macabre*, his exemplar and type cases before him, his composing stick in his left hand. Although Gutenberg may have printed the Latin Bible one page at a time, it rapidly became common practice to print multiple pages simultaneously. Depending on the number of pages to be printed per sheet, the compositors placed the type-set pages into a specific order and orientation, then locked them into an iron frame with wooden wedges to create a *forme*. The orientation of the pages was critical. Each piece of paper would have two formes, one to print each side. If the imposition of the individual pages was incorrect, the wrong pages might back onto each other, or pages might appear upside-down. Although compositors were extremely skilled, mistakes were frequently made – **figure 6** shows a sheet from an early sixteenth-century almanac, discarded as waste paper because it was incorrectly imposed. These errors in imposition were discovered at the time of folding. The individual sheets would be folded in a particular way to form small booklets, *quires* or *gatherings*, and each quire was usually identified with a running letter. These letters, known as *signatures*, made the accurate arrangement of multiple quires into a whole book much simpler.

M. ANTONII COCC
AB VRBE CONDITA
ERS
ris r
orſu
ſe a
tas
mag
dire
quo
rint
cti :
xi : qui lucubrationis huius

7

Unlike the printing of text, where Gutenberg's 42-line Bible can be regarded as a near perfect specimen of the printer's craft, the printing of pictures in books only developed in fits and starts in the second decade after the invention of printing. Early printers experimented with printing rubrics and decorative initial letters, then went back to the manuscript tradition of supplying them by hand after the text was printed. Some of the earliest illustrated technical books have hand-drawn rather than printed illustrations and even as late as 1482 a Venetian edition of the Bible printed by Franz Renner has spaces left for hand-drawn illustrations in the commentary. In Germany printing of illustrations developed rapidly, beginning in 1461 with a beautiful fable book, *Der Edelstein*, printed in Bamberg by Albrecht Pfister. Illustrations were primarily printed using woodcuts or occasionally metal cuts, relief blocks cut on metal rather than wood, but printed in the same way: together with the text of the book. Illustration rapidly reached a high degree of sophistication and versatility; comparing the woodcuts of the *Nuremberg Chronicle* of 1493 (see pp. 136–139) and the *Hypnerotomachia Poliphili* printed by Aldus Manutius in Venice in 1499 (see pp. 164–167) demonstrates the huge range of pictorial effects that were being achieved by fifteenth-century block cutters at the end of the century. A few printers experimented with the use of engraved plates, but these represent only a tiny fraction of surviving illustrations. Among these rarities are the engraved volvelles, printed scientific instruments, in Beham's *Buch von der Astronomie*, Cologne, 1476 (see pp. 52–53), the first known use of engraving in a scientific printed book, and the monumental Florentine Dante of 1481, with engravings after drawings by Botticelli (see pp. 88–89).

8

9

7. An initial decorated by the Pico Master, from Sabellico (1436?–1506) *Decades rerum Venetarum* (Venice: Andreas Torresanus, de Asula, 21 May 1487); SSS.2.3.

8. Thomas Rotherham's inscription, from Vincent of Beauvais (died 1264) *Speculum naturale* ([Strassburg: The R-Printer (Adolf Rusch), not after 15 June 1476]); Inc.0.A.2.2[81.1–2]).

9. The Mongol invasion of Hungary in 1241, from János Thuróczy (born about 1435) *Chronica Hungarorum* [Latin] (Augsburg: Erhard Ratdolt, for Theobaldus Feger, 3 June 1488); Inc.5.A.6.18[829], from the Holdsworth bequest.

Today we understand authors, publishers, printers and book sellers as distinct trades, but in the incunable period these distinctions were much less clear. Many printers were also book binders or book sellers, and the fifteenth-century printing house sometimes incorporated a variety of different yet related trades. A printing house might employ a *rubricator*, a scribe employed to insert simple hand-fashioned letters or other features into spaces left on the printed sheets, or an *illuminator*, an artist employed to add more lavish decorative letters and designs. Books were often bound in the printing house and, as in the 1499 *Danse macabre*, the printing house could also function as book shop, selling books produced by the press and importing books from elsewhere for sale.

In order to compete with the existing thriving manuscript market, printers had to create books that met the expectations of patrons accustomed to books tailored to their taste and pocket. Consequently, many early printed books were decorated by hand in the same style by the same artists as their manuscript counterparts. Richly gilded and highly coloured initials and borders were added by hand into spaces left deliberately blank by printers (**Figure 7** and see also pp. 102–105). The hand-colouring of some types of book was an essential part of their marketing. In Paris in the 1480s a number of printers began to produce

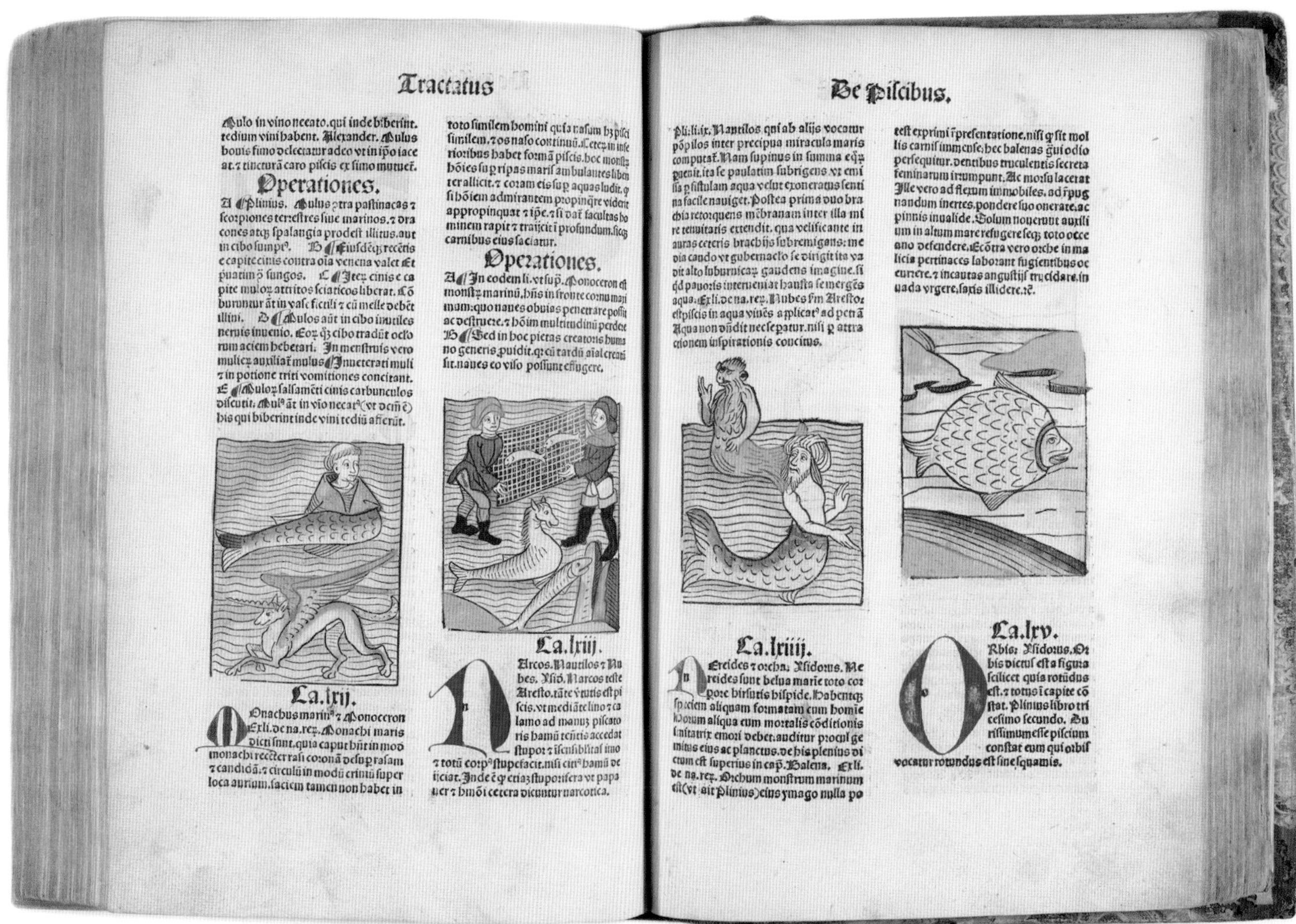

10

luxury printed Books of Hours, entering a market still dominated by manuscript. The wood and metal cuts within these printed hours were often lavishly hand coloured, mirroring and competing with those produced by specialist manuscript illuminators (see pp. 118–121). Some early books were decorated in the printing house, with different copies sharing characteristic decorative features (see pp. 8–11). The majority of books, however, were rubricated and decorated individually, some close to the place of printing, others in distant towns and countries. Some were decorated by book sellers to increase their saleability, others undertaken in-house at religious institutions or as bespoke commissions from favoured artists for private owners. On a more rudimentary level, everyday owners of books also often added their own colour to printed images, enhancing and decorating a treasured possession.

In the same way that buyers of books in this period were offered a number of decorative options, they were also offered a variety of states and types of book binding. They could buy a text unbound as loose sheets to be bespoke bound elsewhere, or they could buy a book folded and sewn, but otherwise uncovered (see pp. 42–43). Alternatively, they could buy books sewn and bound in a simple paper binding, in sheep, pig or calfskin, simply blind-tooled, or later more elaborately decorated with gold tooling. Binding took place in a variety of locations and contexts. Printers bound their own books, along with books imported from elsewhere, and individual owners developed relationships with specific binders. Monasteries frequently bound their own books, or had them bound by a local binder in uniform style (see pp. 46–47). In university towns, binders produced cheaper bindings marketed for students and academics (see pp. 84–87). The dramatic increase in demand for bound books stimulated by the printing press led to major changes in binding practice. New decorative techniques speeded up and lowered the cost of binding books: the roll, an engraved wheel, could impress a border with a repeating pattern rapidly, and the panel, a cast metal plate, could impress a large decoration directly onto leather.

The early book trade thus soon developed the means to tailor the product to the potential buyer. Once the books were in the hands of owners, further opportunities for personalization arose. Early printed books that we now regard as precious artefacts from a distant past were everyday objects to their contemporary readers. The daily use of practical books for study, leisure or devotion has led to low survival rates for what were once popular texts (see pp. 74–75). Scholars and literati used the ample blank margins of classical texts to record their comments and to highlight significant passages (see pp. 18–21).

10. Beasts of the sea, from *Hortus sanitatis* (Mainz: Jacob Meydenbach, 23 June 1491); Inc.3.A.1.8[37], from the collection of Bishop John Moore.

11. The Last Supper from *Horae* [Dutch] (Gouda: Collacie Broeders, 3 October 1496); Inc.5.E.3.10[2890], purchased by Henry Bradshaw at the sale of the library of the Enschedé family.

11

University students often added a lecturer's commentary, or translated and paraphrased difficult Latin and Greek passages. Later donated or bequeathed to colleagues and friends, these books remain one of the primary sources of the transmission of Renaissance knowledge (see pp. 14–17). The readers of romances, poems and encyclopaedic compilations often added classical quotations, verse, music, domestic accounts and medical recipes to the margins of their books (see pp. 160–161). Missals, Breviaries and Books of Hours suffered abuse during the Reformation as forbidden prayers and images of controversial saints were obliterated.

The precise output of the printing press in its earliest years is difficult to assess because much has been lost. Single-sheet publications in particular are rare, due to their fragile nature and the ways in which they were used; calendars, public notices and medical charts were pinned to walls and frequently consulted (see pp. 6–7 and 144–145), whilst indulgences were personal and time-limited. Single-sheet printed devotional images were pasted to walls, glued to wooden panels, inside boxes or to pieces of furniture and, consequently, only a handful of the thousands of impressions produced have survived. The practice of pasting these images into books, both printed and manuscript, to act as devotional aids and stimuli has ensured some endure. These prints offer us a unique insight into the contemporary use of devotional images and the complex interplay between manuscript and print (see pp. 70–71 and 148–149). Elsewhere, where single sheets have survived it is generally due to later repurposing; paper and parchment were expensive commodities, and printed sheets were recycled once their initial usefulness had passed. Bookbinders used waste of all types to line the spines and boards of books (see pp. 100–101).

Cambridge University Library possesses one of the world's most significant collections of incunabula, some acquired on or soon after publication. Amongst the Library's earliest benefactions is the 1475 gift of Thomas Rotherham (1423–1500), Archbishop of York and Chancellor of England, which included both manuscripts and incunabula (**Figure 8**). The collection today numbers 4650, and continues to grow; more than a dozen incunabula have been added over the lifetime of the Mellon-funded project. Its particular strengths are books printed in England, Italy and the Low Countries. In keeping with many institutional collections heavily supplemented in the late nineteenth and early twentieth centuries, the Library's collecting policy at that time was to attempt to represent as far as possible in its collections the spread of printing across Europe, with examples of the work of as many printers as could be located and afforded. The definitive history of the incunabula collections at Cambridge University Library has already been written and published as the introduction to J.C.T. Oates's monumental printed catalogue of the collection as it stood in 1954, but particular mention should be made here of the activities of some of its most notable benefactors.

After Rotherham, the next significant gift of incunabula arrived in the mid-seventeenth century, when the remarkable library of Richard Holdsworth (1590–1649), Master of Emmanuel College, was bequeathed to the University. His collection of some 10,000 books included more than 200 incunabula (**Figure 9**), including the first fifteenth-century English imprints to enter the Library's collections. In 1667 Tobias Rustat (1608–1694), Yeoman of the Robes to Charles II, gave the kind of benefaction every librarian dreams of: an investment in lands of £1000, bringing income to be used 'in buying the choicest and most usefull Bookes for the Publique Library'. Over the 320 years since Rustat's death some 600 incunabula have been purchased through his benefaction, making him in terms of numbers the single most significant donor.

The largest gift of incunabula to come as part of a single collection was the 465 received in 1715 with the collection of Bishop John Moore of Ely (1646–1714). Given to the University by George I, this collection totalled over 30,000 volumes and at a stroke trebled the size of the Library (**Figure 10**). Moore's books can be identified amongst the main collection by their bookplate, designed by John Pine and produced in numerous sizes to suit the variety of formats within the collection. Moore's own marks can also be found in some of the books, and his interests covered not only the expected theology and classics, but also significant numbers of early English imprints, including the *Book of St Albans* (see pp. 96–99), poems by John Lydgate (see pp. 50–51), and the unique extant copy of Chaucer's *Queen Anelida and the false Arcite*.

In terms of sheer numbers the next most significant donor is one often overlooked. Over a number of decades in the first half of the twentieth century, but chiefly in 1934, the year of the opening of the current Library building, Stephen Gaselee (1882–1943) gave a total of 318 incunabula. As Oates noted, "only a monarch gave more". His primary interest was in collecting imprints from the smaller printing towns in Spain, Italy and Germany, many of his books being selected to fill bibliographical gaps, rather than as objects of beauty. Consequently, his remarkable donation is too often overshadowed by the glories of other benefactions.

Samuel Sandars (1837–1894) donated more classically beautiful books. He, like Gaselee, deliberately purchased books the Library did not already possess, but his areas of interest – liturgical books, fine bindings, works printed on vellum – mean that his books were significantly more glamorous. Consequently, while numbering only around 100, Sandars's printed books are represented disproportionally within the present catalogue.

After Moore's remarkable collection, the other transformative benefaction was the donation in 1933 by barrister Arthur Young of Trinity College (1852–1936). A modest man who collected discreetly, his gift and bequest nevertheless included books which, to quote Oates, "the Library had long ago given up all hope of possessing", including the Gutenberg Bible, Caxton's first edition of the *Golden Legend*, and fine copies of both the Foligno and Mantua editions of the *Divina Commedia* (see pp. 34–37). While the gift included only 27 incunabula, Young's interest in collecting early English Bibles and early biblical translations means the collection is of immense importance, and was described by the chairman of the Library Syndicate in 1934 as "probably the most valuable benefaction that has been received from any private individual in the long course of our Library's history".

Finally, the activities of members of Library staff in the development of the fifteenth-century collections cannot be overlooked. The work of nineteenth-century Librarian Henry Bradshaw (1831–1886) was fundamental to the creation of a schema by which to arrange the books, a schema which is now followed by most other libraries. He organised his *Museum typographicum* by country, then city, then printer, following the chronological spread of printing from Germany outwards across Europe. Regrettably this necessitated the division of numerous volumes containing disparate works into their constituent parts, so that they might be placed correctly according to location and printer, but subsequent librarians have been able to trace the majority of these divisions, enabling their provenances to be reconstructed. Bradshaw was responsible for the purchase of some 600 incunabula for the Library, primarily from continental sales (**Figure 11**), including 90 from the great Culemann sale of 1870, amongst them the *Licht der Seelen*, (see pp. 92–93) and the fragments of *Reynard the Fox* (see pp. 100–101). Bradshaw was a pioneering bibliographer and his influence on his own and later generations was immense and (see pp. 152–153).

Amongst incunabulists, the work of J.C.T. Oates (1912–1990) is widely recognised. *A catalogue of the fifteenth-century printed books in the University Library, Cambridge* (Cambridge, 1954) remained unsurpassed for over 60 years and was the only way to access the Library's holdings of these remarkable books until the present project began. Oates's catalogue follows the arrangement begun by Bradshaw, and the copy held in the University Library's Rare Books Reading Room is interleaved with the addition of nearly 300 incunabula acquired since its publication. Oates's reference numbers remain one of the standard identifiers for incunabula, and consequently are included in the concordance to this book (see pp. 175–176).

Thanks to the generosity of the Andrew W. Mellon Foundation, Cambridge University Library's incunabula collections now have an electronic catalogue fit for the twenty-first century. This publication celebrates the conclusion of that catalogue and reflects our enduring fascination with the earliest fruits of the printing press in western Europe.

Ed Potten and Emily Dourish
Editors
September 2014

CATALOGUE

PICTURED:

1. The compositor's mark before the word 'et' in the second line, delineating the opening of a new page, highlighted in the margin with a #.
2. The corresponding opening of a new page in Eggestein's edition of about 1469. Inc.1.A.2.3 [84].
3. The opening of the first letter of Peter in the Gutenberg Bible, showing Eggestein's compositor's marks. A manuscript correction is also visible in the left-hand margin.
4. A pair of intertwined initials from the opening of the first book of Maccabees in the Gutenberg Bible.

The Gutenberg Bible

Biblia latina

[Mainz: Johann Gutenberg and Johann Fust, about 1455]
Inc.1.A.1.1[3761]

In 1933, without fanfare, an eighty-one-year-old London barrister and Cambridge graduate, Arthur William Young, made a spectacular book gift to Cambridge University Library, comprising eighteen medieval manuscripts, twenty-eight incunables, and several hundred later printed books of great significance and value. It is recognized as the most important benefaction made to the University Library since the arrival of the Royal Library in 1715.

Young's collecting interests were focused on the Bible. The Gutenberg (-Fust) Bible of 1455, the first large-scale project of Gutenberg's invention of typographic printing, was obviously the high spot of his collection. This copy had appeared on the London market in the winter of 1889 when the seventh Earl of Hopetoun, about to sail to Australia to take up the governorship of Victoria, put up at Sotheby's the antiquarian library formed by his eighteenth-century ancestor the first Earl. In the early eighteenth century the significance of the Gutenberg Bible was not fully appreciated, and the binding identifies this copy simply as an 'editio antiqua'. Only when Tom Hodge of Sotheby's was packing up the books for shipment to London did he discover the greatest treasure in the collection. At auction the copy was bought by Bernard Quaritch, who sold it a few months later to Young.

The interest of Cambridge's Gutenberg Bible was magnified some fifty years after Young's gift, when it was noticed that this copy had been carefully marked up and used as setting copy for a Latin Bible printed in Strasbourg by Heinrich Eggestein, completed in late 1469 or early 1470. On every page of the Gutenberg Bible are small marginal hash-marks, pointing to small vertical strokes within the text, corresponding exactly, with a few indicative errors, to the page endings of Eggestein's edition. Moreover, various books contain manuscript marginal variant readings which Eggestein's compositors introduced into their settings. In other words, the text of Eggestein's Bible drew partially on a second, manuscript source. Presumably this manuscript was also the source of variant readings in other books that were also brought into Eggestein's text, perhaps at a correction stage. The hundreds of changes did not systematically improve on the Gutenberg Bible's text, but they are the earliest example of editorial work on that text, and Eggestein apparently took pride in this. A printed broadside advertisement for his edition survives, in which he boasted that the edition had been collated by men 'deep-dyed in humane letters'.

Paul Needham *is Librarian of the Scheide Library, a collection of manuscript and printed Bibles at Princeton University.*

1

2

Aurū et argentū vestrū eruginauit: ⁊
erugo eorꝫ in testamentū vobis erit: et
manducabit carnes vr̄as sicut ignis.
Thesaurizastis vobis irā ī nouissimis
diebus. Ecce merces operariorꝫ q̄ mes-
suerunt regiones vr̄as que fraudata
est a vobis clamat: et clamor eorū in
aures dn̄i sabaoth introiuit. Epulati
estis sup terrā: et in luxurijs enutristis
corda vestra. In die occisionis addixi-
stis et occidistis iustū: et nō restitit vobis. Patientes igit̄ estote fratres usqꝫ
ad aduentū dn̄i. Ecce agricola exspe-
ctat p̄ciosum fructū terre · patienter ferēs
donec accipiat temperaneū ⁊ serotinū.
Patiētes igit̄ estote ⁊ vos ⁊ ɔfirmate
corda vr̄a: quoniā aduētus dn̄i appro-
pinquabit. Nolite ingemiscere fratres
in alterutrū: ut nō iudicemini. Ecce iudex ante ianuā assistit. Exemplū accipite fratres laboris ⁊ patiētie ꝓphetas:
qui locuti sunt ī noīe dn̄i. Ecce beatifi-
camus eos q̄ sustinuerūt. Sufferentiā
iob audistis: et finē dn̄i vidistis: qm̄
misericors est dn̄s et miserator. Ante
omnia aūt fratres mei nolite iurare:
neqꝫ p celū neqꝫ per terrā neqꝫ aliud qd̄-
cunqꝫ iuramētū. Sit aūt sermo vester
est · ē · non · nō: ut nō sub iudicio decida-
tis. Tristat̄ aūt aliq̄s vr̄m: oret equo
animo et psallat. Infirmat̄ quis in
vobis: inducat p̄sbiteros eccl'ie ⁊ orēt
sup eū unguētes eū oleo ī noīe dn̄i. Et
oratio fidei saluabit infirmū: ⁊ alle-
uiabit eū dn̄s: ⁊ si in peccatis sit dimit-
tentur ei. Cōfitemini ergo alterutrum
peccata vr̄a: et orate pro inuicē ut sal-
uemini. Multū enī valet deprecatio iu-
sti assidua. Helias homo erat similis
nobis passibilis: et oratione orauit
ut nō plueret sup terrā: ⁊ nō pluit annos tres ⁊ mēses sex. Et rursū orauit:
et celū dedit pluuiā: ⁊ terra dedit fructū
suū. Fratres mei · si quis ex vobis erra-
uerit a veritate ⁊ ɔuerterit quis eū · scire
debet: quoniā qui ɔuerti fecerit pecca-
torē ab errore vie sue saluabit animā
eius a morte: ⁊ operit multitudinem
peccatorū. Explicit ep'la iacobi.
Incipit prologus in ep'la petri:

Discipulos saluatoris in-
uicti toto orbe diffusos et
peregrinos in hoc seculo
mōstrat · et p̄terite vite pe-
nitere suadet: ⁊ in nouā vitā proficere
tota cū sollicitudine exhortat̄ symon
petrꝰ filius iohānis prouincie galilee
vico bethsaida frater andree apostoli.
Explicit prologus Incipit ep'la
Petri:

Petrus apl'us: ihesu
cristi · electis aduenis
dispersionis pōthi
galatie capadotie
asie et bithinie secū-
dum presciētiā dei
pr̄is in sanctificationē spiritꝰ in obe-
dientiam et aspersionē sanguinis ihesu cristi: gratia vobis ⁊ pax mltiplicēt.
Benedictus deus et pater dn̄i nr̄i ihesu cristi q̄ scd̄m misericordiā suā ma-
gnā regenerauit nos ī spem viuam p
resurrectionē ihesu cristi ex mortuis in
hereditatē incorruptibilē ⁊ incontami-
natā et inmarcessibilē cōseruatam ī
celis: in vobis qui ī virtute dei custodi-
mini p fidē in salutē · paratā reuelari
in tēpore nouissimo. In quo exultabi-
tis: modicū nūc si oportet cōtristari ī
varijs temptationibꝫ: ut probatio ve-
stre fidei multo p̄ciosior sit auro qd̄ p
ignē probat̄: inueniat̄ in laudē ⁊ gloriam et honorē in reuelatione ihesu

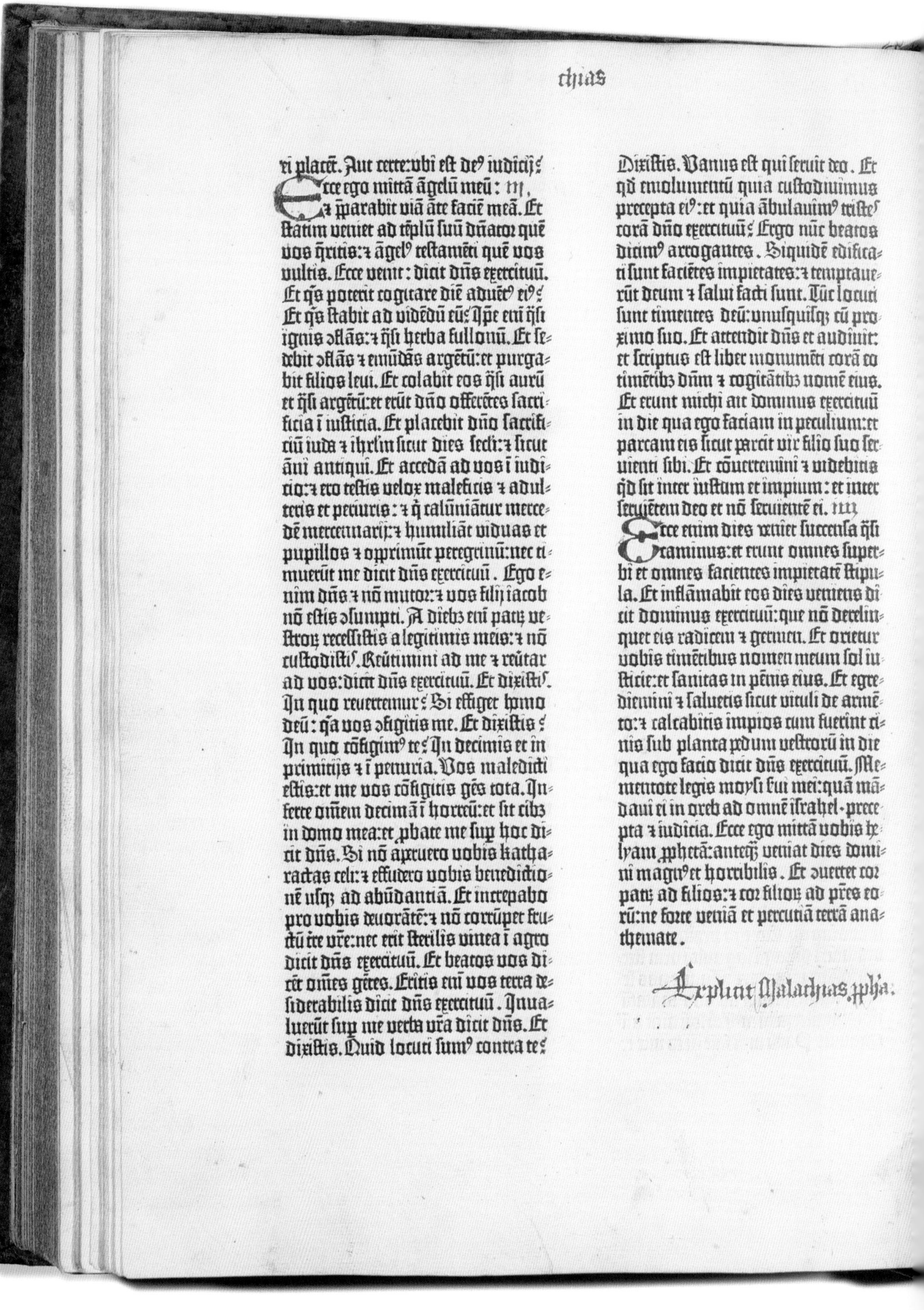

ri placet. Aut certe:ubi est de⁹ iudicij?
Ecce ego mittā āgelū meū: iij.
⁊ ꝑparabit viā āte faciē meā. Et
statim veniet ad tēplū suū dn̄ator quē
vos q̄ritis: ⁊ āgel⁹ testamēti quē vos
vultis. Ecce venit: dicit dn̄s exercituū.
Et q̄s poterit cogitare diē aduēt⁹ ei⁹?
Et q̄s stabit ad vidēdū eū? Ipe eni q̄si
ignis ɔflās: ⁊ q̄si herba fullonū. Et se-
debit ɔflās ⁊ emūdās argētū: et purga-
bit filios leui. Et colabit eos q̄si aurū
et q̄si argētū: et erūt dn̄o offerētes sacri-
ficia i iusticia. Et placebit dn̄o sacrifi-
ciū iuda ⁊ ihr̄lm sicut dies secli: ⁊ sicut
ānī antiqui. Et accedā ad vos ī iudicio: ⁊ ero testis velox maleficis ⁊ adul-
teris et periuris: ⁊ q̄ calūniātur merce-
dē mercennarij: ⁊ humiliāt viduas et
pupillos ⁊ opprimūt peregrinū: nec ti-
muerūt me dicit dn̄s exercituū. Ego e-
nim dn̄s ⁊ nō mutor: ⁊ vos filij iacob
nō estis ɔsumpti. A diebꝫ eni patꝝ ve-
stroꝝ recessistis a legitimis meis: ⁊ nō
custodistis. Reūtimini ad me ⁊ reūtar
ad vos: dicit dn̄s exercituū. Et dixistis.
In quo reuertemur? Si affiget homo
deū: q̄a vos ɔfigitis me. Et dixistis?
In quo cōfigim⁹ te? In decimis et in
primicijs ⁊ ī penuria. Vos maledicti
estis: et me vos cōfigitis gēs tota. In-
ferte omēm decimā ī horreū: et sit cibꝫ
in domo mea: et ꝓbate me sup hoc dicit dn̄s. Si nō aperuero vobis katha-
ractas celi: ⁊ effudero vobis benedictionē usqꝫ ad abūdantiā. Et increpabo
pro vobis deuorātē: ⁊ nō corrūpet fructū tre vr̄e: nec erit sterilis vinea ī agro
dicit dn̄s exercituū. Et beatos vos di-
cēt om̄es gētes. Eritis eni vos terra de-
siderabilis dicit dn̄s exercituū. Inua-
luerūt sup me verba vr̄a dicit dn̄s. Et
dixistis. Quid locuti sum⁹ contra te?

Dixistis. Vanus est qui seruit deo. Et
q̄d emolumentū quia custodiuimus
precepta ei⁹: et quia ābulauim⁹ tristes
corā dn̄o exercituū? Ergo nūc beatos
dicim⁹ arrogantes. Siquidē edifica-
ti sunt facientes impietatē: ⁊ temptaue-
rūt deum ⁊ salui facti sunt. Tūc locuti
sunt timentes deū: unusquisqꝫ cū pro-
ximo suo. Et attendit dn̄s et audiuit:
et scriptus est liber monumēti corā eo
timētibꝫ dn̄m ⁊ cogitātibꝫ nomē eius.
Et erunt michi ait dominus exercituū
in die qua ego faciam in peculium: et
parcam eis sicut parcit vir filio suo ser-
uienti sibi. Et cōuertemini ⁊ videbitis
q̄d sit inter iustum et impium: et inter
seruiētem deo et nō seruientē ei. iiij.
Ecce enim dies veniet succensa q̄si
caminus: et erunt omnes super-
bi et omnes facientes impietatē stipu-
la. Et inflāmabit eos dies veniens dicit dominus exercituū: que nō dereliu-
quet eis radicem ⁊ germen. Et orietur
vobis timētibus nomen meum sol iu-
sticie: et sanitas in pēnis eius. Et egre-
diemini ⁊ salietis sicut vituli de armē-
to: ⁊ calcabitis impios cum fuerint ci-
nis sub planta pedum vestrorū in die
qua ego facio dicit dn̄s exercituū. Me-
mentote legis moysi serui mei: quā mā-
daui ei in oreb ad omnē israhel: pcep-
ta ⁊ iudicia. Ecce ego mittā vobis he-
lyam ꝓphetā: anteqꝫ veniat dies domini magn⁹ et horribilis. Et ɔuertet cor
patꝝ ad filios: ⁊ cor filioꝝ ad pr̄es eorū: ne forte veniā et percutiā terrā ana-
themate.

Explicit Malachias ꝓpha.

4

Explicit malachias Incipit prologus
btī Iheronimi in libro machabeoꝝ

Machabeorū libri duo pno-
tant prelia · inter hebreoꝝ
duces gentēq; persarū:
pugnā q; sabbatoꝝ · ⁊ no-
biles machabei ducis triūphos: ex cui⁹
noīe ⁊ libri ipi eciā sūt nūcupati. Hec q;
historia cōtinet eciā inclita illa gesta
machabeoꝝ fratrū: qui sub antiocho
rege pro sacris legibꝫ dira tormenta
perpessi sunt. Quos mater pia dum
diuersis supplicijs vrgerent non solū
nō fleuit: sed et gaudēs hortabat̄ ad
gloriā passionis. Explicit prologus

Incipit liber machabeoꝝ. C I

Et factū est postq̄ per-
cussit alexander phi-
lippi rex macedo qui
primus regnauit ī
grecia egressus de ter-
ra cethim dariū regē
persarū ⁊ medoꝝ: cōstituit prelia multa:
et obtinuit omniū munitiōnes: et in-
terfecit reges terre. Et ptransijt vsq; ad
fines terre: ⁊ accepit spolia multitudinis
gentiū: ⁊ siluit terra in cōspectu eius. Et
cōgregauit virtutē ⁊ exercitū fortem ni-
mis: et exaltatū est et eleuatū cor ei⁹: et
obtinuit regiones gentiū ⁊ tirannos
et facti sunt illi in tributū. Et post hec
decidit in lectū: ⁊ cognouit quia more-
retur. Et vocauit pueros suos nobiles
qui secū erant nutriti a iuuentute sua:
et diuisit illis regnū suū cum adhuc
viueret. Et regnauit alexander annis
duodecim: ⁊ mortu⁹ ē. Et obtinuerūt
pueri ei⁹ regnū vnusquisq; ī loco suo:
et imposuerūt oēs sibi diademata
post mortē ei⁹ ⁊ filij eoꝝ post eos annis
multis: et multiplicata sūt mala ī terra.
Et exijt ex eis radix peccati · antiochus
illustris fili⁹ antiochi regis qui fuerat
rome obses: et regnauit in anno cen-
tesimotricesimo et septimo regni greco-
rum. In diebꝫ illis exierunt ex isrl' filij
iniqui: ⁊ suaserūt multis dicentes. Ea-
mus ⁊ disponam⁹ testamentū cū gen-
tibus que circa nos sūt: quia ex quo
recessim⁹ ab eis inuenerūt nos multa
mala. Et bonus visus ē sermo ī oculis
eoꝝ. Et destinauerūt aliqui de pplo ⁊
abierūt ad regē: et dedit illis potestatē
ut facerēt iusticiā gentiū. Et edificaue-
rūt gymnasiū in iherosolimis scdm
leges naciōnū · ⁊ fecerūt sibi pputia: ⁊ re-
cesserūt a testamēto sancto · ⁊ iuncti sūt
nationibꝫ: et venūdati sunt ut facerēt
malū. Et paratū ē regnū in conspectu
antiochi: ⁊ cepit regnare ī terra egipti:
ut regnaret sup duo regna. Et intrauit
in egiptū in multitudine graui in curri-
bus ⁊ elephantis ⁊ equitibꝫ: ⁊ copiosa
nauiū multitudine. Et constituit bellū
aduersus ptolomeū regē egipti: ⁊ veri-
tus ē ptolomeus a facie eius ⁊ fugit:
et ceciderūt vulnerati multi. Et compre-
hendit ciuitates munitas in terra egipti: ⁊ accepit spolia terre egipti. Et con-
uertit antiochus postq̄ pcussit egiptū
in centesimo ⁊ quadragesimo ⁊ tercio anno ⁊ ascendit ad isrl': et ascendit iherosolimis ī multitudine graui. Et intrauit
in sanctificationē cū supbia: ⁊ accepit
altare aureū ⁊ candelabrū luminis ⁊
vniuersa vasa eius ⁊ mensam ppositi-
onis ⁊ libatoria ⁊ fialas ⁊ mortario-
la aurea ⁊ velū ⁊ coronas ⁊ ornamen-
tum aureum qd in facie templi erat: ⁊
cōminuit oīa. Et accepit argentum ⁊
aurū et vasa cōcupiscibilia: et accepit
thesauros occultos quos inuenit: et
sublatis omnibꝫ abijt ī terrā suā. Et
fecit cedem hominū: et locutus est in

1456

PICTURED:

Cambridge University Library's unique, if damaged, copy of the *Kalender*.

An aid to memory

Cisiojanus (Kalender)
[Mainz: Johann Gutenberg?, about 1456–1457]
Inc.0.A.1.2[6]

As preparation for the work of printing his famous 42-line Bible (see pp. 2–5), Johann Gutenberg produced two large printing-types. The larger of these two seems to have been designed and made first, but the smaller was in the end preferred for the Bible. When the printing business set up by Gutenberg was dissolved shortly after the Bible was completed, his typographic materials were divided with his former partners, and he seems to have ended up with the larger, earlier of these types. By 1461 the type was in the hands of Albrecht Pfister in Bamberg, who used it to print the Bible that no doubt Gutenberg had originally conceived. In the meantime, a number of broadsides and small pamphlets were produced using the type, and it seems likely that it was then still in Gutenberg's hands.

These short texts only survive today in single copies or in fragments, leading us to conclude that more of these brief texts may have originally been produced than are now known. What we can guess from the survivors is that many were concerned with the passage and meaning of time, such as almanacs and prognostications. They are among the earliest pieces of printing in the German language known to exist.

One of the odder-looking of these (to modern eyes) is the *Cisiojanus*, a mnemonic poem in twelve verses – one for each month – designed to help the user remember saints' days and the dates of other church feasts, important in an age when many official documents were dated in this fashion rather than by calendar dates. The name derives from the first two words of the Latin versions, '*Cisio*', short for Circumcision, and '*Janus*' short for St Januarius, the two first feast days in January.

This German example, of which no other copy is known, consists of nonsense verses where the number of words in each verse corresponds to the number of days in the month, with a saint's day appearing at the appropriate place. So the fourth word in the first line for April is Ambrosius, indicating that St Ambrose's day is 4 April, and we can also easily see the feast of St Remigius (or Remy) on 1 October – here curiously called Herbstmonat, a name more commonly used in German for September.

John Goldfinch *is Acting College Librarian at Eton College, and was formerly Curator of Incunabula at the British Library.*

Dis ist der Cisianus zu dutsche und

Horent do crist' wart besnitten ... gericht
Hartmant — Und opperē dem herrē lobesan ... sebestian
Agnes sal do mit paulus gene ... ne
Do maria sal mit aga then gan Jhesum ... schone
Hornung — Do rieffe valentinus wir macht Frauwent ... nacht
want petrus und mathias Komment schiere ... as
Mertz fert do her mit bii thoman Uñ spricht er ... egoriū han
Mertze — Mit dem wolle er disputeren So kōmet benedictu ... wil hofferē
Marien unszer drostetin Und dem iungen kindelin
Apprille und bischoff ambrosius Farent do here un ... us
Aprille — Die ostern wollē tiburciū brengē So wil valerius das ... ngē
Sprechen georgius und marcus zu hant · wiste das ... t
Meye das crutze funden hat Johannes ... adi
Meye — Gordian sprach zu servatius · wir wollen zwar ... baden a
Gang und sage auch urban snelle Das er uns brenge peter
wir sollen frolichen leben Bonifacius wil es alles vir geben
Brachmāt — Als barnabas mir hat geseit Vitus sprach mit bescheiden
Gervasius uñ alban wollē iagē Johēs uñ heselin sollē dz pet sagen
Ewaldus maria und ulrich · wollen in die erne gem ... ch
Haumāt — Des frauwet sich margreta gar fast Uñ machet d ... gast
Uñ magdalen wil auch iacob liep ha. Daz ödru ... ermā
Peter und steffan wonnedich Oswal. ... xtus des
Augst — laurencius sprach daz wisz almelich Maria wil f ... ch
Bühart ging dz sagē bartelme lodwig sprch dz ... geuot er
Egidius bliesz us eyn horn Frauwent ach mari ... n
Folmāt — lassent uns das crutze erheben So wirt der her ... gen
Matheus mauricius sprechen ia Des wart cosm ... michel fro
Remigius der hiesze frantzen Mit gertruden frolic ... tzen
Herbstmāt — Dionisi' sprch waz beruder daz Es were galle uñ lu ... dē das
Ursula sprach wer dantzen wil Der sy symonis un ... n geselle
Alle heilgē fragē noch gutem win · willibrord' sp ... laussent hien
Slachtmāt — Martinus schencket guten most Und hat do by vil guter kost
Cecilia clemēs sagiten katherinen das Silbilt hie komen andreas
wanne kommet iungfrau barbara Sprach nicolaus zu maria
Wintermāt — wie lange sal din lucia beiden Das sie dem kindelbette bereiden
wā tomā brenget nu die wynacht Steffa ... omā hat gedocht

PICTURED:

1. The fine red morocco binding of the Lactantius, executed in the eighteenth century.
2. and 4. Illuminations by the Master of the Barbo Missal.
3. Sweynheym and Pannartz's elegant Greek type.

The first dated book printed in Italy

Lactantius (about 240–about 320)
Opera
Subiaco: [Conradus Sweynheym and Arnoldus Pannartz], 29 October 1465
Inc.3.B.1.1[1122]

In the early 1460s, two journeymen took up residence in the abbey of Subiaco with the intention of printing books, probably in consequence of violent political upheavals in Mainz, the birthplace of printing. Nobody knows what took Sweynheym and Pannartz to this secluded spot in the Apennine foothills fifty miles east of Rome, but they found there a thriving community of Benedictine monks, mostly Germans like themselves, and a site of international pilgrimage as the first foundation of St Benedict. From a later list of their publications, we know that their first book was a Donatus, all trace of which has long disappeared. Other documentary evidence shows that they completed an undated Cicero, *De oratore*, before 30 September 1465. The Lactantius which followed is the first Italian printed book with a date; in absolute terms the third book printed in Italy. It is also the only one of the three surviving editions (the last being Augustine's *City of God* of 1467) to mention the place of printing; the Subiaco printers never revealed their own names.

1

The fourth-century Church Father Lactantius became known to the Renaissance as 'the Christian Cicero' for the stylistic purity of his apologetic works. He was extraordinarily popular with the humanists and clerics at whom the products of the first Italian press were aimed. Following their move to Rome in 1467, Sweynheym and Pannartz published two further editions over the course of their nine-year partnership, totalling over 800 copies. The 1465 Lactantius was set in a type of surpassing beauty, essentially roman but retaining gothic traits from their German homeland. Good judges have thought it the finest of all Renaissance types. A further distinction was the first appearance anywhere of a complete Greek font to render quotations in the text.

The Cambridge Lactantius is one of twenty copies (among 53 extant) finely illuminated by a north Italian artist known as the Master of the Barbo Missal. He also illuminated several copies of the Subiaco Cicero and one of the Augustine, besides plentiful manuscript work. Surprisingly, his hand is found in a number of books printed in Mainz by Fust and Schöffer, the supposed masters of Sweynheym and Pannartz, in the years 1459 to 1462. The most probable explanation is that the two Germans initially came to Italy to sell Mainz books and, finding a market for these novel products, decided to take up printing on their own account.

Martin Davies *was Head of Incunabula at the British Library from 1992 to 1998.*

lactancii firmiani de diuinis institucionibus aduersus gentes primus liber incipit

Quanta sit et fuerit semper cognicio ueritatis. Et quot nec sine religione sapiecia nec sine sapiencia probanda sit religio

MAGNO & excellēti īgenio uiri quom se doctrinę penitus dedidissent: quicquid laboris poterat impendi: contemtis omnibus publicis & priuatis actionibus: ad inquirēdę ueritatis studiū se contulerūt: existimātes multo esse pręclarius humanarū diuinarūq; rerū inuestigare ac scire rationē q̄ struēdis opibus aut cumulandis honoribus inherere: Quibus rebus quoniam fragiles terrenęq; sunt: & ad solius corporis ptinent cultum nemo melior: nemo iustior effici potest. Erāt quidē illi ueritatis cognitione dignissimi quam scire tātopere cupiuerūt: atq; ita ut eam rebus omnibus anteponerēt: Nam & abiecisse quosdā res familiares suas et renūtiasse uniuersis uoluptatibus constat: ut solā nudamq; uirtutē: nudi expeditiq; sequerent̄: tantū apud eos uirtutis nomen et auctoritas ualuit: ut in ea omne summi boni premium p̄dicarēt. Sed neq; adepti sūt id quod uolebāt: & operā simul atq; industriā pdiderūt: quia ueritas idest archanū sūmi dei qui fecit omnia ingenio ac ꝓpriis sensibus nō potest comp̄hēdi: alioquin nihil inter deū hominēq; distaret si cōsilia & dispositiones illius maiestatis ęternę cogitatio assequeret̄ humana. Quod quia fieri nō potuit ut homini p se ipsū ~~ideo~~ diuina noscere̅t: non est passus hominem deus lumē sapientię requirentem diutius errare: ac sine ullo laboris effectu uagari per tenebras inextricabiles: aperuit oculos eius aliquando: & notionem ueritatis munus suū fecit: ut & humanā sapientiā ratio

2

NVnc reliqua subnectā. Veniet igit̄ sūmi & maxī dei filius. ut uiuos ac mortuos iudicet. Dicēte sibilla sic. πασης γαρ γαιης τοτε θνητων συγχυσις εσται αυτος ο παντοκρατωρ οταν ελθη βηματι κριναι ζωντων και νεκυων ψυχας και κοσμον απαντα. Id ē totius ei terrę mortaliū cōfusio tūc erit. et ipse oīpotēs cū uenerit i solio iudicare uiuoꝝ mortuorūq; aīas et mūdū omnē. Verū ille cū deleuerit iiustitiā: iudiciūq; max im fecerit: ac iustos q a p̄ncipio fuerūt ad uitā r̄staurauerit: mille ānis iter hoīes uersabit̄. eosq; iustissīo īpio reget. qđ alibi sibilla uaticinās furēsq; ꝓclamat. κλυτε δε μου μεροπες βασιλευς αιωνιος αρχει. Id ē Audite me hoīes rex sēpiternus dn̄at̄. Tūc q erūt i corpibus uiui nō morient̄. sed p eosdē mille ānos in-

3

Lactancij firmiani de officio opificio dei uel formatione hoīs capitulum: Prohemiale capitulum ad demetrianum in quo narrat cur hoc opus assumpserit.

Q Vam minime sim quetus etiam summis necessitatibus ex hoc libello poteris existimare: quem ad te rudibus pene uerbis ꝓut igenii mediocritas tulit Demetriane perscpsi: ut et quotidianũ studiũ meum nosces. et non deessem tibi ꝑceptor etiã nũc: sed honestioris rei: meliorisq; doctrinę. Nam si te in lr̃is nihil aliud q̃ liguã instruẽtibus auditorẽ satis strẽnuum ꝑbuisti: quantomagis in his ueris et ad uitã pertinentibus docilior esse debebis. apud quem nunc ꝓfiteor: nulla me necessitate uel rei uel temporis ipediri: quo minus aliquid excudam. quo philosophi nostrę sectę quam tuemur instructiores doctioresq; i posterũ fiant: q̃uis nũc male audiãt. castigentq; uulgo ꝙ aliter q̃ sapiẽtibus conuenit uiuãt. et uitia sub obtẽtu nominis cęlent. qbus aut mederi oportuit: aut ea prorsus effugere. ut beatũ atq; incorruptũ sapiẽtię nomen: uita ipa cũ pręceptis congruẽte prestarẽt. Ego tamen ut nos ipos simul et cęteros instruã: nullum laborem recuso. neq; enim possum obliuisci mei: tum presertim cum maxime opus sit meminisse. sic ne tu quidem tui ut spero & opto. Nam licet te publicę rei necessitas a ueris et iustis operibus auertat: tñ fieri nõ potest: quin subinde in cęlũ aspiciat mens sibi conscia recti. Ego qdem lętor: omnia tibi quę pro bonis habenẽ prospere fluere. sed ita si nihil de statu mẽtis imutẽt. Vereor ei ne paulatim consuetudo & iocũditas earũ rerũ sicut fieri solet: in animũ tuũ repat. Ideoq; te moneo. ne oblectamẽta ista terrę ꝓ magnis aut ueris bonis habere te credas. quę sunt non tm̃ fallacia quia dubia: uerũ etiã insidiosa quia dulcia. Nam et ille colluctator & aduersarius noster: scis q̃ sit astutus. et idem ipe uiolentus. sicuti nũc uidemus. Is hęc omnia quę illicere possũt pro laqueis habet. et qdem tam subtilibus: ut oculos mẽtis effugiãt: ne possint hominis ꝓuisione uitari. Summa ergo prudentia est pedetẽtim: qm̃ utrobiq; saltus insidet. et offensacula pedibus latẽter opponit. Itaq; res tuas ꝓprias in quibus nũc agis suadeo: ut ꝓ tua uirtute aut contemnas si potes: aut non magnope mireris. Memento & ueri parentis tui. et in qua ciuitate nomẽ dederis. et cuius ordinis fueris. Intelligis ꝓfecto qd loquar. Nec eni te supbię arguo. cuius in te ne suspicio qdem ulla ẽ: sed ea quę dico. ad mentẽ referẽda sunt non ad corpus. cuius omnis rõ ideo compata ẽ: ut animo tanq̃ domino seruiat et regaẽ nutu eius. Vas ẽ enim quodammodo

4

fictile quo animus. id est homo ipe uerus continet̃. et qdem nõ a Prometheo fictũ ut poetę loquunt̃: sed a summo illo rerũ cõditore ac artifice deo. cuius diuinã ꝓuidẽtiã pfectissimãq; uirtutem nec sensu cõphendere: nec uerbo enarrare possibile est. Temptabo tñ quoniã corporis & animi facta mẽtio ẽ. utriusq; rationẽ q̃tum pusillitas intelligẽtię meę ꝓuidet explicare. quod offitiũ hac de cã maxime suscipiendũ puto. qd̃ Marcus Tullius uir ingenii singularis in quarto de re publica libro cũ id facere temptasset: materiam late patentẽ angustis finibus terminauit leuiter summa queq; decerpẽs. Ac ne ulla esset excusatio: cur eum locũ nõ fuerit exequutus ipe testatus ẽ. nec uolũtatem sibi defuisse nec curam. In libro ei de legibus primo cũ hęc idem summatim stringeret sic ait. Hunc locũ satis ut mihi uidet̃ i his libris quos legistis expressi Scipio. Postea tñ in libro de natura deoꝝ secũdo. hoc idem latius exequi conatus. Sed qm̃ nec ibi quidem satis expressit: aggd̃iar hoc munus et sumã mihi audacter explicandũ: quod homo dissertissimus pene omisit intactũ. Forsitan repħendas: ꝙ in rebus obscuris coner aliqd dispu-tare. cũ uideas tanta temeritate hoĩes extitisse q uulgo philosophi noiant̃. ut ea que obstrusa ꝑsus atq; abdita deus eẽ uoluit scrutarent̃. ac naturam rerũ celestiũ terrenarũq; conquirerent. quę a nobis longe remote neq; oculis contrectari: neq; tangi manu: neq; ꝑcipi sensibus possunt. Et tam de illarũ oĩm rõe sic disputant. ut ea quę afferũt ꝓbata et cognita uideri uelint. Quid est tãdem cur nobis inuidiosũ qsq̃ putet. sed rõem corporis nr̃i inspicere et contẽplari uelimus? Que plane obscura nõ ẽ. q̃a ex ipis membroꝝ offitiis et usibus partiũ singularũ q̃ta ui ꝓuidẽtię quisq; factus sit itelligere nobis licet. Que deus homini & que ceteris animantibus dedit.

OEdit eni homini artifex ille noster ac parens deus sensũ atq; rõnem. ut ex eo appareret nos ab eo esse generatos. quia ipe intelligentia: ipe sensus ac ratio ẽ. Cęteris aiantibus qm̃ rõnalem istã uitam nõ attribuit. queadmodũ tamẽ uita earũ tutior esset ante prętiidit. Omnes eni suis ex se pellibus texit. quo facilius possẽt uim pruinarũ ac frigora sustinere. Singulis autẽ generibus ad ꝓpulsandos impetus externos sua ꝓpa munimẽta constituit. ut aut naturalibus telis repugnẽt fortioribus: aut quę sũt imbe-cilliora subtrahant se ꝑiculis: ꝑnicitate fugiendi: aut quę simul et uiribus & celeritate indigẽt astu se ꝓtegãt. aut latibulis sepiãt. Itaq; alia eoꝝ uel plu-mis leuibus i sublime suspensa sunt: uel suffulta ungulis: uel instructa cor-nibus: quibusdam in ore arma sunt dentes: aut in pedibus adunci ungues. nulliq; munimentũ ad tutelam sui deest. Si qua uero in prędam maioribus

PICTURED:

The markings round the edge of this partial leaf show where it was later re-used in a book binding.

Printing schoolbooks: little and often

Aelius Donatus (4th century AD)
Ars minor
Mainz: Peter Schöffer, [after 30 October 1466]
Inc.3.A.1.3b[13]

Among the earliest evidence for printing with movable type are fragments of *Ars minor,* a Latin grammar for beginners by Aelius Donatus, a fourth-century Latin teacher in Rome. Some printed Donatus fragments predate the Gutenberg Bible (see pp. 2–5), but although the Cambridge fragment displays the type of the Gutenberg Bible, it has been suggested that it was not printed until after the death of Johann Fust (30 October 1466): Schöffer and Fust normally signed their books jointly but the colophon found in a matching fragment in the Bibliothèque nationale de France only mentions Peter Schöffer. Fust had been in a business relationship first with Gutenberg and then with Schöffer. This edition of Donatus demonstrates the continuity of the successor company in the very early days of printing, through the ownership of equipment and through elements of a business model.

The many fragmentary pieces of evidence for Donatus editions suggest that there were more editions than we have surviving evidence for. The numerous editions also suggest that, although the text could be expected to sell continuously, the early printers chose to produce new editions as required, rather than to produce fewer editions with, relatively speaking, larger print-runs. For printers who, like Gutenberg, and Fust and Schöffer, typically produced big books on which the return on investment would have been slow, schoolbooks like this could have been a way of generating a quicker cash flow.

Early Donatus editions have largely been preserved because the vellum they were printed on constituted a valuable commodity for reuse by book binders. The Cambridge fragment comes from the binding of a book printed in Cologne in about 1470–1472. The splendid large metal-cut P, here printed in blue and red, was first used by Fust and Schöffer in 1457, although by 1466/1467 it was quite damaged and apparently touched up subsequently by hand. Schöffer mentions the use – rather extravagant for a schoolbook – of these capitals specifically in the colophon, and they are not found in other Donatus editions. Apart from the large capitals, the printed layout provides no help with understanding the structure of the text. The Paris fragment has been fully marked up by a professional hand to make it easier to use. The Cambridge fragment, however, has few such helpful additions, so it is possible that it was never used as a book before being used by the binder.

Kristian Jensen *is Head of Arts and Humanities at the British Library, and has a special interest in how the new business of publishing in printed form affected texts as the relationship changed between producers, readers and buyers of books.*

quā quandoq̄ [illegible] quinetiā quatenus [illegible] sine [illegible] n
ut nisi nisi [illegible] interea quamobrē pīerea [illegible] itē
alioqui preterea. Da racōnales ut ita itaq; enī [illegible]
ꝑpter quā quoniā quidem quippe nempe ergo [illegible] ur [illegible]
ꝑpterea [illegible] figure [illegible] iunctionū quot sūt· due· q̄ simp
ꝯposita ut nāq; [illegible] iunctionū in quo est· quia aut p
iunctionis sūt [illegible] at ac ast· aut subiunctiue ut q; neque· au

P[illegible]posicio quid ē· pars oracōis [illegible] ut ergo
que ꝑposita aliis partibus in oracōe [illegible] gui
[illegible] aut ꝯplet aut mutat aut minuit. Ore
quot accidūt· unū· quid· casus tantum [illegible] Qu
[illegible] ·q̄· accus· et ablatiuus. Da ꝑposiciones c
ut ad apud ante aduersū cis citra circū circa [illegible] erga
intra infra iuxta ob pone ꝑ ꝑpe ꝑpter scd̄m post [illegible] ul
supra circiter usq; secus penes. Quō· dicimus eni [illegible] pa
villā ante edes aduersū inimicos cis renū citra [illegible] circ
circa templū [illegible] hostes erga ꝑpinquos [illegible] nos
[illegible] intra menia infra tectū iuxta [illegible] ū ob au [illegible] p
[illegible] ꝑ parietē ꝑpe fenestrā ꝑpter disciplinā scd̄m [illegible] po
trans ripam ultra fines ꝑter officiū supra celū [illegible]
q; [illegible] secus viā penes arbitros. Da ꝑposicōnes casu
ut a ab abs cū corā clam de e ex ꝓ p̄ palā sine [illegible] tu
dicimus enim· a domo ab [illegible] abs quolibet [illegible]
[illegible] ex ꝓfectura ꝓ clientibus p̄ [illegible]
lā [illegible] tenus pube [illegible] nos

PICTURED:

1. The guilty party owns up to his error.
2. A fine opening from volume 2, displaying the illuminated initial 'C' with annotations from early readers.

Blotting your copy-book

Livy (59 BC–about 17 AD)
Historiae Romanae decades
[Venice]: Vindelinus de Spira, 1470
Inc.1.B.3.1b[1330.1–2]

On 1 December 1482, an unfortunate student at the University of Padua made a large red inkblot in this precious edition of Livy's *History of Rome*. He was annotating Livy's account of Hannibal's invasion, giving brief summaries of the narrative; 'Fabius Pictor sent to Delphi to the oracle' and so forth. After several pages, he lost concentration and made a large glaring blot. All he could do was 'own' it – 'I stupidly made this blot on the first of December 1482' – and press on. Three weeks later, reaching the end of Livy's account of the war, he proudly wrote, 'I have completed this task studiously.'

The book he was annotating had been produced in nearby Venice in 1470, a year after the first printed edition of Livy appeared in Rome. The work of the German printer Wendelin, it is a particularly lovely specimen, the handsome typeface complemented by luxuriously illuminated initials with white vine-stems in glorious gold and colours.

When the book left the Italian peninsula we do not know, but we can reconstruct part of its journey from Padua to Cambridge. One of the early pages has a floral border and coat of arms added in a distinctively northern style, very likely Austrian, around 1500, suggesting a stay there. But it was to move on, into the library of that voracious bibliophile, John Moore, before coming to the University of Cambridge, thanks to the generosity of George I.

In fact, it was only half of Livy's lengthy *History*. Our Paduan student had been working on the second of two volumes. By the time it reached Moore's library, it had become separated from volume 1. In 1784, to complete the pair a London bookseller, George Nicol, gave to the University a first volume of Wendelin's 1470 edition, acquired from the sale of the library of another famous book collector, Robert Hoblyn (1710–1756). The two volumes had not originally gone together, as differences in the illumination make clear, but this second volume is also beautifully decorated in Venetian style, with a heading to the whole work added by hand in gold.

Nicol's letter of donation remains attached to the end-papers. On it, the Librarian has added a few words of celebration. This edition, he writes, is not in 'any known Library in England'. Together, he continues (presumably with a glint in his eye), 'the 2 Vols are worth at least 50 £!'.

Mary Beard *is Professor of Classics at the University of Cambridge.*

modo: sed etiam equitum interfectorum rati occasionē supplicii patere: misso retro nuntio: perfuga autē Romanus erat: ut sine arbitro milites: quę uellent: agerē. ℂOppidanos per muros: urbisq; opportuna loca in statiōibus disponūt. ℂCustodias: uigiliasq; in eam noctē intentius instruunt. circa portā: qua uēturū hostem rebantur: quod roboris in pręsidio erat: opponunt. ℂAnnibal quarta uigilia ferme ad urbē accessit. ℂPrimi agminis erant perfugę Romanorum. & arma Romana habebāt. Ii ut ad portam est uentum: latinę omnes loquentes: excitāt. uigiles. Apeririq; portā iubent. Consulem adesse. ℂVigiles uelut ad uocem eorū excitati: tumultuari. trepidare. moliri portā: cataracta clausa erat. Eam partī uectibus leuāt. partim funibus subducunt in tātum altitudinis: ut subire recti possent. Vix dum satis patebat iter. quom perfugę certatī ruunt per portā. & cum sexcenti ferme intrassent remisso fune: quo suspensa erat: cataracta: magno sonitu cecidit. ℂSalapiani alii per fugas negligenter ex itinere suspensa humeris: ut iter pacatos: gerētes arma: īuadūt. Alii e turri eius portę: murisq;: saxis: sudibus: pilis: absterrēt hostem. ℂIta inde Annibal: sua & ipse fraude captus: abiit. profectusq; ad Locrorum soluendam obsidionē: quā cētius summa ui operibus: tormētorūq; omī genere ex Sicilia aduecto: oppugnabat. ℂMagoni iā haud ferme fidenti recenturū: defensurumq; se urbem: pria spes morte nuntiata Marcelli adfulsit. Secutus inde nūtius Annibalem Nūidarū equitatu pręmisso: ipsum quātū accelerare poss&: cum peditum agmīe sequi. ℂItaq; ubi primū Numidas edito e speculis signo: aduentare sensit: & ipse patefacta repente porta: ferox ī hostes erumpit. ℂEt primo magis quia īprouiso id fecerat: q̄ q̄ par uiribus ess&: anceps certamen erat. Deinde ut superuenere Numidę tātus pauor Romanis ē iiectus: ut passim ad mare ac naues fugerēt: relictis operibus: machinisq;: quibus muros quatiebāt. ℂIta aduētu Annibalis soluta Locrorū obsidio est. ℂCrispinus postq̄ ī Brutios profectum Annibalē sēsit: exercitū cui Collega pręfuerat. M. Marcellū Tribunū Militum Venusiā adducere iussit. Ipse cū legiōibus suis Capuā profectus uix lecti exagitationē: pręgrauitate uulnerum: patiens: Romam litteras de morte Collegę scripsit: quātoq; ipse in discrimine ess&. Se comitiorum causa nō posse Romā uenire: quia nec uię laborē passurus uideret. Et de Tarento sollicitus ess&: ne ex Brutiis Annibal eo cōuerter& agmē. ℂLegatos opus eē ad se mitti: uiros prudētes: cū quibus quę uell& de Re. P. loqueretur. ℂHę litterę recitatę: & magnū luctū morte alterius Consulis: & metum de altero fecerūt. ℂItaq; Q. Fabium filium ad exercitum Venusiā miserunt. ℂEt ad Consulē tres Legati missi. Sex. Iulius Cęsar. L. Licinius Pollio. L. Citius Halimetus: cū paucis āte diebus ex Sicilia rediss&. Hi nuntiare Consuli iussi: ut si ad cōitia ipse Romā uenire nō poss&: Dictatorē in agro Romano dicer& Comitiorū causa. si Cōsul Tarētū profectus ess& Q. Claudiū Prętorem placere ī eā regionē inde adducere legiones: in q̄ plurimas sociorū urbes tueri poss&. ℂEadē ęstate Valerius cum classe centum nauium ex Sicilia in Africā transmisit. & ad Clupeam urbē: excursione facta: agrum late nullo ferme obuio uastauit. Inde ad naues rapti prędatores recepti: quia repente fama accidit classem Punicā aduētare. Lxxx. erāt & tres naues. Cū iis haud procul Clupea: prospere pugnat Romanus. Decē & octo nauibus captis: fugatis aliis: cum magna nauali: terrestriq; pręda Lilybęū redit. ℂEadē ęstate & Philippus implorantibus Achęis auxiliū tulit. quos & Machanidas Tyrānus Lacedęmoniorū finitimo bello urebat. Et Aetoli nauibus per fretū quod Naupactum & Patras interfluit: Rhion incolę uocāt: exercitu traiecto: depopulati erant. ℂAttalum quoque Regem Asię: quia Aetoli sūmū gentis

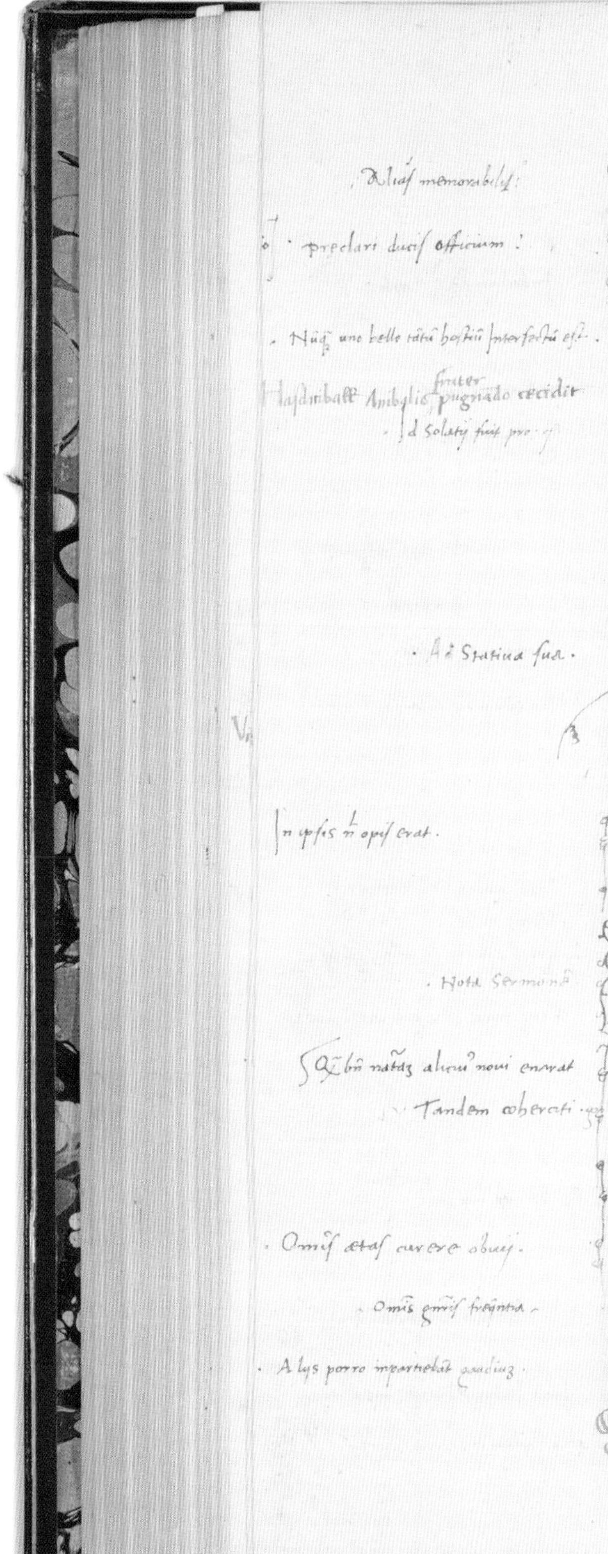

instituerat Dux: cũ ſepe alias mẽorabilis: tũ illa precipue pugna. Ille pugnãtes
hortando: pariterq; abeundo pericula: ſuſtinuit. Ille feſſos: abnuẽtiſq; tedio &
labore: nunc precando: nunc caſtigando: accendit. Ille fugientes reuocauit.
omiſſamq; pugnã aliquot in locis reſtituit. Poſtremo cũ haud dubie fortuna
hoſtiũ eſſ&: ne ſupereſſ& tãto exercitui: ſuum nomen ſecuto: concitato equo
ſe in cohortẽ Romanã immiſit. Ibi: ut patre Hamilcare: & Annibalis fratre
dignũ erat: pugnãs cecidit. Nunq̃ eo bello una acie tãtũ hoſtiũ ĩterfectũ eſt.
Redditaq; equa Cannenſi clades uel Ducis uel exercitus interitu: uidebatur.
Quinquagĩta ſex milia hoſtiũ ceſa. Capta. v. milia & quadringenti. Preda
magna. alia tum oĩs generis: tum auri argẽtiq;. Ciuium etiam Romanoꝝ:
qui capti apud hoſtes erãt. ſupra quattuor milia capitũ recepta. Id ſolatii fuit:
pro amiſſis eo proelio militibus. Nam haud quaq̃ incruenta uictoria fuit.
octo ferme milia Romanoꝝ: ſocioꝝq; occiſa. Adeoq; etiã uictores ſanguinis:
cediſq; coeperat ſatietas: ut poſtero die: cũ eſſ& nuntiatũ Liuio Conſuli Galloſ
Ciſalpinos Liguresq;: qui aut proelio nõ affuiſſent: aut ĩter cedem effugiſſent:
uno agmĩe abire ſine certo duce: ſine ſignis: ſine ordĩe ullo: aut imperio: poſſe
ſi una equitũ ala mittatur: omnes deleri. Superſint inquit aliqui nuntii &
hoſtiũ cladis: & noſtre uirtutis. Nero ea nocte. que ſecuta eſt pugnã: citati
ore: q̃ inde uenerat agmine: die ſexta ad ſtatiua ſua: atq; ad hoſtẽ: peruenit.
Iter eius frequẽtia minore quia nemo preceſſerat nuntius. letitia uero tãta: uix
ut compotes mentium: pre gaudio eſſent: celebratum eſt. Nã Rome neuter aĩ
habitus ſatis dici: enarrariq; poteſt. nec quo incerta expectatiõe euẽtus ciuitas
fuerat: nec quo uictorie famã acceperit. Nunq̃ per oẽs dies ex quo Claudium
Conſulem profectum fama attulit: ab orte ſole: ad occidentẽ: aut Senator q̃q̃
a Curia: atq; ab magiſtratibus abſceſſit. aut Populus e foro. Matrone: quia
nihil in ipſis opis erat: in preces obteſtationeſq; uerſe per omnia delubra uage:
ſuppliciis: uotiſq; fatigare deos. Tam ſollicite ac ſuſpenſe ciuitati fama ĩcerta
primo accidit. Duos Narnienſes equites in caſtra: que in faucibus Vmbrie
oppoſita erant: ueniſſe ex proelio: nuntiãtes ceſos hoſtes. Et prĩo magiſ auri
buſ: q̃ aĩſ: id acceptũ erat. ut maiuſ letiuſq;: q̃ quod mẽte capere: aut ſatis credere
poſſẽt. & ipſa celeritas fidẽ ĩpediebat: q biduo ãte pugnatũ dicebat̃. Littere
deĩde ab L. Manlio Acidino miſſe: ex caſtris: afferunt̃ de Narnienſiũ equitũ
aduentu. Ee littere per forum ad tribunal perlate Senatum in Curiã exciuerãt.
tantoque certamine ac tumultu Populi ad fores Curie concurſum eſt: ut adire
nuntiuſ non poſſ&. traherenturq; a percontãtibus: uociferantibuſq;: ut ĩ roſtris
priuſq̃ in Senatu littere recitarentur. Tandem cõmoti & coerciti a magiſtra
tibus: diſpenſarique letitia inter impotentes eius animos potuit. In Senatu
primum: Deinde in Contione littere recitate ſunt. & pro cuiuſque ingenio:
aliis iam certum gaudium: aliis nulla ante futura fides erat: q̃m Legatos Con
ſulum: uel litteras: audiſſent. Ipſos deinde appropinquare Legatos allatum
eſt. Tunc eninuero oĩs etas currere obuii. primus quiſq; oculis. auribuſq;
haurire tantum gaudium cupientes. Ad Molinum uſque pontem cõtinẽs
agmen peruenit. Legati erãt L. Veturius Philo P. Licinius Varus. Q. Ce
cilius Metellus. Circunfuſi omnis generis frequentia in forum peruenerũt.
Cum alii ipſos: alii comites eorum: quae acta eſſent: percontarẽtur: & ut quiſq;
audierat: exercitum hoſtium: Imperatoremq; occiſum. Legiones Romanas
incolumes: ſaluos Cõſules eſſe: extemplo aliis porro ĩpertiebãt gaudiũ ſuũ.
Cũ egre in curia puẽtũ eẽt: multo egregius ſũmota turba: ne Pr̃ibus miſceret̃.
Litterę ĩ Sẽatu recitatę ſũt. Inde in Contionẽ introducti legati. L. Veturius

2

litteris recitatis:ipſe planiuſ omnia quę acta erant expoſuit cum īgēti aſſēſu: Poſtremo etiam clamore uniuerſę Contionis.cū uix gaudium aīmiſ caperēt. Diſcurſum inde ab aliis circa tēpla deum:ut grates agerent.ab aliiſ domoſ: ut cōiugibus.liberiſq;.tam letum nunciū impertirēt. Senatus ꝙ M.Liuius & C.Claudius Conſules incolumi exercitu ducem hoſtium:legioneſq; occi diſſent:ſupplicationē in triduum decreuit.Eā ſupplicationem A.Hoſtilius Prętor pro concione edixit.celebrata a uiris:foeminiſq; eſt. Omnia templa p totum triduum ęqualem turbam habuere. cum Matronę āpliſſima ueſte.cū liberis:perinde:ac ſi debellatum for&:omni ſolutę metu:deiſ immortalibus grates agerent.Statum quoq; ciuitatis ea uictoria mouit:ut iam inde haud ſecus quam in pace:res inter ſe contrahere uendēdo:emēdo:mutuum dādo. argentum creditum ſoluēdo:auderent .C .Claudius Conſul cum in caſtra rediiſſ&:caput Haſdrubalis:quod ſeruatū cū cura attulerat:proiici āte hoſtiū ſtationes: captiuoſq; afroſ uictos ut erant:oſtēdi:duos etiā ex hiiſ ſolutoſ ire ad Annibalem:& expromere quę acta eſſent:iuſſit.Annibal tanto ſimul publico:familiariq; ictus luctu:agnoſcere ſe fortunā Carthaginiſ fert dixiſſe Caſtris inde motis: omnia auxilia:quę diffuſa latius tueri non poterat: In extremum Italię āgulum Brutios contraxit:& Metapōtinos ciuitatē uīuerſā excitos ſedibus ſuis:& Lucanoſ q ſuę ditionis erāt: ī Brutium traduxit

· Senat⁹ supplicandes ī triduū decreuit.

· E qualem turbam habuere.

· Suę dicionis erant

Vm tranſitu Haſdrubalis:quātum ī Italia declīauerat belli:tantum leuatę Hiſpanię uiderētur:renatum ibi ſubito par priori bellum eſt.Et Hiſpanias ea tēpeſtate ſic habebāt Romaī.poeniq;.Haſdrubal Giſgoīs filius ad Oceanū penitus:Gadeſq; cōceſſerat.Noſtri maris ora:omniſq; ferme Hiſpania:qua in orientem uergit: Scipionis ac Romane ditionis erat .nouuſ Imperator Hāno in locū Barchini Haſdrubalis:cū nouo exercitu ex africa tranſgreſſus:Magoniq; iūctus:quom in Celtiberia:quę media īter duo maria eſt:breui magnum hominū numerū armaſſ&:Scipio aduerſus eum.M.Syllanum:cū decem milibus peditum:equitibus quingentis:miſit Syllanus quātis maximis potuit itineribus:Impediebant autē & aſperitates uiarum.& anguſtię:ſaltibus crebris ut pleraq; Hiſpanię ſunt:incluſę:tamen non ſolum nuntios:ſed etiam famam aduētus ſui pręgreſſus:ducibus īdidē ex Celtiberia tranſfugis ad hoſtem puenit.Eiſdē auctoribus cōpertum eſt: ꝙ decem circiter milia ab hoſte abeſſent.Bina caſtra:circa uiam:qua irēt:eſſe leua Celtiberos:nouum exercitum:ſupra nouem milia hominum:dextra Punica tenere caſtra.Ea ſtatioībus:uigiliis: omī iuſta militari cuſtodia:tuta & firma eſſe.Illa altera ſoluta neglectaq; ut Barbaroꝝ :& tyronum.& minus timentium:ꝙ in ſua terra eſſent.Ea prius aggredienda eſſe ratus Syllanus ſigna quā maxime ad leuam iubebat ferri:Necunde ab ſtationibus Punicis cōſpiceretur.Ipſe pręmiſſis ſpeculatoribus citato agmine ad hoſtem pergit Tria milia ferme aberat:cum haud dum:quis q̄ hoſtium ſenſerat.confragoſa loca & obſita uirgultis:tenebant colles.ibi in caua ualle atque ob id occulta cōſidere militem:& cibum capere iubet.Interim ſpeculatores :trāſfugarum dicta affirmantes uenerunt.Tunc ſarcinis in medium coniectis arma Roāni capiunt.acieq; iuſta in pugnam uadūt.Mille paſſuum aberāt:cum ab hoſte conſpecti ſunt.repenteq; trepidari coeptum.Mago ex caſtris citato equo ad

PICTURED:

1. and 3. Examples of the beautiful foliate decorations which appear on initials throughout the book.
2. The annotation identifying Pietro Barbo as Pope Paul II.

A date and topical notes

Biondo Flavio (1392–1463)
Roma instaurata
[Rome: Printer of Statius, before March 25 1471]
Inc.2.B.2.39[1320]

In 1443, after ten years away, the *curia* returned to Rome, and in 1446 Biondo dedicated to Eugenius IV his first work, *Roma instaurata* (Rome restored), an attempt at identifying its ancient ruins. In 1474 Gaspare Biondo, publishing his father's *Italia illustrata* (Italy displayed), speaks of having already published *Roma instaurata*, whose printer was incapable of signalling topics in the margin. An edition with a blank margin does indeed survive, known since 1905 to antedate 6 August 1471, when someone bought a copy now in Paris. The copy illustrated here, given to the Library in 1917, takes it further back – and does more.

In red ink, someone has repeated in the margin the numbered chapter headings that precede each book. At 3.78, where Biondo mentions Pietro Barbo, the heading is followed by this: *1470 Petrus Barbo cardinalis Sancte Marie Nove Eugenii iiii nepos, qui nunc est PAULUS PAPA SECUNDUS* ('1470 … now POPE PAUL II'). In some calendars the year 1470 ended on what is now called March 24 1471, which becomes the latest possible date of publication.

A note in black ink on the same page concerns the 'unlucky' mansion known today as the Palazzo Doria-Pamphilj, 'where four cardinals died in quick succession; its current occupant is the patriarch of Antioch, none too lucky so far'. This annotator admires the building programme of Sixtus IV and his nephew Giuliano della Rovere but also gives details otherwise unattested about the whereabouts of ancient masonry: the obelisk that today dominates the Spanish Steps 'lies behind the Cardinal of Novara's vineyard', 'most of the Septizonium recently collapsed, and the stones were carried off for use on the basilica of Ss. Apostoli'. The latest event mentioned, the appointment of Guillaume d'Estouteville as Chamberlain to Sixtus IV, fell in August 1477.

Who was this annotator? He occasionally signs notes as *H* and twice addresses *Blonde pater*. As Maurizio Campanelli has noticed, Biondo had another son Girolamo (Hieronymus), *doctor utriusque iuris* by 1459, who in a manuscript with the arms of Biondo framed by *H B* assembled letters of his father's, between copies of *Roma instaurata* and *Italia illustrata*; there too *Blonde pater* occurs. Nothing is known about his career, but in the spirit of his father's work he has left us this record of Rome reborn.

Michael Reeve *was Kennedy Professor of Latin at the University of Cambridge from 1984 to 2006.*

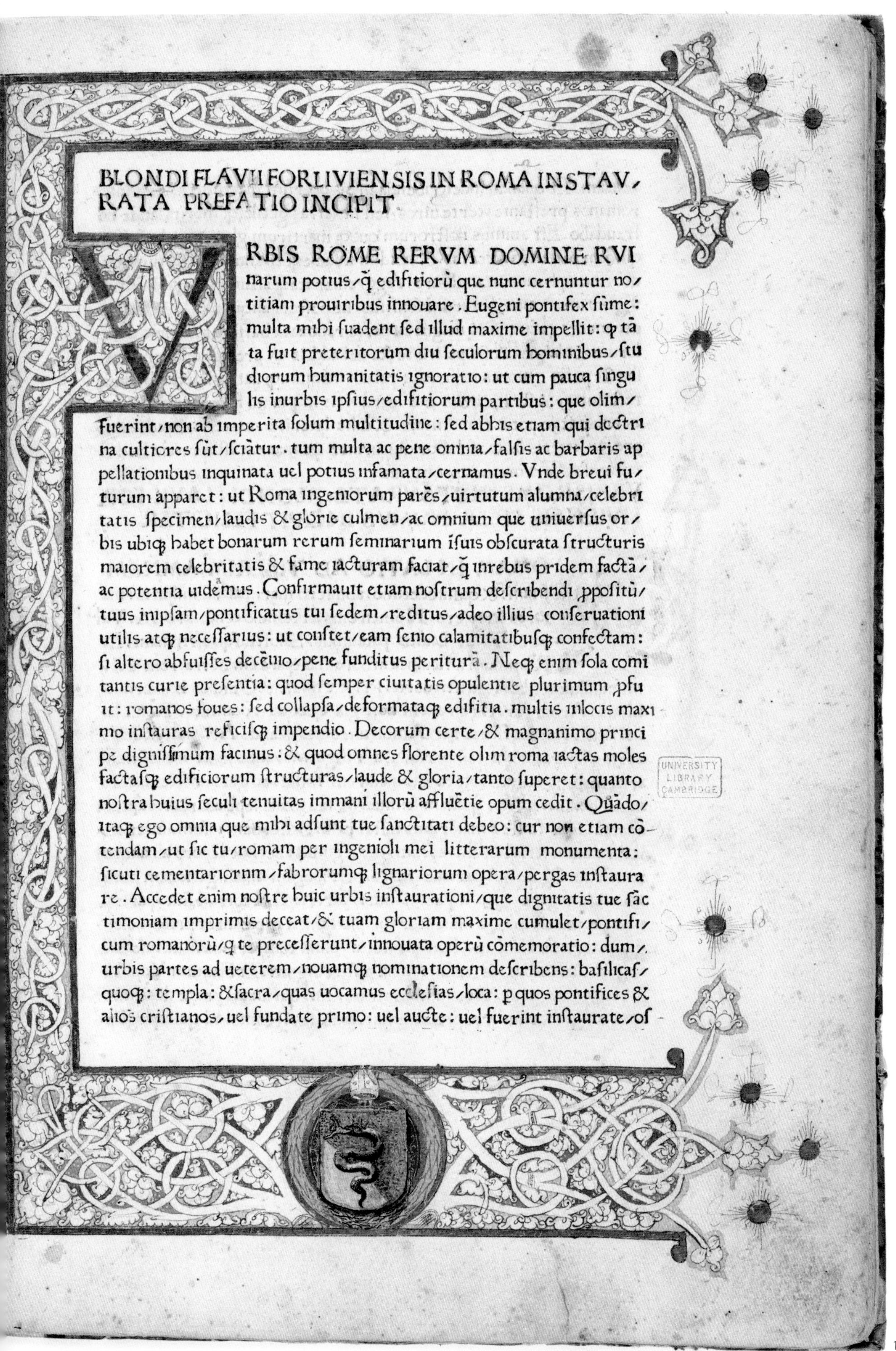

BLONDI FLAVII FORLIVIENSIS IN ROMA INSTAV-
RATA PREFATIO INCIPIT

VRBIS ROME RERVM DOMINE RVI
narum potius/q̄ edifitiorū que nunc cernuntur no/
titiam prouiribus innouare. Eugeni pontifex sūme:
multa mihi suadent sed illud maxime impellit: q̄ tā
ta fuit preteritorum diu seculorum hominibus/stu
diorum humanitatis ignoratio: ut cum pauca singu
lis inurbis ipsius/edifitiorum partibus: que olim/
fuerint/non ab imperita solum multitudine: sed abhis etiam qui doctri
na cultiores sūt/sciātur. tum multa ac pene omnia/falsis ac barbaris ap
pellationibus inquinata uel potius infamata/cernamus. Vnde breui fu/
turum apparet: ut Roma ingeniorum parēs/uirtutum alumna/celebri
tatis specimen/laudis & glorie culmen/ac omnium que uniuersus or/
bis ubiq; habet bonarum rerum seminarium īsuis obscurata structuris
maiorem celebritatis & fame iacturam faciat/q̄ inrebus pridem factā/
ac potentia uidemus. Confirmauit etiam nostrum describendi ꝓpositū/
tuus inipsam/pontificatus tui sedem/reditus/adeo illius conseruationi
utilis atq; necessarius: ut constet/eam senio calamitatibusq; confectam:
si altero abfuisses decēnio/pene funditus periturā. Neq; enim sola comi
tantis curie presentia: quod semper ciuitatis opulentie plurimum ꝓfu
it: romanos foues: sed collapsa/deformataq; edifitia. multis inlocis maxi
mo instauras reficisq; impendio. Decorum certe/& magnanimo princi
pe dignissimum facinus: & quod omnes florente olim roma iactas moles
factasq; edificiorum structuras/laude & gloria/tanto superet: quanto
nostra huius seculi tenuitas immani illorū affluētie opum cedit. Quādo/
itaq; ego omnia que mihi adsunt tue sanctitati debeo: cur non etiam cō-
tendam/ut sic tu/romam per ingenioli mei litterarum monumenta:
sicuti cementariornm/fabrorumq; lignariorum opera/pergas instaura
re. Accedet enim nostre huic urbis instaurationi/que dignitatis tue sāc
timoniam imprimis deceat/& tuam gloriam maxime cumulet/pontifi/
cum romanorū/q te precesserunt/innouata operū cōmemoratio: dum/
urbis partes ad ueterem/nouamq; nominationem describens: basilicas/
quoq;: templa: &sacra/quas uocamus ecclesias/loca: ꝑ quos pontifices &
alios cristianos/uel fundate primo: uel aucte: uel fuerint instaurate/os-

1

iis que forent reliqua exiſtimamus futura: tamē paucissima inposterū
certa oſtendere speramus. Siquis enim urbis Rome etatis noſtre par
tes singulas uel mēte uel oculis luſtrando peruagabitur: ea que populo
nunc & domibus frequētata sunt/a nobis pene intacta intelliget: quod
quidem nulla a nobis neglientia/aut in aduertentia magis factum eſt/
q̄ ne ignota impudenter asserere: aut impossibilia uarie & leuiter co/
nari compellamur. Libet tamē aliqua ex parte ipsam scribendi sine an
tiquis & dignis fide teſtibus audaciam qualis futura fuerit oſtendere.
Ea in regione omnium presentis urbis populo frequentissime/quam
capitolio exquiliis: campomartio: & panthzone uidemus clausam/eccle
sia eſt sancti Marci: quam tuus Eugenii pontifex nepos/Petrus gēte
Barba patricius uenetus & sancte Marie noue Cardinalis inhabitat.
Eam scribit Petrus bibliothecarius: a Marco pontifice Romano/eius
nominis primo: iuxta pallaturas fuisse edificatam: & licet multorum ut
apparet in gentium olim edifitiorum ruine: multa nunc cernantur fun
damenta: quid tamen ille fuerint pallature ignoro. Proximā illi ecclesiā
basilice duodecim apoſtolorum nunc inhabitat/& cardinalatus titulo te
net Bisarion ex conſtantinopoli grecus/cui niceno uulgaris eſt appella/
tio. Quis uero ipsam edificauerit ecclesiam: aut que fuerint edificia/
quorum ingentia apud eam cernuntur ueſtigia/mihi penitus eſt igno
tum & tamen extantia ipsius ecclesie monumenta/ante annum trecente
simum scripta/fuisse dicunt inter ipsius ecclesie parrochiam/& prope
capitolium/Veneris hortū cognomine mirabilem: & multa haud quaq̄
ignobilia quorum loci & situs nullam scire possumus certitudinem. Ec/
clesiam uero sancti Marcelli/quam Nicolaus patria surrentinus/& ei/
usdem ecclesie tituli cardinalis appellatione Capuanus inhabitat. Scri/
bit Bibliothecarius a Lucina nobili muliere uia salaria fuisse edifica/
tam/in catalubio. quod mazentii carnifices animalium ſtabulo habere
consueuissent. quo in sordidissimo loco tentus & passus fuerit Beatus
Pontifex Marcellus. Sed eius palatii quod idem cardinalis elegantissi
mum/apud sancte Marie inuialata ecclesiam edificat: ruine inter ce/
teras urbis conspicue. quid olim fuerint nullo in loco scriptum inueni/
mus: & tamē quātū ex Sexti Ruffi descriptione urbis possumus asse/
qui coniectura/Isidis templum ibi fuisse tenemus: apud quod in porte
triumphalis descriptione Vespasianum & Titum triumphatores/noc
te illa que triumphum precessit: quieuisse oſtendimus. Scribit enim

.ROME INSTAVRATE.L.I.INDICES

PICTURED:

1. and 2. Annotations signalling ownership by a Cambridge scholar and a king.

A Henrician stray

Cicero (106–43 BC)
Orationes
Venice: Christophorus Valdarfer, [not after 9 November] 1471
Inc.2.B.3.3[1366]

A promising young Cambridge scholar, Thomas Langton (about 1430–1501) travelled to Italy first in 1464 and then again for a longer period from 1468 to 1473. Abroad to prepare himself for a career in the Church, he was duly created doctor of canon law by the University of Bologna in 1473. He then embarked on a meteoric career in England that culminated in his election as Archbishop of Canterbury on 22 January 1501, just five days before his sudden death of the plague. A scourge of heretics, he is now best remembered for his laudatory comments about Richard III, maintaining that 'I never liked the conditions of any prince so well as his'.

Langton would later claim that he owed his ecclesiastical preferments to his learning, and he appears to have amassed a small but interesting collection of manuscripts and printed books: these can be identified by the inscription of his name in them, normally in the form 'Mastyr Langton'. Although his will does not mention books other than a small antiphoner for the chapel at Pembroke College, Cambridge, they seem to have passed to Henry VII, and four were later stored at Westminster Palace, where characteristic inventory numbers were inscribed in them. Several others were kept at Hampton Court or Greenwich Palace. Two later came into the possession of John Moore, Bishop of Ely, and passed with the rest of his collection to Cambridge University Library in 1715. Both were no doubt acquired during Langton's second Italian sojourn. One, a copy of Cicero's *Orationes*, edited by the humanist scholar Ludovico Carbone, contains a characteristic 'No 628'. It corresponds to the matching entry in the inventory taken of the Upper Library at Westminster Palace in 1542 for '*Orationes Ciceronis*'. This can thus be indisputably identified as the royal copy.

1

This edition was described by Thomas Frognall Dibdin in *Bibliotheca Spenceriana* (1814) as one of the most magnificent productions of the Venetian press, and a note in another copy, dated 20 January, 1471/2, gives a price of two gold ducats. Scholars cite the purchase on 13 January 1474 of the Rome 1471 edition of *Orationes* by John Shirwood (later Bishop of Durham) as one of the earliest acquisitions by an Englishman of an Italian book. The Langton *Orationes* probably anticipates this, and may well be the first printed copy of this collection to arrive in England.

James P. Carley *is Professor of the History of the Book at the University of Kent.*

non minore labore tueor quā cōparo. Pro his igitur oībus rebus: ꝑ meis ī oēs singularibus studiis pro q; hac q̄m pspicitis ad cōseruādū po. ro. diligentia: nihil a uobis nisi huius temporis totiusq; mei cōsulatus memoriam postulo: quæ dū erit in uestris infixa mētibus firmissimo me septum esse muro arbitror. Quod si meā spem uis improborū fefellerit atq; superauerit: cōmendo uobis paruum meū filium cui profecto satis erit præsidii non solum ad salutē uerū etiā ad dignitatē si eius qui hæc omnia suo solus periculo cōseruarit illū filium esse memineritis: Quapropter de summa salute nostra P.C. Po: Q. ro. de uestris coniugibus: ac liberis: de aris: de focis: de fanis atq; templis: de totius urbis tectis ac sedibus: de imperio ac libertate: de salute Italiæ: de uniuersa rep. decernite diligenter: ut statuistis ac fortiter. habetis enim eum consulē qui & parere uestris decretis non dubit&: & ea quæ statueritis quoad uiuet defendere: & per seipsum præstare possit.

Germani ingenii quis non miretur acumen:
Quod uult germanus protinus efficiet:
Aspice quam mira libros impresserit arte:
Quam subito ueterum tot monumenta dedit
Nomine Cristophorus: Valdarfer gentis alumnus:
Ratisponensis gloria magna soli:
Nunc ingens Ciceronis opus: causasq; forenses
Quas inter patres dixit & in populo.
Cernis quam recto: quam emendato ordine struxit
Nulla figura oculis gratior esse potest:
Hoc autem illustri Venetum perfecit in urbe
Præstanti Mauro sub Duce Christophoro:
Accipite hunc librum quibus est facundia cordi
Qui te Marce col& sponte disertus erit.

M.CCCC.LXXI. LODO.CARBO.

Chap pr. Langton

2

PICTURED:

1. Benedetto Bordon's glorious architectural frontispiece.
2. and 3. Examples of the decorated initials found throughout the book.
4. A detail of the manuscript dedicatory leaf, imitating print.
5. Although restored, portions of the original Italian knot work binding survive.

An ancient manual for Renaissance rulers

Dio Chrysostom (about AD 40–about AD 115)
De regno
[Venice: Christophorus Valdarfer, not after 9 November 1471]
SSS.15.5

This book epitomizes the relationship between early printing, humanistic scholarship and deluxe illumination in Renaissance Venice. Printed by Christophorus Valdarfer, who began his career there in 1470, it contains a treatise on government by the Greek rhetorician and philosopher Dio Chrysostom. The work was translated into Latin by Gregorio Tifernate at the request of Pope Nicholas V, and Tifernate's address to the Pope opens the volume. The editor, Francesco Piccolomini, dedicated the translation to the Habsburg prince and future Holy Roman Emperor Maximilian I. Dated 1 January 1469, Piccolomini's dedication to the ten-year-old Maximilian praises the wise rule of the prince's father. In most copies the dedication was printed, whereas in this copy it is written by hand. This had until now remained undetected, a measure of the scribe's skill in mimicking the font. The dedication is penned on a bifolium which belongs to the volume's contemporary binding. If the original text block included the printed address, a stub glued to the leaf that now contains the manuscript version might be all that remains of it. Perhaps it was replaced with the manuscript copy because it was damaged when the facing page received its illumination?

The frontispiece has been attributed to Benedetto Bordon, one of the most versatile artists of the Veneto. His earliest signed illuminations, found in two legal incunables printed in 1477 and 1479, provide the closest parallels for the illumination in this volume. It shows Bordon creating a design that became typical throughout his career: borders with mythological or historical characters set in atmospheric landscapes. It also shows the first stages in the development of the architectural frontispiece, conceived in four planes and full of three-dimensional conceits. The distant landscape is partially blocked by the text, which is written on a parchment scroll. Strings attach the scroll to the ankles of *putti*, the cherubs ubiquitous in Renaissance painting and sculpture. They stand on top of a Roman arch, a symbol of imperial triumph, while in the foreground Dio Chrysostom and Trajan converse in the company of three youths. The last line of text, just above the figures, recalls the philosopher's friendship with the Emperor and continues overleaf with an account of their frequent strolls in the countryside. The clever text–image amalgam would have delighted an attentive reader–viewer. Image and text seem to merge in this thoughtful creation of Renaissance illusionism, a sumptuous example of hand illumination on the printed page.

Stella Panayotova *is Keeper of Manuscripts and Printed Books at the Fitzwilliam Museum, Cambridge, and Director of the Cambridge Illuminations and MINIARE research projects.*

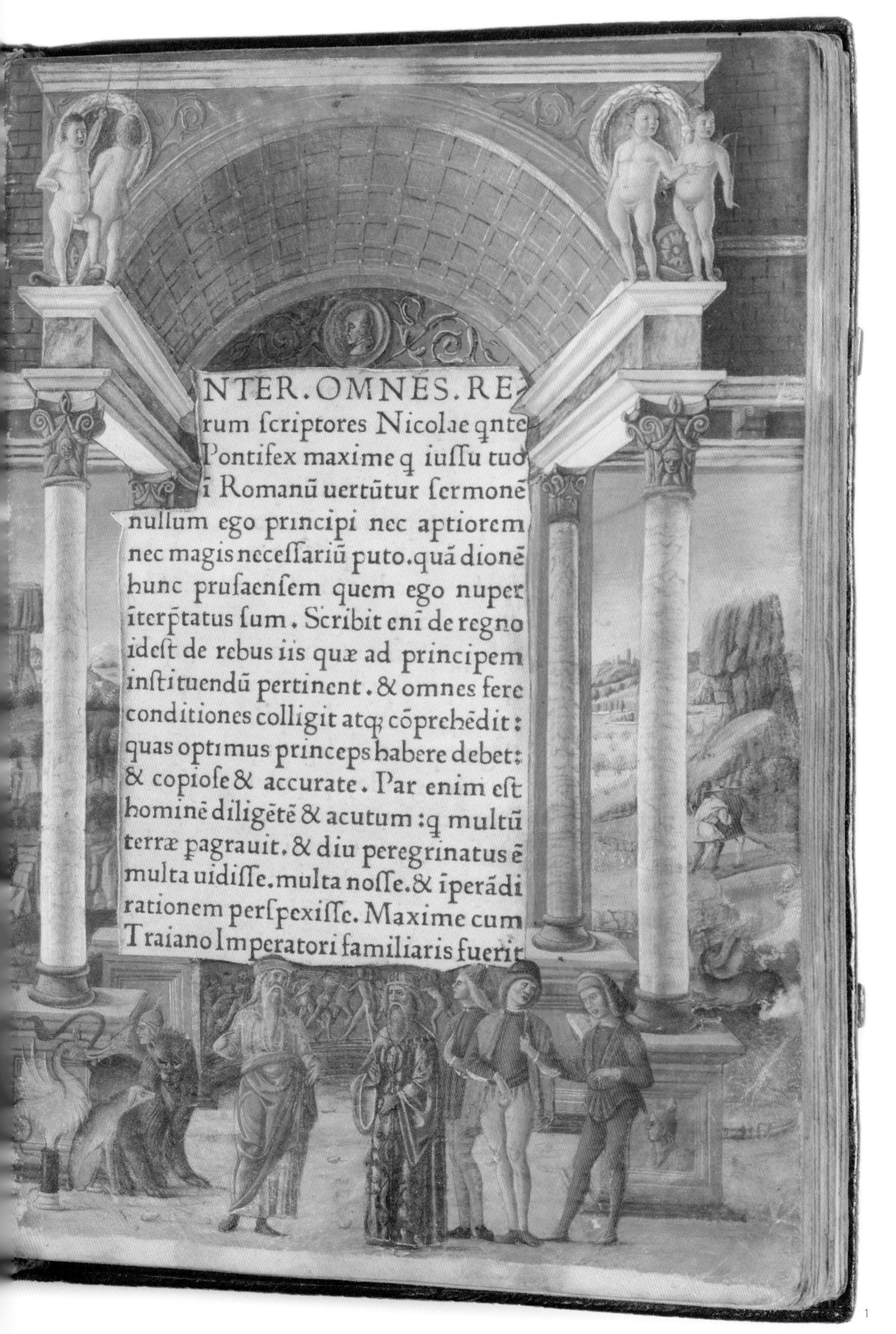

NTER . OMNES . RE
rum ſcriptores Nicolae qnte
Pontifex maxime q iuſſu tuo
ī Romanū uertūtur ſermonē
nullum ego principi nec aptiorem
nec magis neceſſariū puto . quā dionē
hunc pruſaenſem quem ego nuper
īterp̄tatus ſum . Scribit enī de regno
ideſt de rebus iis quæ ad principem
inſtituendū pertinent . & omnes fere
conditiones colligit atq; cōprehēdit :
quas optimus princeps habere debet :
& copioſe & accurate . Par enim eſt
hominē diligētē & acutum : q multū
terræ p̄agrauit . & diu peregrinatus ē
multa uidiſſe . multa noſſe . & īperādi
rationem perſpexiſſe . Maxime cum
Traiano Imperatori familiaris fuerit

1

2

3

Ad Illuſtriſſimũ & Sereniſſimum
dominum dominũ Maximilianum
diui Cæſaris Friderici Tercii filium
Franciſcus de Picolhomineiis Seneñ.
.S. Euſtachii Cardinalis.

4

5

1472

PICTURED:

1. and 4. Examples of the remarkable woodcuts of military equipment throughout the book.
2. The armorial device of Elisabeth Auguste von Sulzbach, on the book's eighteenth-century red morocco binding.
3. The visible marks of later owners.

Owners and users: two different approaches

Roberto Valturio (1405–1475)
De re militari
[Verona]: Johannes Nicolai de Verona, 1472
Inc.2.B.19.1[2158]

This handsome volume is a study in miniature of the fashions and reasons for owning incunabula down the centuries. *De re militari*, a treatise on military devices and stratagems by the fifteenth-century Italian engineer Roberto Valturio, is celebrated for its numerous woodcuts of weapons, and this copy has extensive contemporary rubrication and additional decorative text to enhance its attraction to the eye. Its gold-tooled armorial binding shows that it was owned in the eighteenth century by Elisabeth Auguste von Sulzbach (1721–1794), wife of the Elector of Bavaria, and thereafter it belonged to numerous well-known book collectors of the nineteenth century. Inscriptions and other evidence on the endleaves show that it passed through the collections of the French statesman Talleyrand (1754–1838) and of William Beckford (1760–1844), builder of Fonthill; when his library was auctioned in 1883, it was bought by the famous London dealer Bernard Quaritch, who sold it on to William Mitchell (1821/2–1908), celebrated for his collections of early woodcuts. In 1907 the book was once again in Quaritch's hands and was sold to John Charrington (1856–1939), alumnus of Trinity College, who gave it to the University Library in 1916.

1

What can we say about the book's history before the eighteenth century? Very little, because such evidence as once existed was deliberately removed when making it fit for aristocratic ownership. There is no trace of the original binding, and several pages bear the shadows of early ink marginalia which have been washed out. Those earlier and now anonymous owners would have been interested in this book primarily as a text, on which the marginalia would have commented; the later owners, whose names we know, valued it as something collectable, as the first printed edition of a military manual and a historic material object. Their annotations, on the endleaves, do not relate to the text but to early bibliographies of incunabula, or previous owners, showing an altogether different approach to where the book's interest lies. Today, we may regret the extirpation of earlier evidence of the book's ownership and use, but the way those later collectors changed and regarded it is all part of the book's individual history, and a reflection of those broader trends in attitudes to books down the centuries.

David Pearson *is Director of Culture, Heritage and Libraries at the City of London Corporation and is a Past President of the Bibliographical Society.*

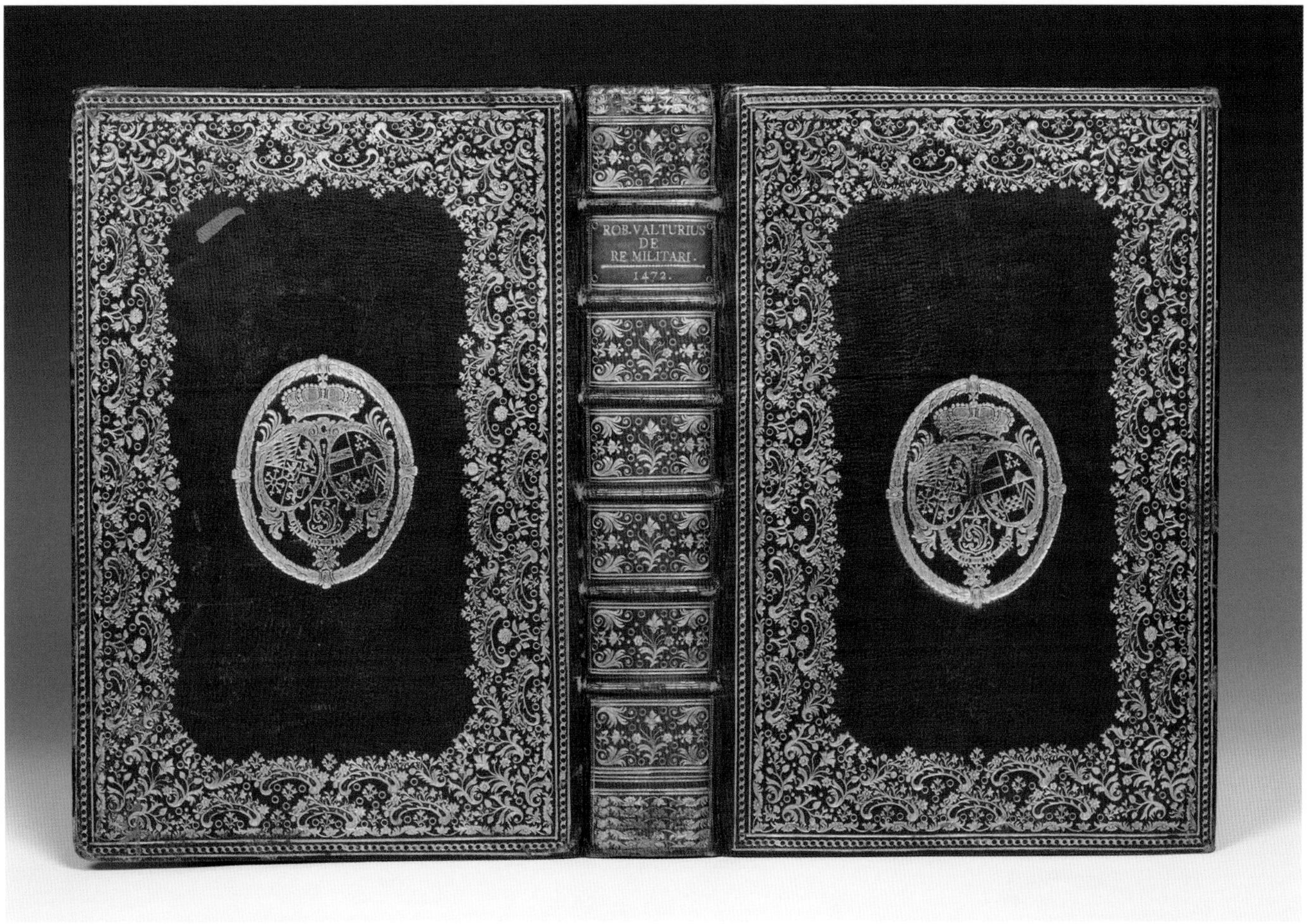

2

3

4

VINEA machina ex lignis leuioribus colligatur latitudine pedū octo: Altitudine septem. longitudine uero. xvi. cuius tectum munitione duplici tabulatis cratibusque contexitur: latera uero uimine sepiuntur: unde nomen ortum putāt: ne saxorum telorumq; impetu penetrentur: Extrinsecus autem ne īmisso concremetur incendio: crudis: uel recētibus coriis: uel cētonibus operit̄. Quomq; plures factę fuerit iunguntur in ordine: ac rotis ducunt̄: his deniq; tuti obsidentes ad subruenda murorū penetrant fundamēta: Lucanus ī. iii Tunc adoperta leui procedit uinea terra: sub cuius pluteis: & tecta fronde latentes: Moliri nunc ima parāt: & uertere ferro. Moenia nūc aries suspensa fortiter ictu: Incussus densi compagem soluere muri: Tēptat & īpositis unum subducere saxis: Liuius ab urb. con. xxi. ad uersus eum uineas agere cōstituit per quas aries moenibus admoueri poss&: idem in eodem itaq; acrius de integro ortum est bellum pluribusq; partibus uix accipientibus quibusdam opera locis uineę cępte agi: admoueriq; Aries. Testudo est scut orū connexio ī modum testudinis: namq; in armorum generibus summunt milites ab animalibus nomina: ut aries: Testudo: hęc ex materia & tabulatis etiam contexitur: quę ne exuratur incēdio coriis uel ciliciis: uel cētonibus uestitur & ad similitudinē uerę testudinis uocabulū sūpsit Nam sicut illam ubi collecta in suum tegmen est: tutam ad oēs ictus uidemus esse: ubi uero caput nudat: & modo reducit modo ꝓfert ictibus patere: Ita machinamenti hoc genere inclusi tuti sunt interdum dum reducunt trabem: Interdumq; eserunt ut fortius cedant: detecti persępe ceduntur Testudo etiam qua accessus ad murum potest haberi: sic erit facienda: Basis compaginatur quadrilatera cui in quibus uersantur supponuntur rotarum axes laminis ferreis conclusi: ita ut habeāt cardines: & foramina quo uectes traiecti uersationes earum expediant: uti ante & post: ad dextrum leuumq; latus: Siue oblique ad angulos opus fuerit ad id uersatis ꝓgredi possit Possunt autem si opus fuerit hi maxime ex octo rotis esse: quibus agatur uerum secundum loci naturam opus erit tēperare. tegatur aūt testudo hec ex omni materia que maxime uim habere possit resistendoq; robur: pręter pinū uel alnum: uel aliud id genus. Hęc enim fragilia sunt: & ignem facile admittentia: ueluti ignis omnino non possit huic machinę obesse: argilla insuper cum capillo subacto: ad eam quam decet crassitudinem inducatur circa

1472

PICTURED:

1. The book's German binding, datable to the 1470s.
2. and 3. The ornamental initials added by the rubricator contrast with Schüssler's gotico-antiqua type.

'Severe, legible, regular and admirably designed' – William Morris

Cassiodorus (about 487–about 580)
Historia ecclesiastica tripartita
[Augsburg]: Johann Schüssler, about 5 February 1472
Inc.2.A.6.2[777]

Flavius Magnus Aurelius Cassiodorus Senator was a Roman administrator from near Catanzaro in southern Italy, who reached high office under the Ostrogoth King Theodoric. Born around 487, he lived to a great age, and in his retirement founded the monastery of Vivarium, following the Benedictine model, on his family estate. His *Historia tripartita*, which dates from this period, is a history of the early Christian church, cobbled together from a number of sources such as Josephus's *Jewish antiquities*. It was a popular work in the Middle Ages, and several versions were printed in the fifteenth century.

This handsome edition was printed in the important early printing city of Augsburg by Johann Schüssler, a shadowy figure who is known for only nine books. It is dated February 1472, and Schüssler died two years later, passing on his type to Günther Zainer. He is known to have had only this one type, of the round blackletter design known as gotico-antiqua. Nevertheless, the tight setting and sharp presswork of *Historia tripartita* make it an impressive piece of work. This copy is heavily rubricated throughout, with sections given more elaborately drawn two-line initials. The typesetting was indented a little to accommodate the initials, except in the case of the letter I, where there is no indentation and the wide variety of elaborate versions of the letter sprawl in the margins. There are also two vigorously drawn initials at the beginning, in red and green with bistre hatching.

William Morris (1834–1896) owned a copy of this edition. For Golden, the first type made for his Kelmscott Press, the fifteenth-century Venetian roman models are well documented. In the case of his second type, Troy (and its smaller cutting Chaucer), we know he based it on the kind of typeface used by Schüssler and the Zainers, but little documentary evidence survives of any definite model; Morris's own published account is fairly vague. He wrote a note in his copy of *Historia tripartita* dated January 1891, just when he was starting work on Troy; it reads, 'Schuszler's [sic] type is amongst the best of the less formal Gothic types: severe, legible, regular and admirably designed, it makes one regret the supplanting of Gothic by even the best Roman; say that of Jenson.' He added, 'the paper of this book is about as good as paper can be.'

Sebastian Carter *ran the Rampant Lions Press for many years, and is a typographical historian.*

1

Igitur athanasius ad
se factam epoꝝ edocui
dantium sibimet sac
nicenum· atqꝫ Theo
Narcissū cilicē·et sim
gentes et nudas valt
componentes. Quo f
imperator ut omne c
diqꝫ congregari prece
Misit itaqꝫ pariter de
largissime expēdi pre
egentibꝫ vniūsis · qu
etiam sacrū altare pa
preciosis decoratum.
Imperator interea arr
deret ꝫ scriptura currēt
prius adinuenerat de
verbis eam et diuīa l
ita se credē · q hec etia
enim eiꝰ expositiōis b
nro impatori Consta

2

Erunt antiquis principibus diligētie studiū
fuisse ut eis amatores quidem ornamentorum
purpuram atqꝫ coronā et his similia prepa=
rarent, Librorum vero habentes intentiōem
circa quasdam fabulas occupati conscriptiōes
agerent que audientiū corda mulcerēt. Porro
bella sectantes ꝫ ut sagittā oportune dirigerēt
bestiam prosternerent· lanceam bene iacularent·aut equum decēter
ascenderent. Prestabantur enim singuli regalibus eorum studentes
rebus illis que forent gratissima domināti, Alius itaqꝫ lapides pre:
ciosos dificile compertos offerebat, Alter tincturā purpure clariorē
Plurimi poemata aut diuersas conscriptiones insinuabant. Aliꝰ
bona cingula aut optimum armoꝝ pandebat vsum. Maxima vo
et imperialis putabatur huius popularis virtutis pars illa fore ꝫ
ad quam tunc amantis intentio declinabat. De pietate autem que
est verus ornatus imperij nulli studiose quodāmodo sermo fuit,

3

PICTURED:

1. The heavily-restored opening leaf, the illumination mimicking a style characteristic of the Veneto in the 1470s.
2. The elegant gold-tooled blue morocco binding.
3. The opening of canto 30 of Dante's *Inferno*.
4. The colophon set by Johann Neumeister, mimicking Dante's *terza rima* form.

The first edition of the first literary classic

Dante Alighieri (1265–1321)
La divina commedia
Foligno: Johann Neumeister and Evangelista [Angelini?], 11 April 1472
Inc.3.B.4.1[3782]

That three editions of the *Divina commedia* were published within a few months of each other in 1472, in three different places, and with three variant texts is a testimony to Dante's pan-Italian popularity in the century after his death and to the strength of a manuscript tradition that in the fourteenth century had been second only to the Bible.

The copy here is the earliest precisely dated edition (11 April 1472) and has long been accepted as the first. An edition dated 18 July 1472 was probably printed at Venice, and another printed at Mantua, although dated just 1472, is thought to be of around the same date.

Fifteen editions were printed in Italy in the fifteenth century, as far apart as Naples and Milan, but it was not until the ninth, in 1481, that one was printed in Dante's native city of Florence (see pp. 88–89). The version of the text printed at Foligno in Umbria by Johann Neumeister, who had come from Mainz in the mid-1460s, and Evangelista Angelini was reprinted only twice – at Naples in 1477 and 1478/9 – but, while it was a textual dead-end, the Foligno Dante has long held a prestige above its much rarer coeval editions.

In 1726, when the London-based Italian composer, librettist and bibliographer Nicola Francesco Haym placed the Foligno Dante at the head of a list of editions of Italian *Poeti epici*, there were probably only two copies in Britain, in the libraries of the Earls of Pembroke and Sunderland. In 1805 Henry George Quin bequeathed a copy to Trinity College, Dublin, and over the next ninety years others entered the Bodleian Library, the British Museum (two) and the John Rylands Library in Manchester. The Cambridge copy was the last to enter a British library.

The early provenance of this copy remains unknown but, to judge by its gold-tooled blue morocco binding of around 1800, it probably left Italy during the Napoleonic Wars. It also had some major paper restoration – the margins of the opening leaf were renewed, the damaged letters at the extremities carefully replaced by hand, and a new illuminated initial N with foliate extensions was painted over the original simple roman capital letter which is still faintly visible. It became what Kristian Jensen has defined as a bibliophilic 'object of luxury', far from the *milieu* of the blacksmith and mule-driver whom Dante's near-contemporary Franco Sacchetti had satirically imagined singing mangled versions of his tercets.

Robert Harding *is a director of the antiquarian bookdealers Maggs Bros., of London, and is a Fellow of the Society of Antiquaries of London.*

COMINCIA LA COMEDIA DI
dante alleghieri di firenze nella q̃le tracta
delle pene et punicioni de uicii et demeriti
et premii delle uirtu: Capitolo primo della
prima parte de queſto libro loq̃le ſechiama
inferno : nel quale lautore fa prohemio ad
tucto eltractato del libro :·

NEL mezo delcamin dinrã uita
mi ritrouai ꝑ una ſelua oſcura
che la diricta uia era ſmarrita
Et quanto adir q̃lera coſa dura
eſta ſelua ſeluaggia aſpra eforte
che nel penſier renoua la paura
Tante amara che pocho piu morte
ma pertractar del ben chio uitrouai
diro dellatre coſe chi uo ſcorte
I non ſo ben ridir come uentrai
tantera pien diſonno inſuquil punto
che la uerace uia abandonai
Ma poi chi fui appie dum colle gionto
la doue terminaua quella ualle
che mauea dipaura el cor compuncto
Guardai inalto et uidde le ſuoe ſpalle
ueſtite gia deraggi del pianeta
che mena drictto altrui per ogni calle
Allor fu la paura un pocho cheta
che nellaco del cor mera durata
la nocte chio paſſai contanta pieta

1

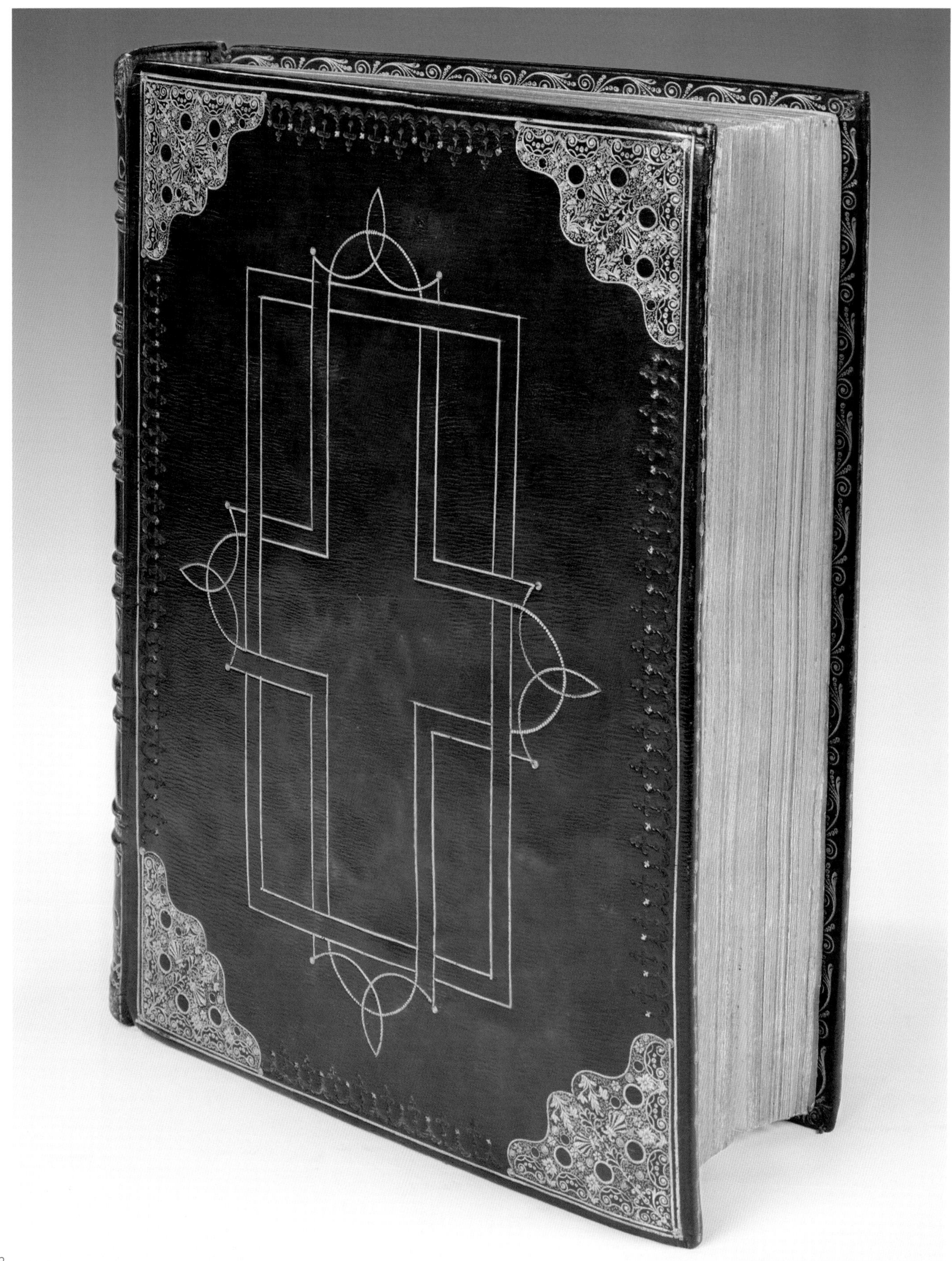

2

Si uedrai chi ſon lombra dicapocchio
che falſai limetalli conalchimmia
et te dee ricordar ſeben ta docchio·
Comio fui dinatura buona ſcimmia
CANTO·XXX ·Oue tracta diquella
medeſima materia et gente detta diſopra :·
NEl tempo che Iunone era crucciata
perſemele contral ſangue thebano
come moſtro una et altra fiata
Atamante diuenne tanto inſano
che ueggendo lamoglie condue filgli
andar carcata daciaſchuna mano
Grido tendian lereti ſichio pilgli
laleoneſſa et leoncini aluarcho
et poi diſteſe idiſpietati artilgli
Prendendo lun cauea nome learcho
et rotollo et percoſſelo adun ſaſſo
et quella ſannego conlaltro carcho

3

Nel mille quatro cento ſepte et due
nel quarto meſe adi cinque et ſei
queſta opera gentile impreſſa fue
Io maeſtro Iohanni Numeiſter opera dei
alla decta impreſſione et meco fue
Elfulginato Euangeliſta mei :·

4

1473

PICTURED:

1–7. Numerous examples of elaborate manicules, highlighting sections of the text deemed significant by successive owners.

Taking the book in hand

Aristotle (384–322 BC)

Ethica ad Nicomachum, Oeconomica, Politica

[Barcelona: Heinrich Botel, Georgius vom Holtz, and Johann Planck, about 1473]

Inc.3.H.2.2[3472–3]

In 1473, three German printers set up shop together in Spain, and this volume – containing three major texts by Aristotle – evidently represents the first fruits of their partnership. It is probably the earliest surviving book printed in Spain: the volume does not contain any publication information but is now thought to have been produced in Barcelona in 1473 or 1474 and not, as the standard sources had it until recently, four years later in Zaragoza, where Botel continued his work with Planck before finishing his career on his own in Lérida. It is not an especially distinguished piece of printing, and this copy has next to nothing in the way of illumination or rubrication. It has every appearance of a scholar's working copy, and the marks preserved in the margins suggest that it was subjected to heavy use by several generations of readers. There is at least one set of notes in a small Spanish hand of the late fifteenth century, and another layer of elegant inscriptions in an English hand of the sixteenth century.

The *Politics* in particular is bristling with marginal summaries, interlinear glosses, knotted brackets, and above all manicules: these are the dramatic pointing hands that may well have been the most common symbol produced by readers between the thirteenth and eighteenth centuries, and remain a familiar feature of public signage, popular advertising and industrial typography. The hand has always played a special role in the apprehension and retention of information: Aristotle himself (in the *De anima* [III:8]) praised the hand as the 'tool of tools' or 'instrument of instruments'. As such, it often stands in for the body of the teacher or student and serves to join the world of words and the world of things. Readers evidently developed their own distinctive styles, and they were usually more concerned with catching the eye than with anatomical accuracy. There are at least three different specimens poking at passages in the pages of this book, one with frilly cuffs, one with furry sleeves (or hairy arms?) and one marked by a dot on the back of the hand.

William Sherman *is Head of Research at the Victoria and Albert Museum, and Professor of Renaissance Studies at the University of York.*

uilibus opificiis occupatus eſt. in paucorū q̄ꝫ guber
natione tenues hoīes ad rem. p. non recipiunt̄. Ex
magno. n. cenſu ad honores rei. p. puenit̄. Artifices
tn̄ ad hanc ſpēm perueniſſe poſſunt: z ſi ſordidi ſint
qm̄ plerūq; diuicius habundāt. Apud thebanos lex
fuit: ut nemo abilis eſſet ad honores rei. p. ſuſcipiē
dos: niſi deceꝫ annos a mercatura deſtitiſſet. in mul
tis aūt rebus. p. attrahunt̄ ad ciuitateꝫ etiā peregri
ni. Eſt. n. lex in qbuſdam ciuitatibus: ut ſatis ſit ex
matre ciue eſſe genitū. z ſpurios q̄dā recipiūt. Atq
propter defectum legittimorum ciuiū tales faciunt
ciues. Paucitate. n. hoīm īducti his utunt̄ legibus.

1

iusmõi lege: q̃ q̃rũ causa optias leges esse oportꝫ: et
cuius gr̃a Socrates cẽset ita instituendũ de natis &
mulieribus. Amicitiã.n. putamus maxĩm esse bonũ
ciuitatibus. Nã sic minie seditiõibus agitabunt̃. &
unã esse ciuitatẽ laudat maxĩe Socrates. qd & uide
tur et ipse ingt esse amicitie opus. vt in amatoriis
sermõibus scimus dicentez. Aristophanẽ ꝑpter exi
miã amãtiũ cupiditatẽ applicari sib̃: & ex duobus
fieri unũ. Hic ergo ncẽm est ambos esse corruptos
uel unũ. At in ciuitatibus ncẽe est amicitiã infirmã
fluxãqꝫ fieri ꝑpter huiusmõi cõunitatẽ: & minie di
cere suuꝫ aut filiũ patrẽ: aut patrẽ filiuꝫ. vt.n paruꝫ
mellis multa in aqua diffusuꝫ insensibilẽ facit mixti
onẽ: sic accidit cõmũitatẽꝫ istã nequaq̃ ncẽam in tali
re.p. a nomibus extimãtibus uel patrẽ ut filii: uel
filium ut patris. vel fratres iuicẽ; Duo sunt q̃ faci
unt hoiem curam hẽre: & amare/propriũ scilicet et
affectio: quoruꝫ neutrum sit necesse est in huiusmo
di re.p. Insuper transs latio illa natorum ex agrico
lis & artificibus in custodes. & ex his in illos mag
nam cotinet difficultatem. queãdmodum tãdẽ fiet.
& cognoscãt ncẽe est dãtes et trãsferentes q̃bus q̃s
dedãt; Preterea et supius dicta magis ĩ his ncẽm
est euenire/puta rixas & plagas et amores ꝫ cedes.
Nã nõ amplius appellãt custodes fratres et filios ꝫ
patres et matres: q alus ciuibus dedunt̃. et rursus
q ex custodibus alus ciuibus: ut caueãt tale aliqd p
petrare ꝑpter cõsanguinitatẽꝫ; De cõitate igĩt na
toruꝫ et mulierũ determiatũ sit in hunc modum;

2

ı̃dẽ simpliciter: hi uero ex
int/sed impfecti. Vetustis
osdã opifices erãt serui: aut
etiã nũc tales plerıqꝫ sunt.
opificẽ faciet ciuem. Q si
est: quã diximus: dicendũ
ꝫ liberi modo/sed eorum q
sint alieni. Necessaria uero
s est. qui aũt publice: uiles
oc paulo adhuc cõsideranti
res habeat. Hoc.n. qd dix

5

Nam cum plures sint
ac prudẽtię. ac fiunt i
multos pedes habeat
sus. Et eodẽ modo ci
propter melius iudicã
rum opibus. Alii .n.
Sed in hoc differunt
ex multitudine: queã
aiunt: ꝫ picta artifici

6

2

tunc habeat: q̃ nũc. Nã nunc quidez nemo dubitat:
ex eo q̃r in singulos diuisę: sunt facultates in quãta
cunqꝫ multitudine. Tunc uero cuꝫ sint indiuise: ne

3

sdam. Quis igitur sit ciuis ex his patet.
abilitas est participande potestatis publi
ratiuę / aut iudiciarię: hunc ciuem esse di
s ciuitatis. Ciuitatem vero talium multi
: quę ipsa per se sufficiens sit (vt simplici
m) ad uiuendum. Consueuerunt autem
m esse ciuem: qui ex duobus ciuibus or

4

constare uideãtur:
abent uarietatem.
dunt detrimenta.
alii ob fortitudinẽ;
s loquẽtes/grosso
tatẽ ostendere: &
ent: de huiusmodi
singula quę de his
eius qui eruditur
e certitudinem exi
recipit: Simile qp
sionem recipere: ꝫ
urere; Quisqꝫ be
qꝫ bon⁹ est iudex.

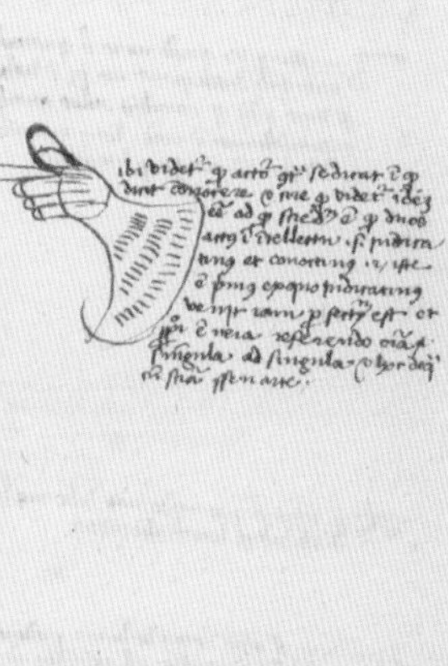

. Simpliciter au
st. Ex quo fit / vt
uditor sit ciuilis di
m: quę in vita uer
e illis est. Sequax
inaniter & inutili
tio/ sed actio; Ni
enis/ an moribus.
: sed in uiuendo /
ni perturbatione.
t ista cognitio/quẽ
s sunt. Qui vero
: his ista scire mꝫ
uditore quidem /
sit: & quid propo
t;

7

PICTURED:

1. John Paston's hand-written book list, mentioning *The play of chess.* © The British Library Board MS Add.43491, f.26.
2. The contents leaf of Caxton's *The play of chess.*

Game of thrones

Jacob de Cessolis (active 1288–1322)
The play of chess
[Ghent? David Aubert?, for William Caxton], 31 March 1474 (also recorded as [Bruges: William Caxton])
Inc.3.F.3.2[3308]

One November day in the late 1470s, Sir John Paston sat down, quill in hand, to draw up a list of the books he owned. He was in his mid-thirties, a Norfolk landowner who had found a place, after years of turmoil in what we now call the Wars of the Roses, at the court of the Yorkist king, Edward IV. Paston was also, his mother thought, a wastrel who did not come home to see her often enough. However unfair that judgement, it was true that his enthusiasm was reserved not for estate management, but for women, jousting and books. His library contained an impressive collection of romances, chronicles, and light religious reading. Among all the manuscripts, one volume stands out: 'A boke in preente off the Pleye of the…' The list is damaged, but it is clear that this new-fangled printed book was *The play of the chess*, William Caxton's translation of a thirteenth-century treatise.

Title notwithstanding, *The play of the chess* is not a how-to manual for aspiring grandmasters. Instead, it is a 'mirror for princes', a discussion of how a kingdom should properly be governed, in this case using the rules of chess as an extended explicatory analogy. To turn the pages of the University Library's copy, knowing that John Paston once owned the same edition, is to experience a telescoping of time. Caxton dedicated his work to Edward IV's ill-fated brother George, Duke of Clarence, whom John Paston knew; in 1468, he had served in the entourage of George and Edward's sister Margaret when she travelled to Bruges to marry the Duke of Burgundy. The book's print is astonishingly fresh, and its text – a store of treasures for a political historian – is full of vivid turns of phrase. 'All love is blind', we are told in the section on the 'alphins' (bishops, in the modern game) who dispense justice on the king's behalf. 'There love is, there can not right judgement be given.' But it is in the chapter on the knights that John Paston is likely to have seen himself, and perhaps also the troubled times in which he lived. 'Where shall thou find a man in these days that will expose himself for the worship and honour of his friend or for the common weal? Seldom or never shall he be found.'

Helen Castor *is a medieval historian, writer and broadcaster, and a Bye-Fellow of Sidney Sussex College, Cambridge.*

1

This booke conteyneth . iiii . traytees / The first traytee is of the Inuencion of this playe of the chesse / and conteyneth . iii . chapitres

The first chapitre is vnder what kynge this playe was founden

The . ii . chapitre / who fonde this playe

The . iii . chapitre / treteth of . iii . causes why hit was made and founden

The seconde traytee treteth of the chesse men / and conteyneth . v . chapitres

The first chapitre treteth of the forme of a kynge and of suche thinges as apperteyne to a kynge

The . ii . chapitre treteth of ye quene & her forme & maners

The . iii . chapitre of the forme of the alphins and her offices and maners

The . iiii . chapitre is of the knyght and of his offices

The . v . is of the rooks and of their maners and offices

The thirde traytee is of the offices of the comyn peple And hath . viii . chapitres

The first chapitre is of the labourers & tilinge of the erthe

The . ii . of smythis and other werkes in yron & metall

The . iii . is of drapers and makers of cloth & notaries

The . iiii . is of marchantes and chaungers

The . v . is of phisicyens and cirugiens and apotecaries

The . vi . is of tauerners and hostelers

The . vii . is of ye gardes of the citees & tollers & customers

The . viii . is of ribauldes disepleyars and currours

The . iiii . traytee is of the meuyng and yssue of them And hath . viii . chapitres

The first is of the eschequer

The seconde of the yssue and progression of the kynge

1474

PICTURED:

1. The exposed spine, showing the single surviving secondary tacket and octagonal reinforcement on the lower sewing support.
2. The calf parchment cover with the envelope flap extending from the right cover.
3. The outside of the right cover with the manuscript title.
4. The partially erased inscription on the left slip of the upper sewing support.
5. The spine of the sewn bookblock on the left with the detached cover on the right.
6. The inscription of Antonio Graziadei on the first leaf of the *Conclusiones*.

Liber sine asseribus – a half-completed fifteenth-century binding

Clemens de Terra Salsa (active fifteenth century)
Conclusiones formales in Thomae de Aquino summam theologicam
[Basel: Printer of the *Modus legendi abbreviaturas*, about 1484]

bound with:
Aristotle (384–322 BC)
Organon
[Louvain: Conradus Braem, 1474–1475]
Inc.4.F.2.3[4152]

The plain parchment cover on this composite volume might not appear remarkable, but the presence of a partially erased late fifteenth-century inscription – possibly once the name of the author of the first work in the volume, Frater Clemens de Terra Salsa – on the upper sewing support slip in the left joint suggests otherwise. It is highly unusual to find an inscription in such a place, and suggests that when it was written, the book had no cover, and that this indication of the author or content, if such it was, was intended to identify it within the book trade before the cover was added. The structure is simple, sewn on only two sewing supports, without adhesive, linings or endbands, though it does use parchment sewing guards in the centre of each gathering, a common feature of paper-leaved books until the 1490s. The use of the first, blank, text leaf as a flyleaf, whilst adding only a single endleaf to protect the textblock (hooked around the final gathering of the volume, which did not provide a blank final leaf), shows a concern for economy. For whom and why the two editions, printed some ten years apart, were sewn together is unknown, but the state of the volume suggests that it was done within the book trade.

Books could be bought as sewn bookblocks from the late fifteenth century to the eighteenth, leaving the choice of cover and decoration to the purchaser. Here, an inexpensive plain calf parchment wrapper with a fore-edge flap was chosen, following a typically Germanic pattern. It was attached to the bookblock by means of four small secondary 'tackets' of cord threaded through octagonal leather reinforcements on the spine and between the elements of the double supports close to each end of the bookblock: only one of the tackets has survived.

This volume was acquired by Antonio Graziadei, Abbot of the monastery of Admont in Austria between 1483 and 1491, who wrote his name (*Anth[onius] Abb[as]*) on the recto of the second leaf, perhaps when he removed manuscripts and printed books from the abbey before his arrest and death in prison. The parchment cover has a possibly slightly later title on the right cover, which could suggest that the cover was supplied only after the book was returned to the monastery. This rare survival was given to the University Library by Sir Stephen Gaselee in 1936.

Nicholas Pickwood *is Director of the Ligatus Research Centre at the University of the Arts London, studying the history of bookbinding.*

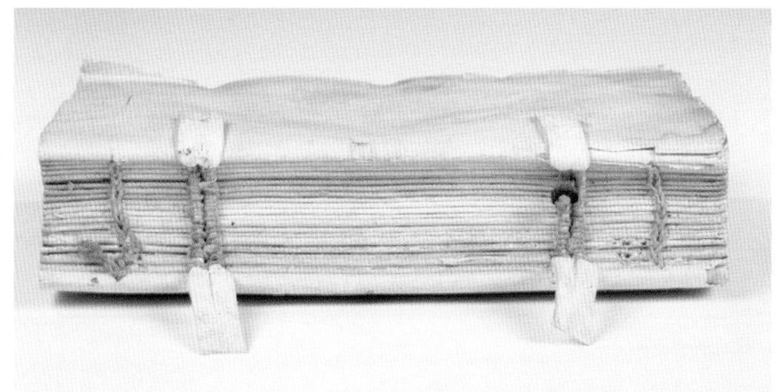
1

2

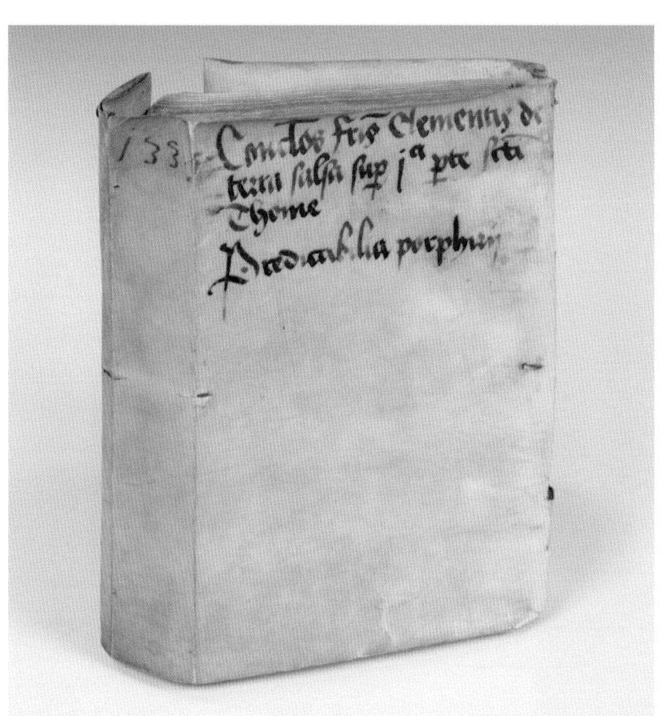
3

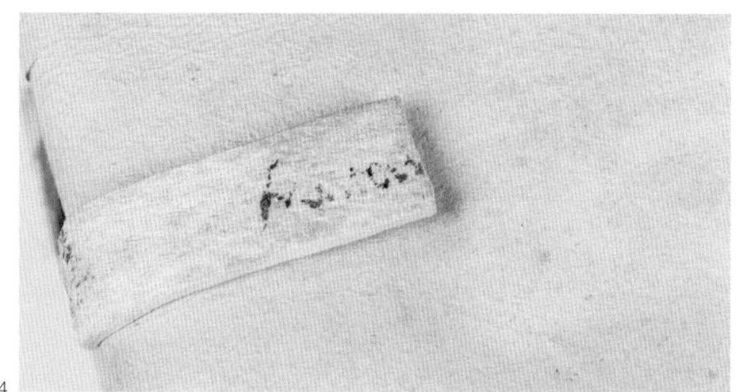
4

5

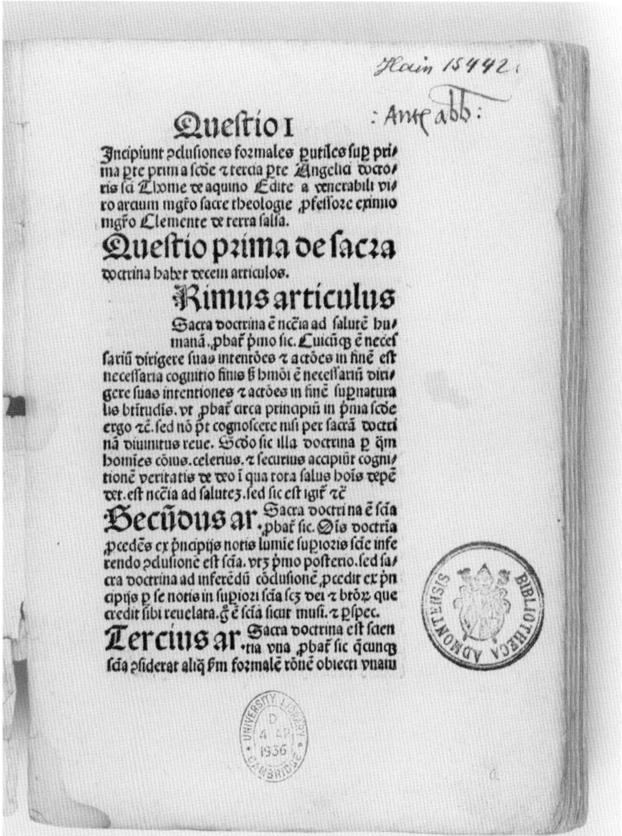
Hain 15442.

: Ante abb:

Questio I

Incipiunt ꝯclusiones formales ꝑutiles sup prima pte prima scđe ꝛ tercia pte Angelici docto-
ris scī Thome de aquino Edite a venerabili vi-
ro arcium mgr̄o sacre theologie ꝓfessore eximio
mgr̄o Clemente de terra salsa.

Questio prima de sacra
doctrina habet decem articulos.

Primus articulus

Sacra doctrina ē nccīa ad salutē humanā. ꝓbať p̄mo sic. Cuicūqꝫ ē necessariū dirigere suas intentōes ꝛ actōes in finē est
necessaria cognitio finis ſ̄ hmōi ē necessariū dirigere suas intentiones ꝛ actōes in finē supnatura-
lis btitudis. vt ꝓbať circa principiū in p̄ma scđe
ergo ꝛc̄. sed nō p̄t cognoscere nisi per sacrā doctri-
nā diuinitus reue. Scđo sic illa doctrina ꝑ q̄m
homies cōīus. celerius. ꝛ securius accipiūt cogni-
tionē veritatis de deo ī qua tota salus hoīs depē-
det. est nccīa ad salutez. sed sic est igiť ꝛc̄

Secūdus ar. Sacra doctrina ē scīa
ꝓbať sic. Ōis doctrina
ꝓcedēs ex p̄ncipijs notis lumie supioris scīe infe-
rendo ꝯclusionē est scīa. vtz p̄mo posterio. sed sacra doctrina ad inferēdū cōclusionē ꝓcedit ex p̄n-
cipijs ꝑ se notis in supiori scīa scz dei ꝛ btōꝝ que
credit sibi reuelata. g̃ ē scīa sicut musi. ꝛ ꝑspec.

Tercius ar. Sacra doctrina est scien-
tia vna ꝓbať sic q̄cunqꝫ
scīa ꝯsiderat aliq̄ ſm formalē rōnē obiecti vnam

6

PICTURED:

1. An early twentieth-century photograph of the Long Gallery at Sudbury Hall, showing it lined with bookcases. © Country Life
2. Bookplates charting the book's later history.
3. and 4. Annotations of earlier owners.

A tale of two libraries

Pope Pius II (1405–1464)
De duobus amantibus Euryalo et Lucretia
[Sant'Orso: Johannes de Reno, about 1475]
Inc.5.B.21.1[4236]

Between the French Revolution and the middle of the nineteenth century, vast numbers of early printed books flowed through the salerooms from the historic collections of continental Europe into the private libraries of aristocratic British book collectors. Many, though by no means all, of these libraries were in great country houses. As often as not changing tastes and declining finances meant that such books were then sold in turn later in the nineteenth century to national and university libraries, and to private collectors in the United States. Changes in the law and the great agricultural depression created a climate where landowners often found it necessary to convert ancestral books into convenient investment capital.

Few libraries have disappeared more completely than that of George Warren, fifth Lord Vernon (1803–1866), a crack shot, fanatical bibliophile and amateur Dante scholar. In its heyday, the Vernon Library filled the whole of the seventeenth-century Long Gallery at Sudbury Hall, the family's ancestral home in Derbyshire. Today perhaps not one National Trust visitor in a thousand realizes that this great room was once crammed with books, but a photograph taken in 1904 shows it shelved end-to-end with no fewer than eighty bookcases. Vernon's famous collection of his favourite poet overflowed into the neighbouring gallery, the Dante Room, and there were still more books in a downstairs drawing room.

1

Parts of Lord Vernon's collection were sold in his own lifetime to Roger Staynor Holford (1808–1892) and they formed the core of Holford's library at Dorchester House in London, which was in its turn sold between 1924 and 1928. Many of the Sudbury books which Vernon did not sell to Holford were sold in 1918, including this copy of *De duobus amantibus*. Although a very early example of an epistolary novel, written in 1444 and a bestselling book of the fifteenth century, the interest of this copy today lies in how its provenance is typical of the fate of bibliomaniac libraries in Britain in general, and of Vernon's in particular. Its buyer in 1918 was the collector C.S. Ascherson of Merton College, Oxford, whose library was in turn purchased by Quaritch in 1944–1945, and this book sold on to Cambridge University Library shortly afterwards.

The Long Gallery at Sudbury was cleared of its bookcases after the final sales of the 1960s and spectacularly, if controversially, redecorated: not a trace of its erstwhile library function survives.

Mark Purcell *is Libraries Curator of the National Trust.*

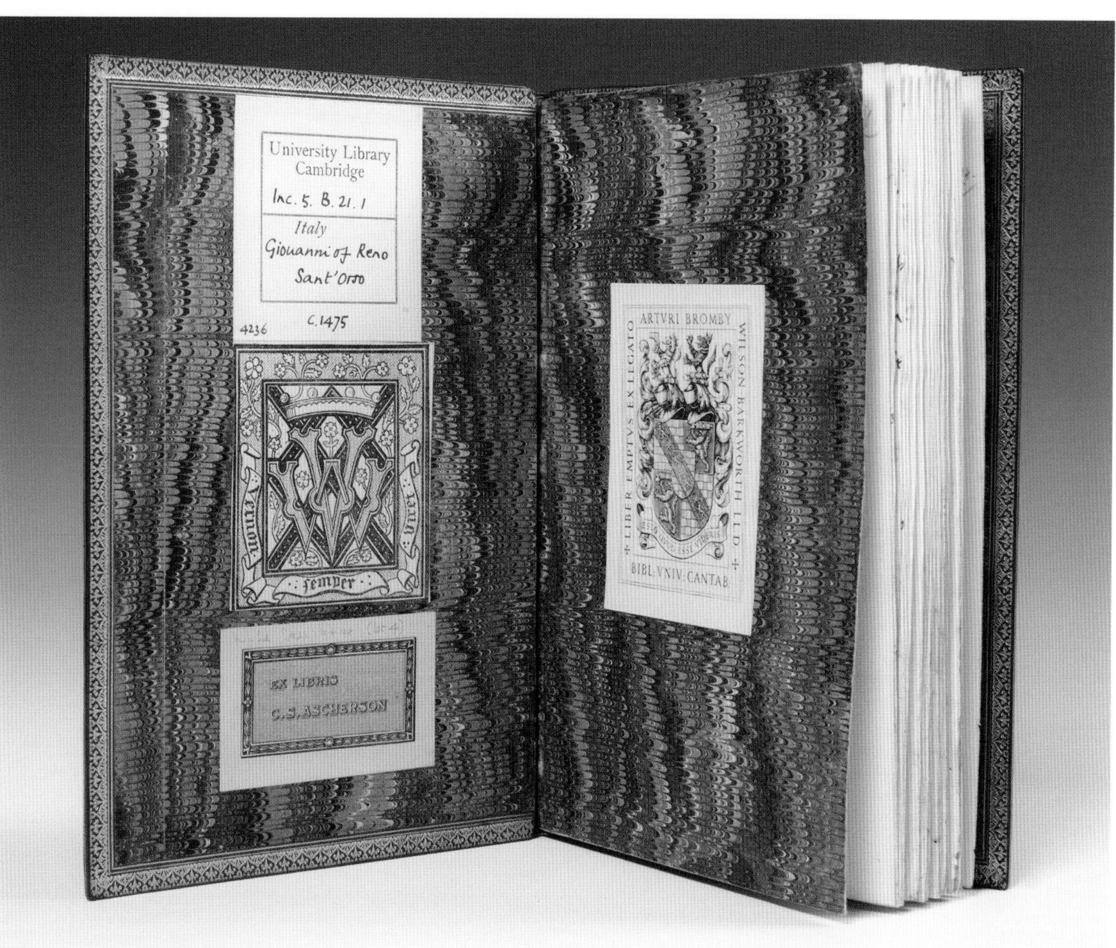

2

Facile est femellam decipere . sed quanto facilius
tanto turpius. Adhuc res integra est: si putas me
deserendam: dicito añ q̃ magis amor ardeat. Nec
ĩcipiam⁹ qđ postmodũ icepisse peniteat. Omniũ re
rum respiciendus est finis. Ego ut fœminarum ẽ
parũ uideo. Tu uir es: te mei & tui curam habere
oportet. Do me iam tibi: tuamque sequor fidem.
nec tua esse cupio: nisi ut sim perpetuo tua. Vale
meum præsidium meæq; ductor uitæ.
Post hæc plures epistolæ missæ utrinq; fuut. nec
tam ardenter scripsit Eurialus: quam feruenter
Lucrecia respondit. unũ iam utrique desiderium
erat simul conueniendi. sed arduum ac pene impo
ssibile uidebatur omnium oculis lucreciam obser
uantibus quæ nec sola unquam egredieba-
tur: nec unquam custode carebat nec tam
diligẽter bouẽ Iunoĩs argus custodiuit: quã Me-
nelaus iusserat obseruari Lucreciam. Vicium hoc
apud italos late patet: fœminam suam quasi the-
saurum quisquis recludit. meo iudicio minus uti-
liter. Sunt enim fere eiusmodi mulieres omnes.
ut id potissimum cupiant quod maxime denega-
tur. Quæ ubi uelis. nolunt: ubi nolis cupiunt ul-
tro. Ex si liberas habent habenas: minus delin-
quunt. Exinde tã facile est inuitam custodire mu

Nota

3

Vbi ad edes lucrecie uentũ ẽ: Euriali oculos pilleo
cõtexit: nec uidebis iqt qđ amas. ego hoc spectacu
lo fruar. Tũ Eurialus. qđ hoc signũ ẽ cesar? Nihil
mihi cũ illa. Sed hoc facere uitandũ ẽ. ne circũstan
tes ĩ suspicionẽ adducas. Erat Eurialo spadix e
quus arduæ ceruicis angustiq; capitis: quẽ & breuis aluus & obesa tergora. spectabilem reddebãt a
nimoso pectore choris luxuriantẽ. q sonante tuba
stare loco nesciebat. Nutabat auribꝰ & collectũ fre
mẽs uoluit sub auribꝰ ignẽ. Densa iuba. & dextra
iactata recõdebat ĩ armo. Et cauãs tellurẽ solido
cornu grauiter sõabat ũgula Similis illi fiebat eu
rialus uisa lucrecia. Que lic& dũ sola fuit. claude-
re uiam destinasset amori. ut tñ illũ aspexit: nec
modũ flãmæ nec sibi ponebat. Sed ut siccus. ager
qui admisso igne conburit. sic chori pflant. altius
sic infelix Lucrecia exardebat. Ita ẽ sane ut sapien
tibꝰ uidet: Humiles tantũ casas ĩhabitat castitas.
Solaq; paupies affectu sano tenet & q̃ domꝰ se co-
herc& modico. Diuites edes nescit pudicicia Quis
qs secũdis rbꝰ exptat sp isolita appetit. Delicatas
eligit domos & pñates magnos dira fortũæ comes
libido. Intuẽs igit eurialũ q̃ sepe trãseũtẽ lucrecia
nec ardorẽ cõpescere potẽs diu secũ cogitauit cui
patefaceret. Nam qui tacitus ard& magis uritur.
aiiii

Iuba capillos sig.
Arm i. humer.

4

1476

PICTURED:

1. A collection of books bound at the monastery of Castrum Sanctae Mariae.
2. A selection of rubbings of the binding tools used on the Marienburg bindings.

Bindings from the Carthusian monastery, Marienburg

1

Cambridge University Library holds the largest collection in Britain of incunabula from the Carthusian monastery of Castrum Sanctae Mariae (Marienburg). It consists of twenty-six books bound in thirteen volumes, all in their original bindings of wooden boards covered in brown calf and decorated with a large variety of engraved brass stamps.The monastery of Marienburg, founded in 1476, was situated at Weddern, a small village a few miles from Duelmen, near Münster. The monks lived a silent, solitary, austere and ascetic life devoted to prayer, reading and writing books. Apart from Sundays and feast days they ate alone, and only came together for three of the many daily church services. They had a sizeable library which was dispersed when the charterhouse was suppressed in 1803, and books with the monastery's ownership inscription can be found in many libraries and traced in auction catalogues, and are still occasionally offered for sale.

We do not know whether the monks bound their own books, or whether the three different sets of stamps used to decorate their bindings imply three outside binders. Many of the bindings have the same structural features, some of which are common to many German bindings of the late fifteenth and early sixteenth centuries, but there are some characteristics which seem typical of the bindings made for Marienburg. Many of the metal plates for the clasps which hold the leather straps in place, for example, are shaped like four-petalled square flowers. The second compartment between the raised bands on the spine has often been painted red, with the title written in black ink, and some spines also have a white-painted top compartment, with what looks like a shelf number in black ink, both probably added in the monastery in the sixteenth century. Three of the bindings have endleaves taken from the same fourteenth-century manuscript.

Most of the University Library's Marienburg bindings have the same decorative tools and several are signed HG, probably the initials of the binder. Three of the Marienburg volumes come from a bindery that also worked for an Augustinian convent in nearby Coesfeld and one, decorated with yet another set of stamps, was left to Marienburg by Hinricus Wacker, one of the officiating priests.

Mirjam Foot *is Professor Emerita at University College London, and an expert in the history of bookbinding.*

A complete list of the Marienburg bindings can be found in the concordance at the end of this volume.

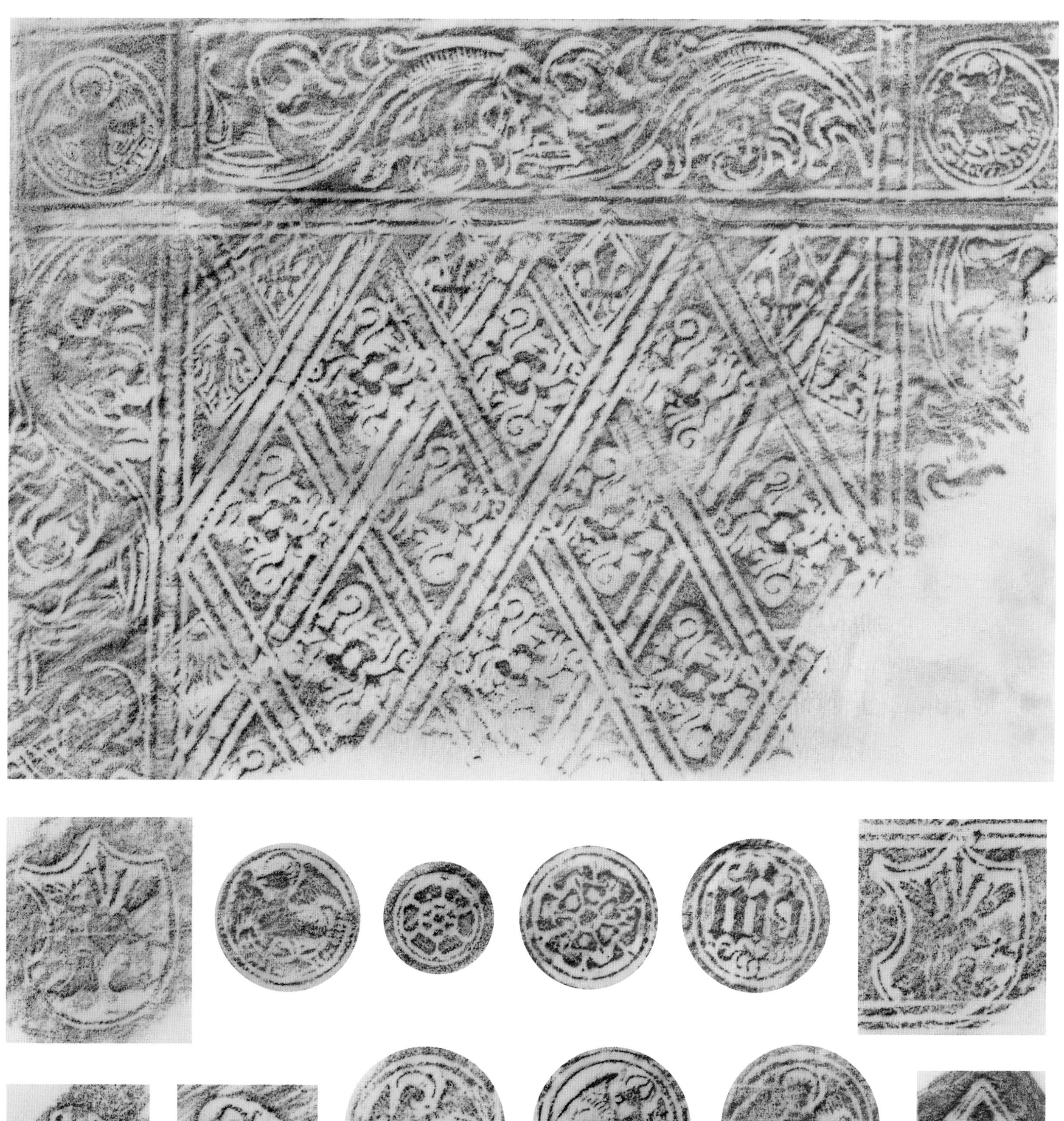

2

1476

PICTURED:

1. and 2. Two of the many sumptuous illuminations added to the book.
3. The architectural frontispiece, attributed to the Master of the London Pliny.

A splendidly illuminated Venetian incunable

Pliny the Elder (23–79 AD)
***Historia naturalis* [Italian]**
Venice: Nicolaus Jenson, 1476
Inc.1.B.3.2[1360]

Arguably the most spectacular incunable in Cambridge University Library is this copy of Pliny's *Historia naturalis*, in the Italian translation by the Florentine humanist Cristoforo Landino, printed on vellum in 1476 by Nicolaus Jenson, the most successful printer in Venice in the 1470s. The text is an encyclopedic work in which the first-century author proudly announces his topic: 'the world of Nature, or in other words, Life'. Jenson's edition is remarkably well documented. Commissioned through the Strozzi banking firm of Florence, Jenson agreed to print 1025 copies on paper, and in addition about twenty were printed on vellum.

The Cambridge Pliny combines monumental dimensions (389 x 250 mm), handsome layout in beautifully designed Roman type, a stunningly beautiful illuminated frontispiece, over thirty large painted initials in gold and brilliant colours, and hundreds of smaller gold initials on coloured grounds. The margins of Book II have been exquisitely painted with motifs that create an 'architectural frontispiece'. Painted around the edge of the printed text is a narrow bronze-coloured frame, illusionistically creating a gigantic inscribed plaque. Surrounding it has been painted an architectural wall-monument to which the plaque appears to be tied with strings of red beads. The colours of this ensemble are sumptuous: a deep purple base, blue columns with golden capitals, a blue-green frieze with fictive reliefs. Delicate chains of gems and cameos hang at the side and base of the monument. The opening initial E also appears to be three-dimensional, composed of red crystalline cylinders with gold fixtures. Dangling from the upper stroke of the E is a cameo with profile busts of the emperor Antoninus Pius (reigned 138–161AD) and his wife Faustina, while on the green plaque behind them is 'carved' a cherub riding on the tail of a triton. The decorative motifs evoke the world of classical antiquity, without referring specifically to the text.

The illumination is attributed to an anonymous Venetian miniaturist known as the Master of the London Pliny. Evidence provided by coats of arms found on other elaborately illuminated Jenson incunables makes it likely that the original owner was a member of the Agostini family, wealthy Venetian merchants who were associates of Nicolaus Jenson, and supplied paper for the Pliny publication. Thus, not only is the Cambridge Pliny a work of outstanding beauty, but it also informs us about the history of printing and Venetian Renaissance culture.

Lilian Armstrong *is the Mildred Lane Kemper Professor of Art, Emerita, at Wellesley College in Massachusetts, where she taught history of Renaissance art for many years.*

1

2

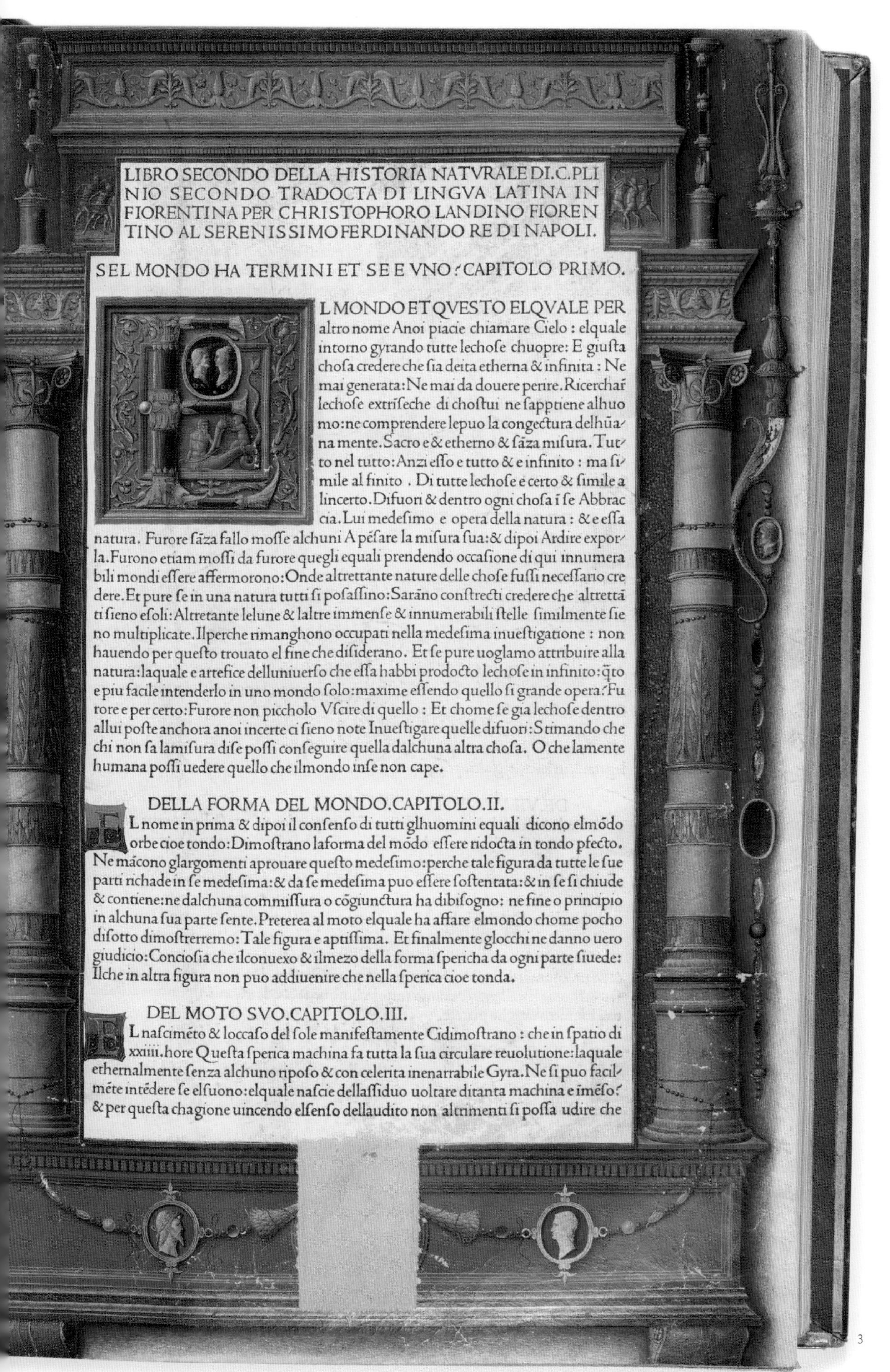
LIBRO SECONDO DELLA HISTORIA NATVRALE DI.C.PLI
NIO SECONDO TRADOCTA DI LINGVA LATINA IN
FIORENTINA PER CHRISTOPHORO LANDINO FIOREN
TINO AL SERENISSIMO FERDINANDO RE DI NAPOLI.

SEL MONDO HA TERMINI ET SE E VNO: CAPITOLO PRIMO.

L MONDO ET QVESTO ELQVALE PER altro nome Anoi piacie chiamare Cielo : elquale intorno gyrando tutte lechoſe chuopre: E giuſta choſa credere che ſia deita etherna & infinita : Ne mai generata: Ne mai da douere perire. Ricerchaī lechoſe extrīſeche di choſtui ne ſapptiene alhuomo: ne comprendere lepuo la congectura delhūana mente. Sacro e & etherno & ſãza miſura. Tutto nel tutto: Anzi eſſo e tutto & e infinito : ma ſimile al finito . Di tutte lechoſe e certo & ſimile a lincerto. Difuori & dentro ogni choſa ī ſe Abbraccia. Lui medeſimo e opera della natura : & e eſſa natura. Furore ſãza fallo moſſe alchuni A pẽſare la miſura ſua: & dipoi Ardire exporla. Furono etiam moſſi da furore quegli equali prendendo occaſione di qui innumerabili mondi eſſere affermorono: Onde altrettante nature delle choſe fuſſi neceſſario credere. Et pure ſe in una natura tutti ſi poſaſſino: Sarāno conſtrecti credere che altrettāti ſieno eſoli: Altretante lelune & laltre immenſe & innumerabili ſtelle ſimilmente ſieno multiplicate. Ilperche rimanghono occupati nella medeſima inueſtigatione : non hauendo per queſto trouato el fine che diſiderano. Et ſe pure uoglamo attribuire alla natura: laquale e artefice delluniuerſo che eſſa habbi prodocto lechoſe in infinito: q̄to e piu facile intenderlo in uno mondo ſolo: maxime eſſendo quello ſi grande opera: Furore e per certo: Furore non picchololo Vſcire di quello : Et chome ſe gia lechoſe dentro allui poſte anchora anoi incerte ci ſieno note Inueſtigare quelle difuori: Stimando che chi non ſa lamiſura diſe poſſi conſeguire quella dalchuna altra choſa. O che lamente humana poſſi uedere quello che ilmondo inſe non cape.

DELLA FORMA DEL MONDO. CAPITOLO. II.

L nome in prima & dipoi il conſenſo di tutti glhuomini equali dicono elmōdo orbe cioe tondo: Dimoſtrano laforma del mōdo eſſere ridocta in tondo pfecto. Ne mācono glargomenti aprouare queſto medeſimo: perche tale figura da tutte le ſue parti richade in ſe medeſima: & da ſe medeſima puo eſſere ſoſtentata: & in ſe ſi chiude & contiene: ne dalchuna commiſſura o cōgiunctura ha dibiſogno: ne fine o principio in alchuna ſua parte ſente. Preterea al moto elquale ha affare elmondo chome pocho diſotto dimoſtrerremo: Tale figura e aptiſſima. Et finalmente glocchi ne danno uero giudicio: Conciosia che ilconuexo & ilmezo della forma ſpericha da ogni parte ſiuede: Ilche in altra figura non puo addiuenire che nella ſperica cioe tonda.

DEL MOTO SVO. CAPITOLO. III.

L naſcimēto & loccaſo del ſole manifeſtamente Cidimoſtrano : che in ſpatio di xxiiii. hore Queſta ſperica machina fa tutta la ſua circulare reuolutione: laquale ethernalmente ſenza alchuno riposo & con celerita inenarrabile Gyra. Ne ſi puo facilmēte intēdere ſe elſuono: elquale naſcie dellaſſiduo uoltare ditanta machina e imẽſo: & per queſta chagione uincendo elſenſo dellaudito non altrimenti ſi poſſa udire che

3

PICTURED:

The final leaf of *The churl and the bird*, annotated by an early owner.

Bite-sized Lydgate: a Caxton speculation

John Lydgate (1370?–1451?)
The churl and the bird
[Westminster: William Caxton, about 1476–1477]
Inc.5.J.1.1[3486]

and:
John Lydgate (1370?–1451?)
The horse, the sheep and the goose
[Westminster: William Caxton, about 1476]
Inc.5.J.1.1[3488]

Shortly after he set up in business at Westminster in 1476, William Caxton set about printing a number of small booklets in quarto format – what he himself called 'pamphlets' – containing mostly single short works by well-known and successful vernacular writers of the previous generation. As they were relatively inexpensive for him to produce and for his clientele to buy, a quick turnover of small quartos would have provided him with some immediate income to invest in larger projects, one of the first of which was to be the *editio princeps* of Chaucer's *Canterbury tales* (1477). The booklets would have also given a wider readership a novel opportunity to choose off-the-shelf contemporary texts to form their own personal collections, without having to go to the trouble of engaging scribes, tracing exemplars, or even copying the works for themselves.

The author most fully represented in Caxton's early quartos is not Chaucer, but rather his prolific fifteenth-century follower and admirer John Lydgate, of the abbey of Bury St Edmunds. Lydgate's vast oeuvre led the nineteenth-century critic Joseph Ritson to describe him as a 'voluminous, prosaic and drivelling monk', a verdict with which some readers have been tempted to concur, but the style of Lydgate's varied and workmanlike writings was very much to the taste of his age, and modern criticism has identified various genuine merits in his work. Caxton's choice of an entertaining dialogue, *The churl and the bird*, and a spirited and learned debate poem, *The horse, the sheep and the goose*, shows that he was alive to where some of the chief attractions in Lydgate's poetry lay. To judge by the number of manuscript copies that have survived, the printer must have calculated upon their popular commercial potential. Though both texts successfully appropriate features of Chaucer's 'low' style, they remain emphatically moral and exemplary pieces, and they would have been an uncontroversial choice of text-type with which to initiate a trend for the large-scale publication of writings in English.

Lydgate's verse is nothing if not sententious, and here we see a contemporary reader who entered into its spirit: to the left of the proverbial

> A childes birde and a knaues wyff
> Haue ofte sithe [times] grete sorowe and
> meschance

he (and it must be a he) has added a pointing hand, and the rueful remark 'and a womans man'.

Richard Beadle *is Professor of Medieval English Literature and Palaeography in the Faculty of English, University of Cambridge.*

Vnto purpos this prouerbe is full ryff
Redde and reported by olde remembrance
A childes birde and a knaues wyff
Haue ofte sithe grete sorowe and meschance
And who hath fredom hath alle suffisance
Better is fredom with litell in gladnes
Than to be thrall with alle worldly riches

Goo litell quayer and recomande me
Vnto my maister with humble affection
Beseke hym lowly of mercy and pyte
Of thy rude makyng to haue compassion
And as touchyng thy translacion
Out of frenssh how that hit englisshid be
Alle thing is said vnder correction
With supportacion of his benygnyte

. Explicit the chorle and the birde .

by John Lydgate

1476

PICTURED:

1. Letterpress tables of planetary positions.
2. Relief-printed eclipse diagrams.
3. Intaglio-printed volvelle, with two moving parts.

An astronomical vade-mecum

Lazarus Beham (15th century)
Buch von der astronomie*, incorporating Regiomontanus, *Kalendarium
[Cologne: Nicolaus Götz, 1476]
Inc.5.A.4.9[514]

This was a widely used basic textbook of astronomy, with tables giving the predicted positions of the heavenly bodies from 1477 to 1537. These positions were calculated by Johannes Müller, known as Regiomontanus (1436–1476) and originally printed in 1474 on the press which he set up in his house in Nuremberg: the first scientific publishing house.

The printer of the University Library's Cologne edition, Nicolaus Götz, was not alone in recognizing the market potential of the *Kalendarium*, an essential tool for astrologers: at least nine editions were printed before 1500. Nor was he the only one to struggle with the technical difficulties that it presented. The tables of planetary positions required an unusually large stock of type for the tables of numbers (one printer abandoned typographic printing and carved the tables on woodblocks); and diagrams for the eclipse predictions were required. More difficult still was the manufacture of two paper instruments with moving parts included in the book. These are used to make the necessary calculations for the use of the tables.

The woodcut eclipse diagrams in the Götz edition are very crude, and we may speculate that Götz did not have access to a block cutter skilful enough to produce the fine lines needed for the instruments. His solution was to print them from intaglio plates, probably engraved by a local scientific instrument maker. This is the first known use of engraving for a scientific diagram in a book. An edition of Boccaccio printed at Bruges in the same year is celebrated as the first book to contain figurative engravings.

It was probably another edition of the *Kalendarium* that got Columbus out of trouble in 1504. Shipwrecked on Jamaica, his raping and pillaging crew upset the native inhabitants to the point that they refused to continue to supply the ship with food. Columbus knew from his *Kalendarium* that there would be a full eclipse of the moon and he told the village elders that if they did not co-operate, God would make the moon disappear from the sky on the following night. When the moon rose and then gradually disappeared, the terrified villagers begged Columbus to intercede on their behalf. The moon was restored to the sky, and Columbus had no further problems with supplies before he was rescued by another Spanish ship.

Roger Gaskell *is an antiquarian bookseller specializing in early scientific and medical books.*

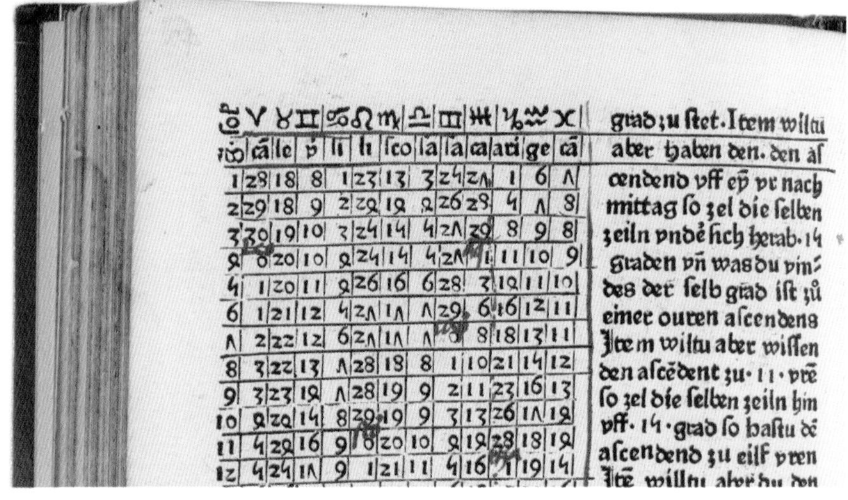

sol	♈	♉	♊	♋	♌	♍	♎	♏	♐	♑	♒	♓
gꝛ	cā	le	v	li	li	ſco	la	la	ca	ari	ge	cā
1	28	18	8	1	23	13	3	25	27	1	6	7
2	29	18	9	2	24	14	4	26	28	5	7	8
3	30	19	10	3	25	15	5	27	29	8	9	8
4	0	20	10	4	25	15	5	27	1	11	10	9
5	1	20	11	4	26	16	6	28	3	14	11	10
6	1	21	12	5	27	17	7	29	6	16	12	11
7	2	22	12	6	27	17	7	[illegible]	8	18	13	11
8	3	22	13	7	28	18	8	1	10	21	14	12
9	3	23	14	7	28	19	9	2	11	23	16	13
10	4	24	15	8	29	19	9	3	13	26	17	14
11	5	24	16	9	0	20	10	4	14	28	18	14
12	5	25	17	9	1	21	11	5	16	1	19	15

grad zu ſtet. Item wiltu aber haben den. den aſcendend vff ey̅ vr nach mittag ſo zel die ſelben zeiln vndē ſich herab. 14 graden vn̄ was du vin- des der ſelb grad iſt zů einer ouren aſcendens Item wiltu aber wiſſen den aſcēdent zu. 11. vrē ſo zel die ſelben zeiln hin vff. 14. grad ſo haſtu dē aſcendend zu eilf vren Itē wiltu aber du den

1

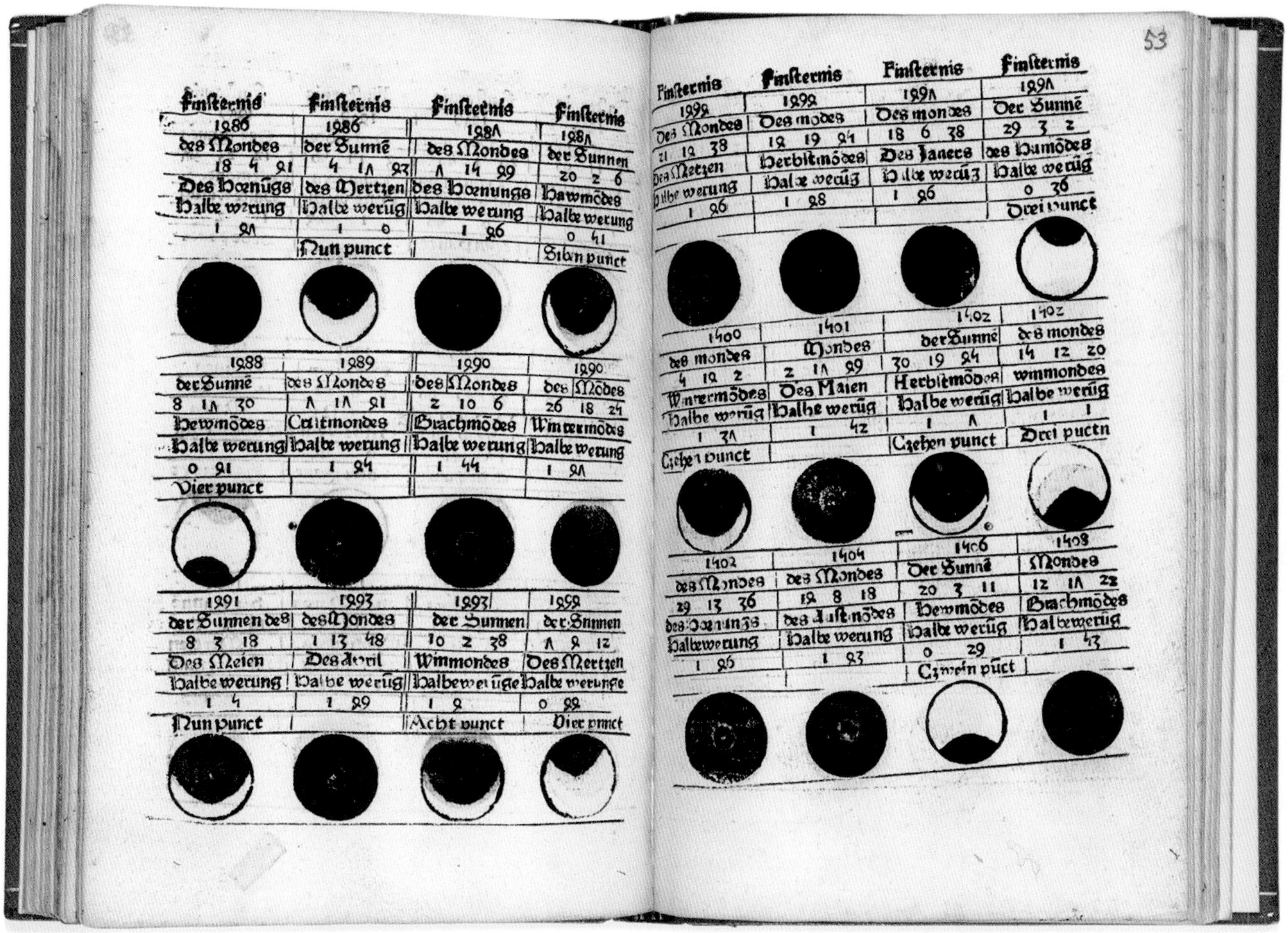

2

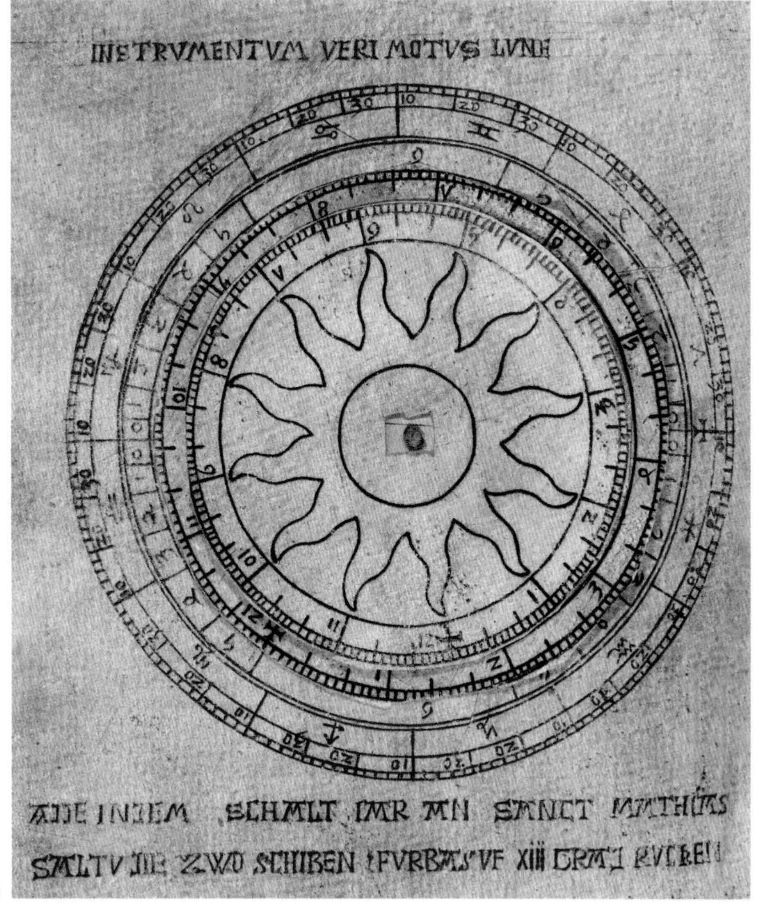

3

1478

PICTURED:

1. Sister Alexia's 1528 annotation.
2. Christ as Man of Sorrows at the opening of the text.
3. Discreet manicules mark texts of significance.

A nun at her private devotions

***Meditationes vitae Christi* [Italian]**
[Venice: Nicolaus Jenson?, about 1478?]
Inc.5.B.3.2[4321]

The *Meditations on the life of Christ*, composed in the thirteenth century, were once attributed to St Bonaventure: all that is known for sure is that the author was a Franciscan. Originally written in Latin, the text was rapidly translated into many European languages. The book presents a series of guided meditative exercises, based on a vivid narration of Christ's Passion which encourages the reader to cultivate the practice of 'reliving' these episodes in the imagination, embracing the human experiences of the protagonists, Christ, Mary and the apostles. The text is dedicated by its author to a member of the Poor Clares, the Franciscan sister-order: the dedicatee is instructed to 'feel yourself present in those places as if the things were done in your presence', and to meditate frequently 'so that these meditations become familiar to you'.

Two nuns, Sister Teofila and Sister Alexia, have identified themselves as owners of this book, and have used it well. Scattered across the pages are manicules and brief notes to remind the user of the important passages as she reads. A small image of Christ as Man of Sorrows on the opening page provides a visual reminder of the physical suffering upon which the reader of this text will be taught to meditate.

Sister Alexia, the most prolific annotator, tells us she received the book from her uncle, a Dominican friar, perhaps as a gift when she entered the convent: a fitting present for a new nun. She added two hymns and a prayer in Latin, in the clear, italic hand of a well-educated girl. A 'Hymn to the Holy Virgin' includes praise for the many female saints who gave their lives to Christ in perpetual virginity, providing a useful gallery of role models for a young nun. At the back of the book another Latin hymn tells of Alexia's own dedication to Christ, describing her as high born and a member of the order of St Ursula. Dedicatory verses of this kind, praising the choice of a spiritual life by individual nuns, were often used together with musical settings at the ceremonies to mark a nun's entry into the convent. This little book allows us privileged access to a private world of female devotion, enclosed behind the high convent walls where many aristocratic women passed their days.

Abigail Brundin *is Reader in Early Modern Literature and Culture at the University of Cambridge.*

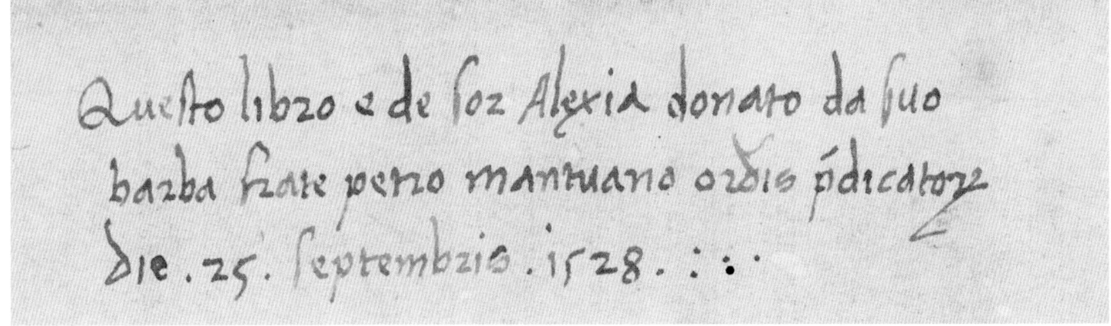
Questo libro e de sor Alexia donato da suo
barba frate petro mantuano ordis pdicatore
die .25. septembrio .1528. :.:

1

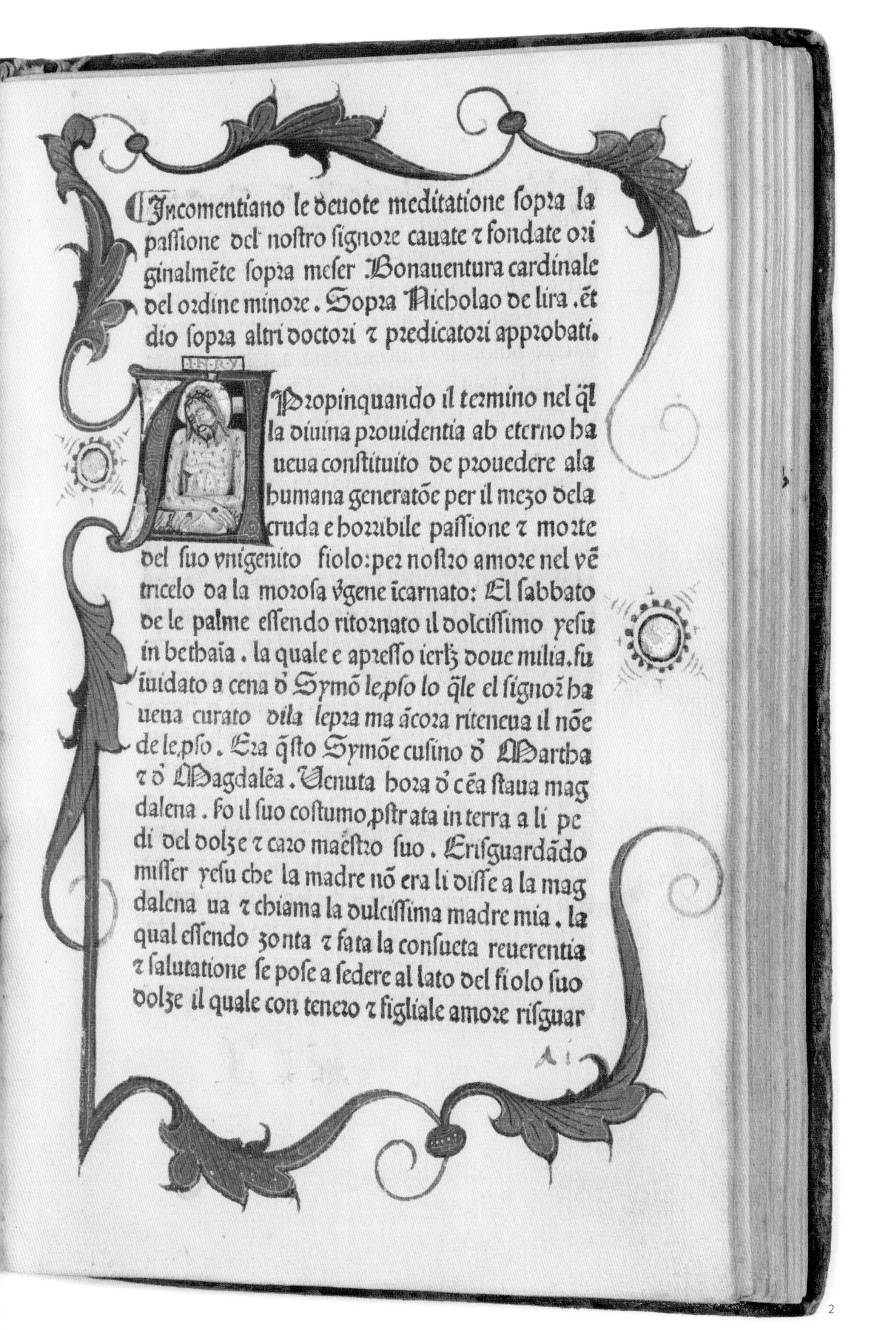

Incomentiano le deuote meditatione sopra la
passione del nostro signore cauate ⁊ fondate ori
ginalmēte sopra meser Bonauentura cardinale
del ordine minore. Sopra Nicholao de lira. ēt
dio sopra altri doctori ⁊ predicatori approbati.

I.N.R.Y.

Apropinquando il termino nel q̄l
la diuina prouidentia ab eterno ha
ueua constituito de prouedere ala
humana generatiōe per il mezo dela
cruda e horribile passione ⁊ morte
del suo vnigenito fiolo: per nostro amore nel vē
tricelo da la morosa v̄gene īcarnato: El sabbato
de le palme essendo ritornato il dolcissimo yesu
in bethaīa. la quale e apresso ierlꝫ doue milia. fu
īuidato a cena d' Symō leꝓso lo q̄le el signor̄ ha
ueua curato dila lepra ma ācora riteneua il nōe
de leꝓso. Era q̄sto Symōe cusino d' Martha
⁊ d' Magdalēa. Uenuta hora d' cēa staua mag
dalena. fo il suo costumo ꝓstrata in terra a li pe
di del dolze ⁊ caro maestro suo. Erisguardādo
misser yesu che la madre nō era li disse a la mag
dalena ua ⁊ chiama la dulcissima madre mia. la
qual essendo zonta ⁊ fata la consueta reuerentia
⁊ salutatione se pose a sedere al lato del fiolo suo
dolze il quale con tenero ⁊ figliale amore risguar

Ai

2

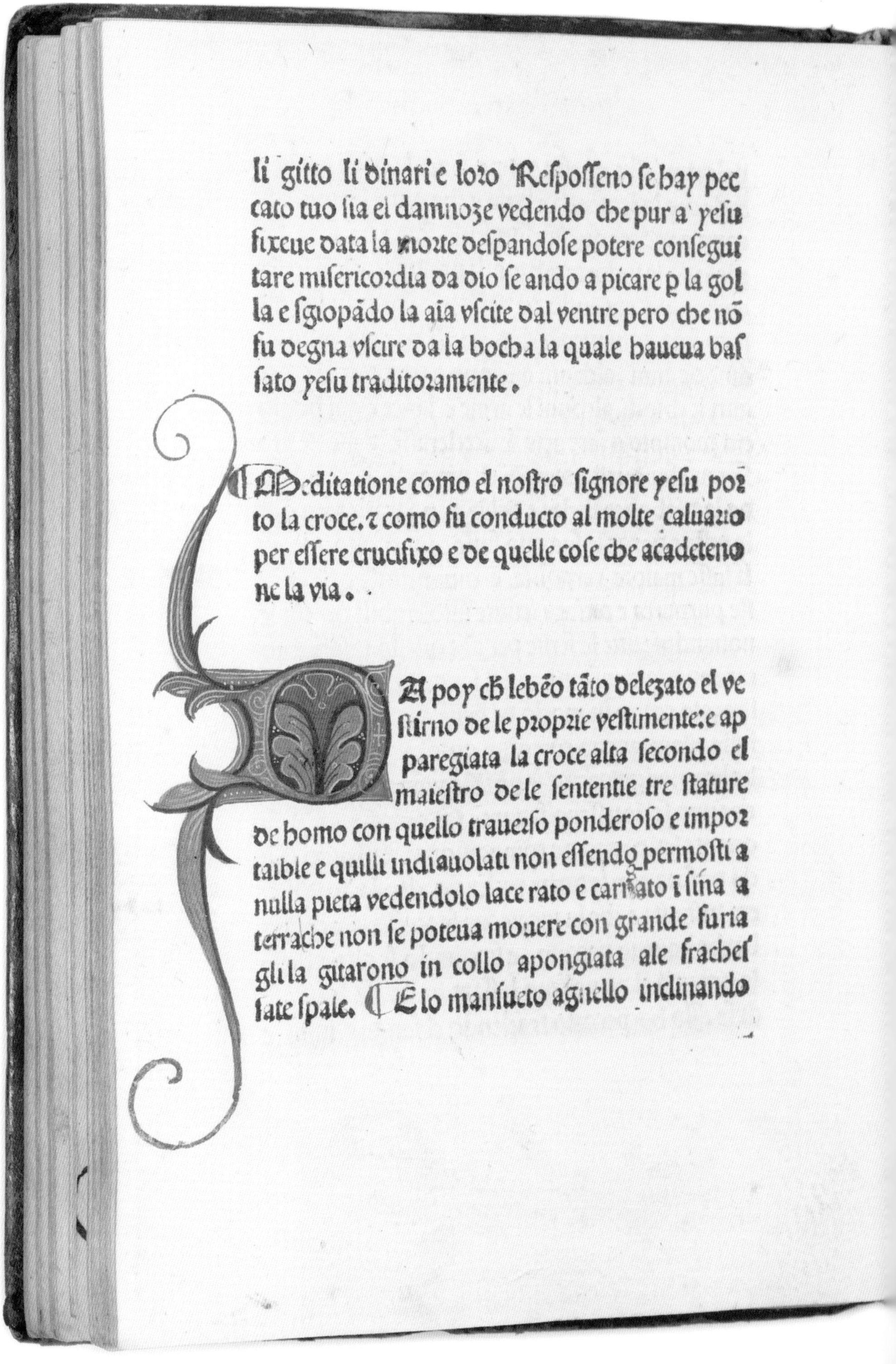

li gitto li dinari e loro Respossено se hay pec
cato tuo sia el damnoze vedendo che pur a yesu
fixeue data la morte despandose potere consegui
tare misericordia da dio se ando a picare ꝑ la gol
la e sgiopãdo la aĩa vscite dal ventre pero che nõ
fu degna vscire da la bocha la quale haueua bas
sato yesu traditoramente.

¶ Meditatione como el nostro signore yesu por
to la croce. ꝛ como fu conducto al molte caluario
per essere crucifixo e de quelle cose che acadeteno
ne la via.

DA poy chꝭ lebẽo tãto delezato el ve
stirno de le proprie vestimente: e ap
paregiata la croce alta secondo el
maiestro de le sententie tre stature
de homo con quello trauerso ponderoso e impor
taible e quilli indiauolati non essendo permosti a
nulla pieta vedendolo lace rato e cargato i sina a
terrache non se poteua mouere con grande furia
gli la gitarono in collo apongiata ale frachesi
sate spale. ¶ E lo mansueto agnello inclinando

3

lo inſpinato capo lo quale capo may non pote
leuare da lora che gli fu metuto la corona de ſpi
ne humilmente la preſe dicendo vene a me cro
ce diuina o mille anni paſſati dal mio padre ſey
a me ordinata: uene a me croce amabile da my
trenta tri anni in queſto mundo con faticha e ſu
dore e morte cercata: vene ame victoria de lo in
ferno. ¶ Uene a me gloria del paradiſo ¶ Ue
ne a me ſtendardo de li mei ſeguitatore. ¶ Ue
ne a me cathedra diuina ſopra te. te voglio la
mia opera conſumare. ¶ O humile obedientia
de yeſu veramente fato obediente inſino ala mor
te. ¶ O benignio yeſu e patientiſſimo e ſuauiſſi
mo yeſu corona de li ſancti ¶ Gloria de li beati
Hora ſey chiamato el re de li ſtulti ⁊ iniqui.
¶ O meliſluo yeſu quanto ſey degno de infima
compaſſione. ¶ O anime deuote como dolora
teue de ſaluberimo dolore de compaſſione le
uate la negligentia. contemplate queſto paſſio
nato ⁊ impacito. yeſu. riſguardate chel uſiſſe dal
pretorio de pillato coronato de ſpine mille acutiſ
ſime ponture de la ſpinoſa corona hano pforato
quello pretioſo capo guardatelo tuto purpurato
ſanguinato e ſtrazato. Adunche o anima pieto
ſa ua uno pocho i cõtra alui adeſſo e uede el tuo
amatore e lo tuo Signore ch porta la croce per

1478

PICTURED:

1–4. Examples of marginal diagrams added to elucidate or illustrate points in the text.

5. The hand-drawn ring bearing initials G O.

6–9. Hand-drawn geometric diagrams.

10. and 11. The colours in these diagrams remain vivid after 500 years.

12. The 'spheres of the Universe'.

Picturing the world

Johannes Sacrobosco (died about 1236)
Sphaera mundi
Venice: Franciscus Renner, 1478
Inc.4.B.3.6d[1389]

Little is known of the life of Johannes Sacrobosco, or John of Holywood – he was most probably of British origin, and certainly taught at the University of Paris. His *Sphaera mundi* is a textbook on Ptolemaic astronomy, though he appears not to have known Ptolemy's *Almagest* directly. The *Sphaera mundi* was widely used in the arts curriculum of medieval universities, and endured as a fundamental text on astronomy into the seventeenth century. Several commentaries are known, the most significant of which was Christoph Clavius's *In sphaeram Ioannis de Sacro Bosco commentarius* (1585).

This edition of Sacrobosco's *Sphaera mundi* was printed by Franz Renner in Venice in 1478. As in other early printed editions of the *Sphaera*, some of its woodcuts are coloured by hand, such as the diagram of eclipses, indicating the relative positions of the sun, earth and moon for lunar and solar eclipses. This particular copy records various past owners, including one (whose name is no longer legible) who began annotating his copy in 1521 and noted that in September 1522 he heard a lecture by 'the most excellent teacher of astronomy, Luca Gaurico'. Gaurico (1476–1558) was a well-known astrologer who served popes and rulers. There are also extensive annotations, including diagrams and figures, made by the same early sixteenth-century hand. These, as it turns out, were images copied from another, later edition of Sacrobosco (Venice: Johannes Lucilius Santritter & Hieronymus de Sanctis, 1488). This later edition contained more woodcuts, which were assiduously copied out by the owner of the earlier edition.

In the 1488 edition, a woodcut image of a ring bears the initials 'I.H.' (presumably the blockcutter's initials), but in the hand-drawn figure in the Cambridge copy (Figure 5), it bears the initials 'GO', which might be a clue to the annotator's name. Transferring corrections or additional material from a later printed edition into an earlier edition was a fairly common practice, presumably to save the costs of acquiring a new copy, but it is rare to find diagrammatic and pictorial material copied in this way.

Sachiko Kusukawa *is Fellow in History and Philosophy of Science at Trinity College, Cambridge, and author of* Picturing the book of nature *(2012).*

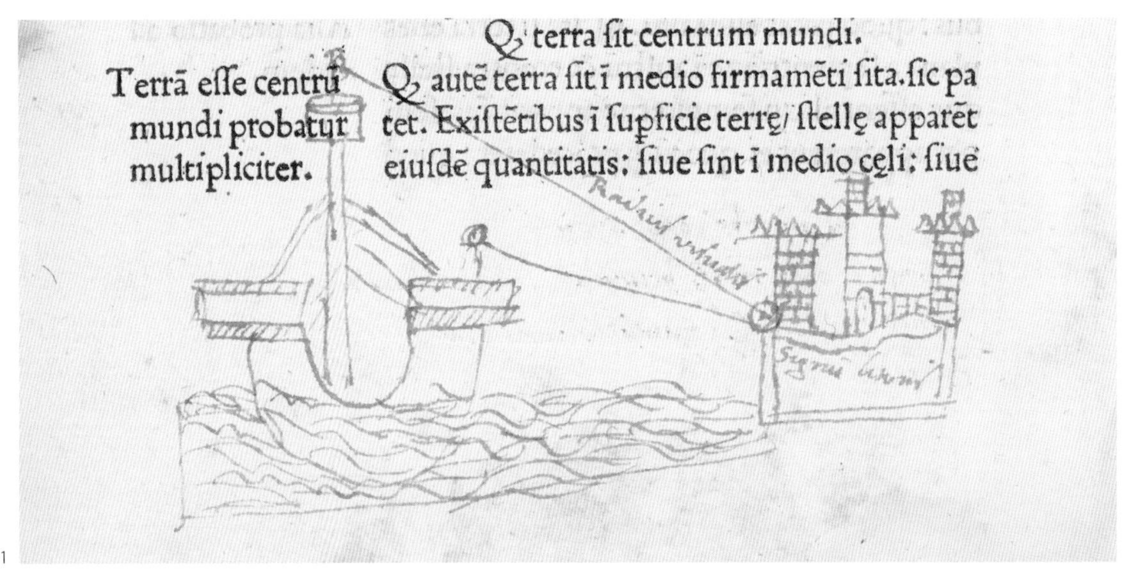

1

linea curua
Diametre
semicirculus
1389

2

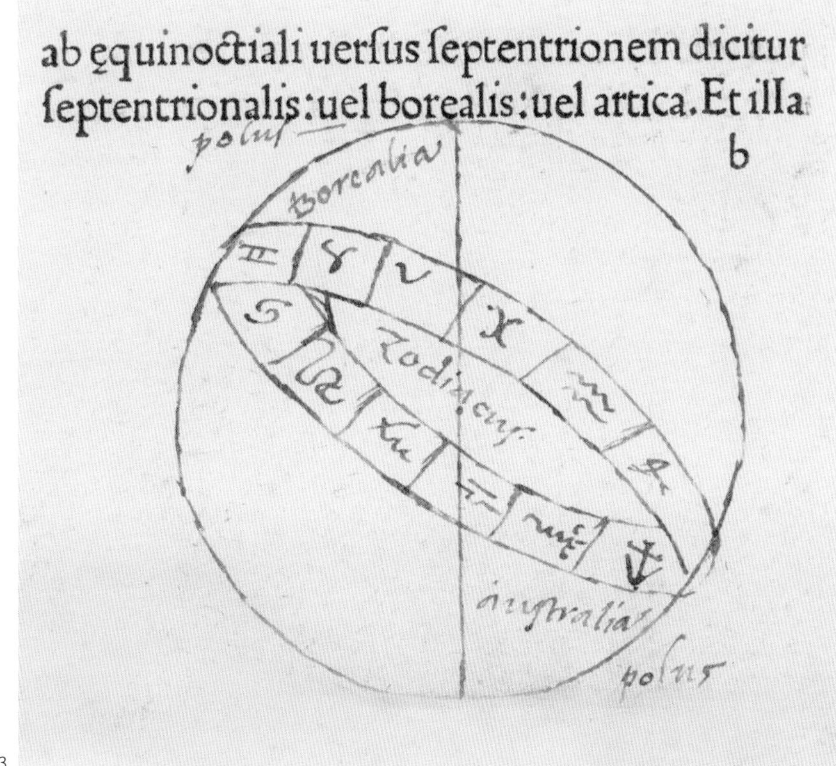

ab ęquinoctiali uersus septentrionem dicitur
septentrionalis: uel borealis: uel artica. Et illa
b
polus
borealis
zodiacus
australis
polus

3

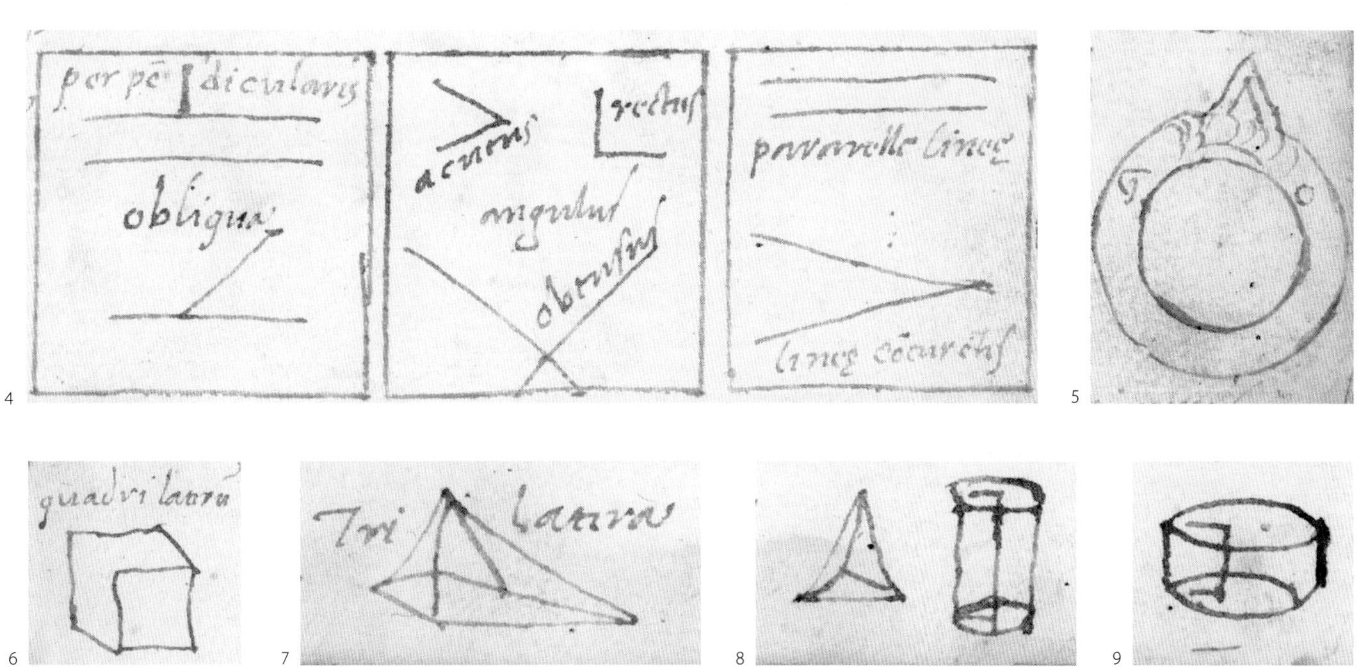

perpendicularis
obliqua
acutus
rectus
angulus

4

5

6

7

8

9

pertranſit motu ꝓprio cōtrario motui firma-
menti qui eſt ab oriente ĩ occidentẽ cōtra firmamentũ & ducit ſecũ augẽ. Quare in quãto
tempore ſol pertranſit firmamentũ / in tanto

Theorica Mercurij inter alias difficilior

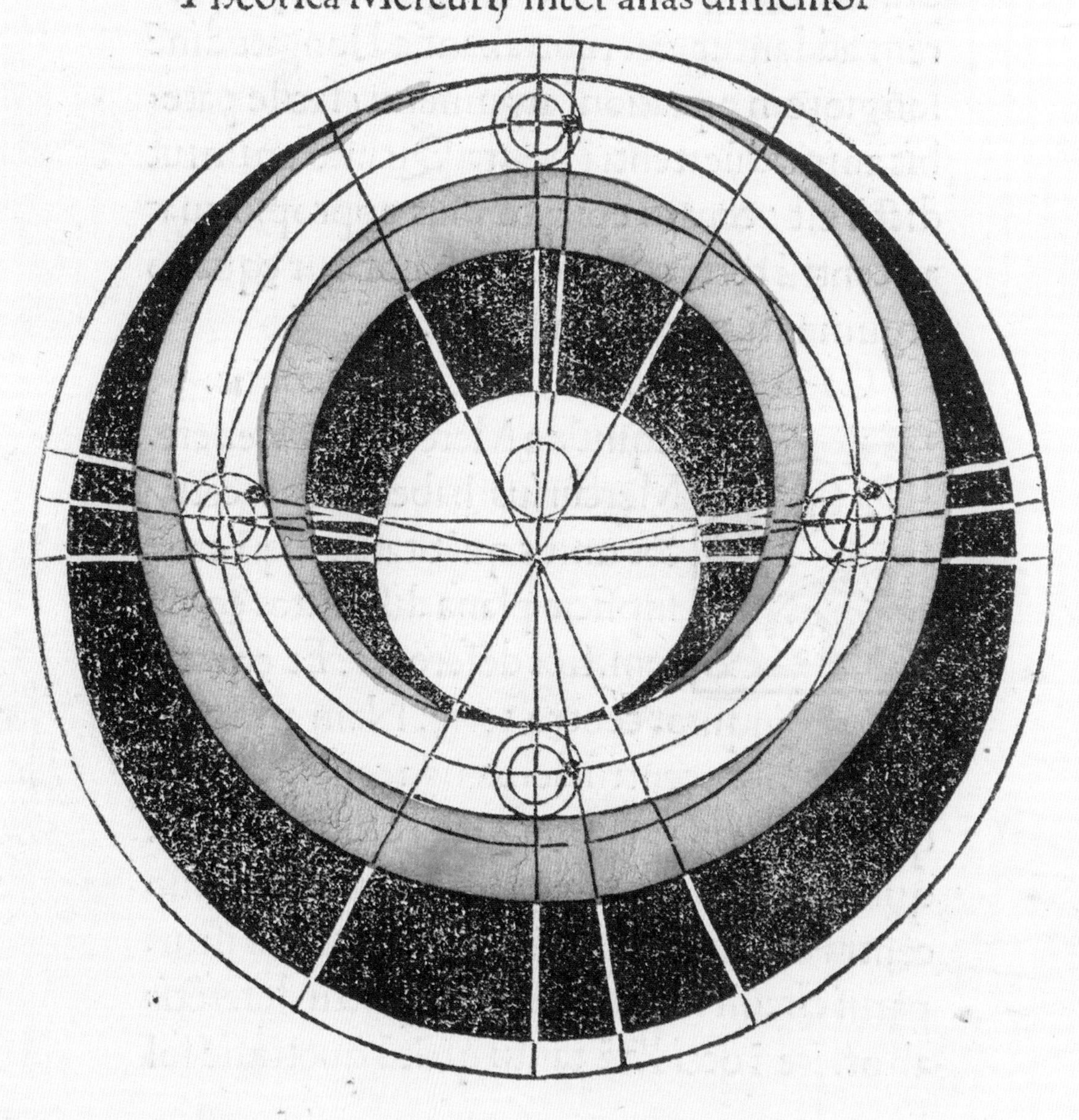

10

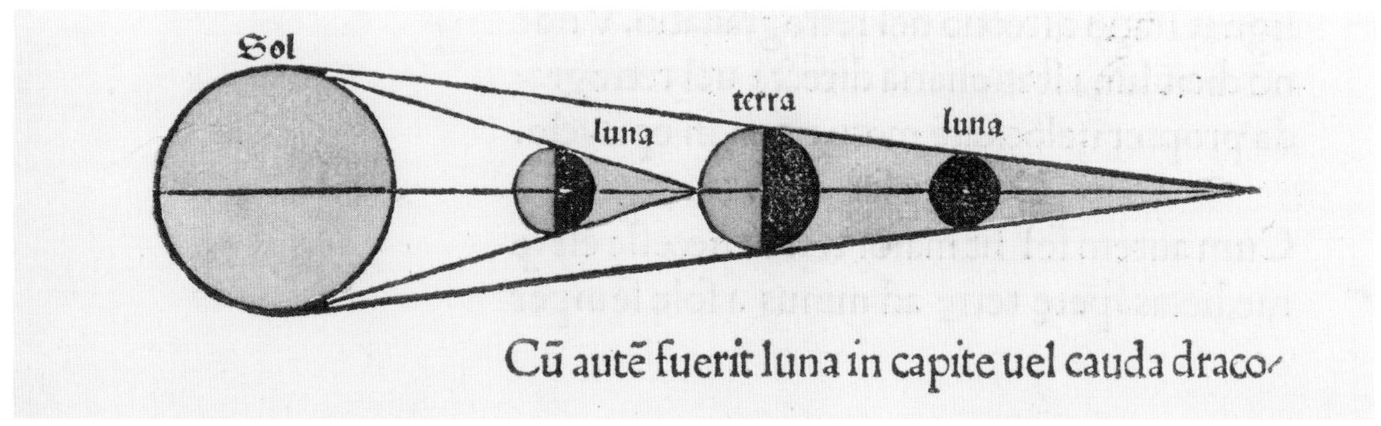

Sol
luna
terra
luna
Cū autē fuerit luna in capite uel cauda draco-
11

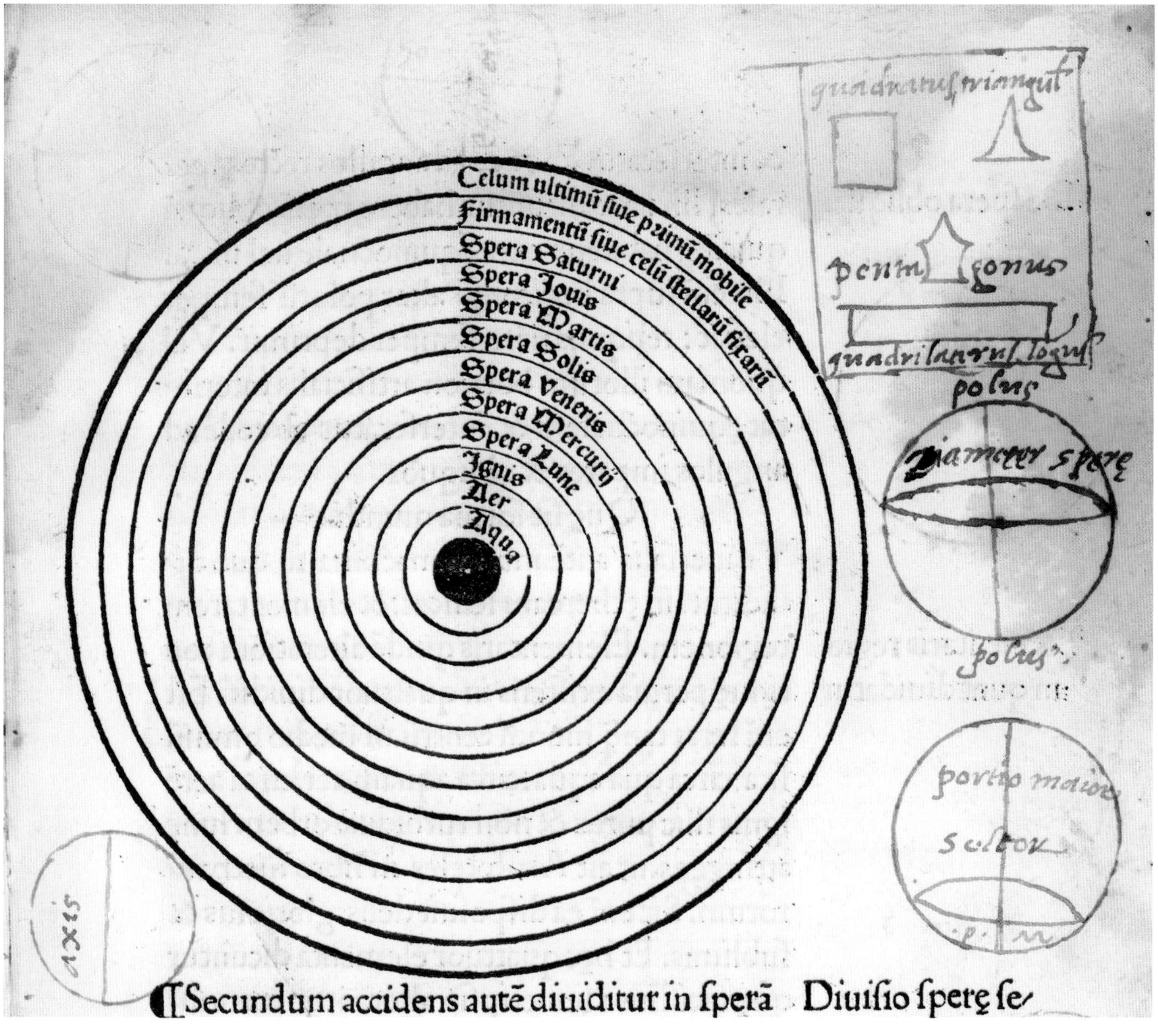

Celum ultimū siue primū mobile
Firmamentū siue celū stellarū fixarū
Spera Saturni
Spera Jouis
Spera Martis
Spera Solis
Spera Veneris
Spera Mercurij
Spera Lune
Ignis
Aer
Aqua
polus
polus
axis
Secundum accidens autē diuiditur in sperā Diuisio sperȩ se-
12

1478

PICTURED:

1. and 2. Text and illustrations entirely printed from incised wooden blocks, then hand coloured.

A book printed from wood blocks

Blockbook Apocalypse
[Germany, about 1470, impression about 1478–1480]
Inc.3[4245]

Blockbook printing, which in its purest form meant the production of books with text and pictures entirely printed from incised wood blocks, emerged in parallel to typographic printing with moveable type, around the middle of the fifteenth century. The earliest such book to have survived completely intact is a blockbook *Apocalypse* printed in the Low Countries and datable on the basis of paper evidence to about 1450–1452, which puts it about four years earlier than Gutenberg's 42-line Bible (see pp. 2–5). Text and images of the blockbook Apocalypse were borrowed from the tradition of English illustrated Apocalypse manuscripts, in particular a small group of 'picture book' manuscripts in which the explanatory text was integrated into the pictures rather than being set out separately. The mode of printing was entirely different from that of the regular printed book: the leaves were printed on one side only, with an iron-gall ink quite different from printing ink, and most examples appear to have been printed in a hand-press or by rubbing.

With the conventional printed books of the incunable period the type had to be dismantled after each set of sheets had been printed, which involved manufacturing all copies of an edition at once, but there was no need for this with blockbooks. One set of blocks would be used again and again to produce small runs, or issues, distinguishable from one another only by the state of the blocks and the paper stocks employed. The blockbook Apocalypse went into six editions in all, each new edition entailing the execution of a new set of twenty-four or twenty-five wood blocks, each with two pages.

The early editions of the Apocalypse were 'stacked-sheet' blockbooks, in which the pages were printed in pairs, side by side, on one side of the paper, and the printed sheets then folded and placed one after another to be bound. The blank pages were usually pasted together. The copy of Edition VI illustrated here is particularly unusual in that it was printed on both sides of the paper on double leaves, with a single image to the left on each side of the sheet, so that when assembled all printed images are versos, and thus positioned to the left when the book is open. The opposite pages, the rectos, remained blank. This is one of only four copies of blockbooks known to have been assembled in this manner.

Nigel F. Palmer *is Emeritus Professor of German Medieval Studies at the University of Oxford; his special areas of research are medieval prayer books, palaeography and codicology, and early printing.*

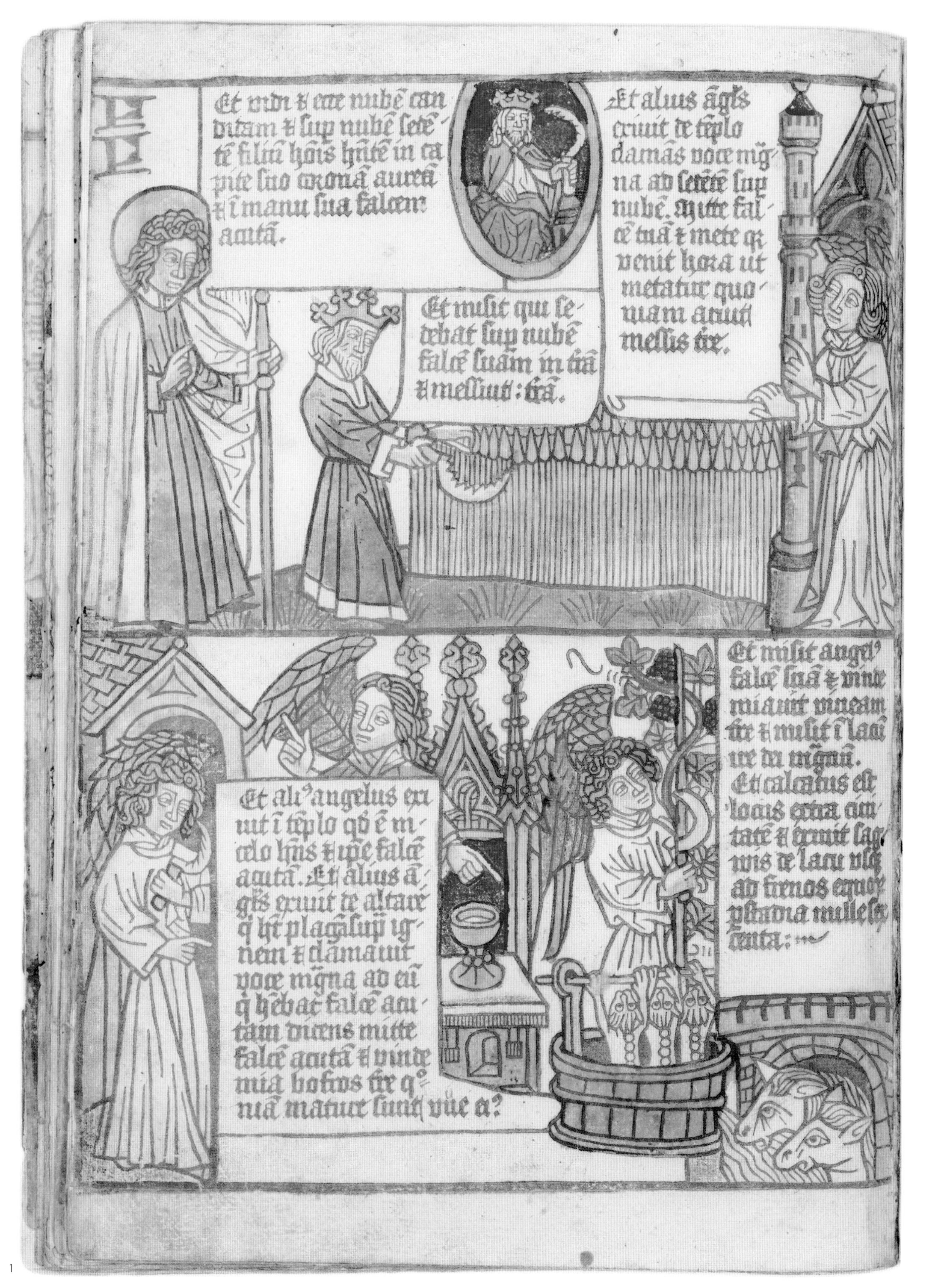
Et vidi & ecce nubē can
didam & sup nubē sedē
tē filiū hoīs hñtē in ca
pite suo coronā aureā
& ī manu sua falcem
acutā.
Et alius āgls
exivit de tēplo
clamās voce mg
na ad sedētē sup
nubē. Mitte fal
cē tuā & mete qr
venit hora ut
metatur quo
niam aruit
messis tre.
Et misit qui se
debat sup nubē
falcē suam in trā
& messuit trā.
Et misit angel'
falcē suā & vinde
miavit vineam
tre & misit ī lacū
ire dei mgnū.
Et calcatus est
lacus extra civi
tatē & exivit sag
wis de lacu usq
ad frenos equor
p stadia mille sex
centa:
Et ali' angelus exi
vit ī tēplo qd ē in
celo hñs & ipē falcē
acutā. Et alius ā
gls exivit de altare
q hȝt ptāt sup ig
nem & clamavit
voce mgna ad eū
q hēbat falcē acu
tam dicens mitte
falcē acutā & vinde
mia botros tre q
niā mature sunt uve ei.

1

Angelus abaton. idest exter minans nomine rex est locu starum et signat dyabolu.
Primum doctrina hereticorum p locu tas multitudo eorum intelligitur.
Sextus an gelus
Solue quatuor angelos qui al ligati sunt in flumine magno eufraten et soluti sunt quatuor angeli qui parati e rant in horam et diem mensem et annum ut occiderent terciam partem hominum.
Eufrates flu uius mag nus.

2

PICTURED:

1. The donkey emulating the pet dog's display of affection with disastrous consequences.
2. The sad story of a tortoise, preyed on by a mighty eagle and a canny crow.

A book from fair Verona

Aesop
***Aesopus moralisatus* [Latin and Italian]**
Verona: Giovanni and Alberto Alvise, 26 June 1479
Inc.4.B.19.2[2161]

Aesop's fables are amongst the most successful bestsellers of all time. Purportedly invented by Aesop, a non-Greek slave, on Samos around the sixth century BC, the corpus of fables originated in an ancient form of oral didactic literature which utilized anthropomorphised animals to teach moral lessons. The fables were used in classical Greece by orators and philosophers and were eventually transcribed in the fourth and third centuries BC. The tales were translated or recreated in a number of Latin prose or verse collections from the first century AD onwards and used as teaching tools. The Middle Ages embraced the didactic moral purpose of the fables once again, with collections appearing in almost all European languages.

Compendia of Aesopian fables in Greek, Latin and vernacular languages survive in no less than 194 incunabular editions from about 1465. The Verona edition of 1479, however, stands out as a quintessentially Renaissance book. Sixty-six fables from the *Romulus*, an early medieval Latin collection, are presented in an elegant twelfth-century re-elaboration in elegiac distichs. Each of the fables is followed by a double verse translation – literal and moral – in Italian vernacular by Accio Zucco da Sommacampagna (active 1364–1372), an obscure but erudite grammarian active in the circle of the Scaligeri court in Verona. Despite its poetic shortfalls, the tone of Zucco's translation is set high by his choice of the sonnet form, the elegant and versatile verse form brought to its highest expression in Italian poetry by his contemporary Francesco Petrarca (1304–1374).

Each fable is illustrated by a woodcut in a type-cast fleuron border. The borders and the title page, designed as a classical epigraphic monument, disclose the participation in the design – if not in the entire editorial plan – of the Veronese antiquary, scribe, goldsmith and typographer Felice Feliciano (1433–about 1480). The iconography of the woodcuts partly derives from the first illustrated edition of Aesopian fables in the German translation by Heinrich Steinhöwel, printed by Johannes Zainer in Ulm about 1476–1477. The lively depiction of the tales and the gusto for the representation of animals in action, however, suggests the involvement of Liberale da Verona (about 1445–1527?), a leading illuminator active in Verona from 1476. His vibrant designs contributed to the popularity of the Verona edition, which influenced the iconography of all subsequent Italian editions, despite being the work of two relatively unknown provincial printers, Giovanni and Alberto Alvise.

Laura Nuvoloni *researches Italian manuscripts and early printed books, and is Research Associate on the Incunabula Cataloguing Project at Cambridge University Library.*

Quod natura negat. nemo feliciter audet
Displicet imprudes,' unde placere studet.

La lingua aſtuta & falſa molto offende
Chel forte per ingiegno liga e prende.

2

SONETTO MORALE.

I tu ben guarde qui laquila prese
Vna gran bissa squara in un bel prato
Ma si coperta tiensi dogni lato
Che dal beccho aquilin si se diffese
E doppo uidde le false contese
Che la grola gli mostra per suo grato
Per hauer quello che se ha imaginato
Gli mostra il modo a portarla suspese
C osi il buon huomo stando in penitentia
Di subito il peccato gli ua adosso
Qual se diffende per la sofferentia
D ice il demonio conuien che remosso
Costui si fia da la ubidientia
E da piu graue temptation percosso
C ome se parte da seruir a dio
C osi sel porta lo inimico rio.

DE VVLPE ET CORVO .F. XVI.

Vlpe gerẽte famẽ/coruũ gerit arbor & escã.
Ore gerens coruus. uulpe loquente silet
Corue decore/decens/cygnũ candore parentas!

PICTURED:

1. A rubricated letter 'O' from the 1479 Utrecht *Homilies.*
2. The woodcut Crucifixion, with manuscript indulgence and colouring.

'The indulgence is larger than any I ever saw.' – Henry Bradshaw

Crucifixion
[The Netherlands: about 1480]
MS Add.5944(11)

Within:
Pope Gregory I (about 540–604)
***Homiliae super evangeliis* [Dutch]**
[Utrecht: Johann Veldener], 22 April 1479
Inc.4.E.1.6[2794]

Single-sheet printed devotional images were used in a variety of ways in the fifteenth century, few of which were conducive to their survival. Pasted to walls, glued to wooden panels, inside boxes and books or onto pieces of furniture, only a handful of the thousands of impressions which were produced have survived. Those that do have invariably been extracted from their context, removed to satisfy the desires of later print collectors.

Many surviving prints were once pasted into books, both printed and manuscript, to act as devotional aids and stimuli. These prints in books offer us a unique insight into the contemporary use of devotional images and into the complex interplay between manuscript and print. One such example is this extraordinary print of the Crucifixion. This graphic woodcut succinctly demonstrates how context is paramount and how evidence of use can be critical in dating and localizing single-sheet devotional images. The Crucifixion is unique and bears no indication of where or when it was produced. Beneath the image is a manuscript indulgence in Dutch, offering the bearer an unprecedented remission from purgatory of 80,000 years. The hand and language suggest that the woodcut circulated in the Netherlands, probably in the east, during the late fifteenth century.

Sinte gregorius omelie op dit selue ewange
lium dat hi predicte den volc te romen in sinte.
Marien kerc der ioncfrowen.:.
Omme dat wi hudē vāder gena-
den gods driewerue celebrieren
sellē die solemniteite der missen so
en moghen wi niet lange sprekē
vander lesen des ewāgelijs. mer
die gheboerte ons heren des verlossers dwinget
ons doch yets wat cortelic te seggen. Wat is
datmen alle die werlt bescriuet als onse heer ge-

1

The extraordinary duration of the indulgence allows us to identify this specific woodcut as the *Ecce homo* mentioned by Henry Bradshaw, University Librarian at Cambridge, in a letter to the Dutch bibliographer J.W. Holtrop, 10 May 1866. Therein, he describes its purchase from the Amsterdam bookseller, Frederik Muller, 'lying loose in a copy of St. Gregory's *Homilies* printed (by Veldener at Utrecht) in 1479'. Bradshaw's later notebooks suggest that Muller may have been wholly unaware of the woodcut's presence at the time of sale. The Utrecht *Homilies* remains in the University collections, and adds further weight to a contemporary Dutch origin for the woodcut. The prolific spurts of blood were added by hand, and stylistically mimic other examples dated to the last quarter of the fifteenth century. The pigment used to colour the Cambridge print is remarkably similar to that used to rubricate the book in which the woodcut was found, suggesting that both may have been undertaken contemporaneously.

That this print survives at all is remarkable, that the link between print and book can be reconstructed doubly so; the combination of evidence permits a tentative dating and locating of a woodcut which otherwise would be impossible to place.

Ed Potten *is Acting Joint Head of Special Collections and Head of Rare Books at Cambridge University Library.*

Soe wie dit ghebet leest mit berou van sijn
sondē die verdient .xxx. dusent iaer aflaets
O Here ihū xpī ic aenbede die heymelike v
borghenheit dijs hertē Indē welckē dat
alle die scatten vā wijsheidē besloten sijn Eñ ic
aenbede die alder hoechste eñ soetste begheerte
eñ mine dijs hertē die vbrochte totter ald' bit
terste pynē des lidēs Om ons daer mede te v
lossen vander ewigher doot Amē Pr nr aue

2

PICTURED:

1. The entry for the Bible in the De Madiis *Zornale*. Marc. It. XI, 45 (=7439), f. 2v.
2. The annotation by Esteveaix, noting the purchase in Paris.
3. The opening of the Book of Judges.

How much did books cost in fifteenth-century Venice?

Biblia latina

Venice: Franciscus Renner, 1480

Inc.4.B.3.6d[1391]

Fifteenth-century printed books sometimes bear on their leaves purchase notes left by their owners recording the price paid, the date, the place, or method of acquisition. This Bible was purchased in Paris, probably still in the fifteenth century, by an as yet unidentified 'Esteveaix'. This indirectly informs us that the book, produced in Venice, was soon shipped to Paris for international distribution. What we do not know was how much it cost.

We are fortunate that the ledger of a Venetian bookseller, Francesco de Madiis, survives in the Biblioteca Nazionale Marciana. During the years 1484–1488 de Madiis recorded the sale and prices of some 25,000 printed books in a document now known as the *Zornale*. In this period in Venice currency was expressed in ducats, lire, and soldi: there were 20 soldi in a lira (£), and 6 lire and 4 soldi in a ducat. In the de Madiis ledger 54 copies of this edition of the Bible were sold between 1484 and 1488; their price initially oscillates between £4 and £5.10 in June, soon to stabilize at £3 during the period from the end of 1484 through to 1488; a copy is sold already bound for £5 in 1487.

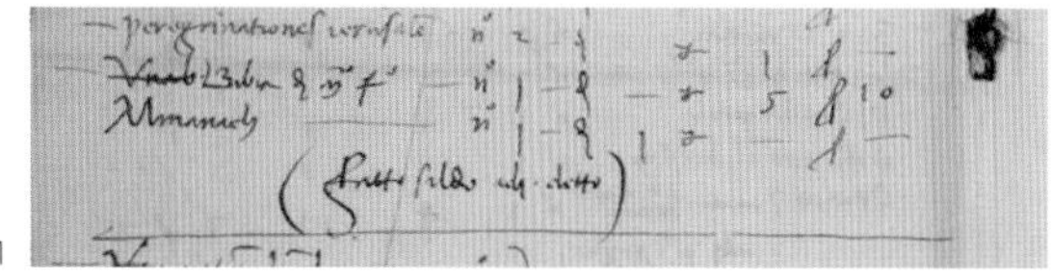

1

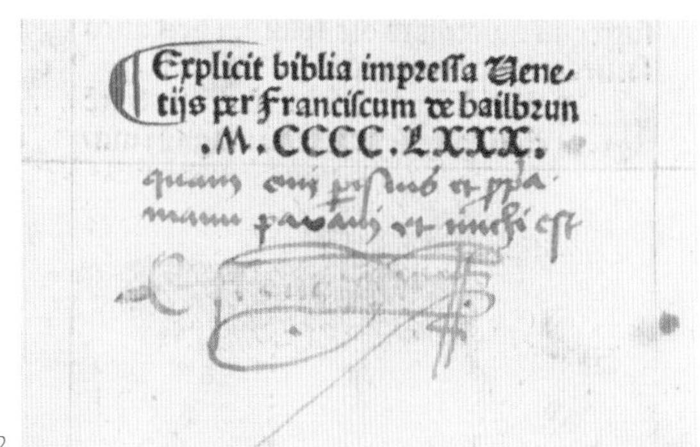

2

For comparison, the Cambridge copy of another Latin Bible, also printed in Venice, by Leonardus Wild in 1481 was purchased in Italy in 1500 from an Italian bookseller for £3.12; in the book an inscription reads: '*Ista biblia est Vrsati de Uilla empta super nundinas de anno 1500 precio libras 3 solidi 12 a magistro Betino cartulario*'.

Thus, there is therefore a certain consistency in price even if the 1480 edition is physically larger than that of 1481; we can already see the price of the book increasing outside its place of production. Venice was the largest printing centre in fifteenth-century Europe and the largest exporter: it will be fascinating to compare Venetian prices with those of copies exported throughout Europe, as recorded in the surviving books themselves.

The cost of this Bible was comparable to the purchase of six chickens or five geese, and was equivalent to three days' wages for a master in the building trade in late fifteenth-century Venice, or six days' for an apprentice. The book was therefore not cheap for a common person, but definitely not unattainable, as a manuscript equivalent would have been only a few years before, and still was.

Cristina Dondi *is Oakeshott Senior Research Fellow in the Humanities, Lincoln College, University of Oxford, and Secretary of the Consortium of European Research Libraries (CERL): she is currently preparing an edition of the de Madiis Zornale with Neil Harris.*

Post mortem iosue· cōsuluerūt filij israhel dn̄m dicentes: Quis ascēdet ante nos cōtra chananeū. ⁊ erit dux belli? Dixitq̨ dn̄s: Judas ascendet. Ecce tradidi terrā in manu eius. Et ait iudas symeoni fratri suo. Ascende mecū in sortē meā. ⁊ pugna ꝯ chananeum: ut ⁊ ego pgā tecū in sortem tuā. Et abijt cū eo symeon. Ascēditq̨ iudas ⁊ tradidit dn̄s chananeū ac pherezeū in man⁹ eorū ⁊ pcusserūt in bezech decē milia viroꝝ. Inueneruntq̨ adonibezech in bezech. ⁊ pugnauerūt ꝯ eū· ac pcusserūt chananeū ⁊ pherezeū. Fugit aūt adonibezech· quē psecuti cōprehenderūt cesis sūmitatib⁹ manuū eius ac pedū. Dixitq̨ adonibezech: Septuagita reges amputatꝭ manuū ac pedū sūmitatib⁹ colligebāt sub mensa mea ciborum reliquias: sicut feci· ita reddidit mihi deus. Adduxeruntq̨ eū in irl'm. ⁊ ibi mortuus ē. Oppugnātes ḡ filij iuda irl'm· ceperūt eā. ⁊ pcusserūt in ore gladij tradentes cunctā incēdio ciuitatē. Et postea descendentes pugnauerūt ꝯ chananeū q̇ habitabat in mōtanis. ⁊ ad meridiē in cāpestribus. Pergensq̨ iudas ꝯ chananeū q̇ habitabat in hebron cui⁹ nomē fuit antiq̄tus cariatharbe· percussit sesai ⁊ hayman ⁊ tholmai: atq̨ inde pfect⁹ abijt ad habitatores dabir· cuius nomē vet⁹ erat cariathsepher. i. ciuitas litterarū. Dixitq̨ caleph: Qui pcusserit cariatsepher ⁊ vastauerit eā· dabo ei axam filiā meā vxorē. Cūq̨ cepisset eam othoniel filius cenez frater caleph minor: dedit ei axam filiam suā cōiugē. Quā pgentē in itinere monuit vir suus ut peteret a pr̄e suo agrū. Que cū suspirasset sedens in asino· dixit ei caleph: Quid habes? At illa r̄ndit. Da mihi benedictionē: q̇a t̄rā arentē dedisti mihi: da ⁊ irriguā aq̄s. Dedit ḡ caleph irriguū sup̱i⁹ ⁊ irriguum inferius. Filij aūt cinei cognati moysi ascenderūt de ciuitate palmaꝝ cū filijs iuda in desertū sortis eius qd ē ad meridiē arath: ⁊ habitauerūt cū eo. Abijt aūt iudas cū symeone fr̄e suo. ⁊ pcusserunt sil'r chananeū qui habitabat in sephat. ⁊ int̄fecerūt eū. Vocatūq̨ est nomē vrbis horma. i. anathema. Cepitq̨ iudas gazā cū finib⁹ suis. ⁊ aschalonē atq̨ accaron cū t̄minis suis. Fuitq̨ dn̄s cū iuda. ⁊ montana possedit. Nec potuit delere habitatores vallis: q̇a falcatꝭ currib⁹ abundabāt. Dederūtq̨ caleph hebron sicut dixerat moyses: q̇ deleuit ex ea tres filios enach. Jebuseū aūt habitatorē irl'm nō deleuerūt filij beniamin: habitauitq̨ iebuseus cum filijs beniamin in irl'm vsq̨ in p̄ntem diē. Dom⁹ q̊q̨ ioseph ascēdit i bethel: fuitq̨ dn̄s cū eis. Nā cū obsiderēt vrbē q̄ p̄us luza vocabat̄· viderūt hoiem egredientē de ciuitate· dixeruntq̨ ad eū: Ostende nobis introitū ciuitatꝭ. ⁊ faciem⁹ tecum m̄iam. Qui cū o͞ndisset eis· percusserūt vrbē in ore gladij: hoiem autē illū ⁊ o͞em cognationē eius dimiserūt. Qui dimissus abijt i t̄rā ethim ⁊ edificauit ibi ciuitatē vocauitq̨ eā luzā q̇ ita appellat̄ vsq̨ in p̄ntē diem. Manasses quoq̨ nō deleuit bethsan ⁊ thanath cū viculis suis. ⁊ habitatores dor ⁊ ieblaam ⁊ maieddo cū viculis suis: cepitq̨ chanane⁹ habitare cū eis. Postq̄ aūt ꝯfortatus ē isrl' fecit eos tributarios ⁊ delē noluit. Effraim etiā nō int̄fecit chananeū q̇ habitabat i gazer: ſ̈ habitauit cū eo. Zabulon nō deleuit habitatores tethron ⁊ naalon: ſ̈ habitauit chanane⁹ i medio ei⁹· factusq̨ ē ei tributari⁹. Aser q̊q̨ non deleuit h̄itatores accho ⁊ sidonis alab ⁊ achazib ⁊ āma ⁊ aphech ⁊ roob: habitauitq̨ i medio chananei habitatoris illi⁹ t̄re· nec int̄fecit eū. Neptalim q̊q̨ non deleuit habitatores bethsemes ⁊ bethanath. ⁊ habitauit int̄ chananeū habitatorē terre: fueruntq̨ ei bethsemite ⁊ bethanite tributarij. Artauitq̨ āmorre⁹ filios dan i mōte: nec dedit eis locū ut ad planiora descenderēt: habitauitq̨ in mōte hares qd interp̄tat̄ testatio i hailon ⁊ salabim. Et aggrauata ē man⁹ dom⁹ ioseph: factusq̨ ē ei tributarius. Fuit aūt terminus āmorrei ab ascensu scorpionis petra ⁊ superiora loca. ¶ II

Ascēditq̨ angel⁹ dn̄i de galgalis ad locū flentiū. ⁊ ait: Eduxi vos de egypto. ⁊ introduxi i t̄rā ꝓ q̄ iuraui patrib⁹ v̄ris. ⁊ pollicitus sum ut nō facerē irritū pactū meū vobiscū in sempit̄nū· ita dūtaxat ut non feriretis fedus cū habitatoribus t̄re hui⁹. ⁊ aras eoꝝ subuerteretꝭ. ⁊ noluistis audire vocē meā. Cur hoc fecistis? Quāobrem nolui delere eos a facie v̄ra: ut habeatis hostes. ⁊ dij eoꝝ sint vobis i ruinam. Cūq̨ loquerer̄ angelus dn̄i h̄ v̄ba ad o͞es filios isrl'· eleuauerūt vocē suā ⁊ fleuerūt. Et vocatū est nomē loci illi⁹ locus flentiū siue lachrymaꝝ

PICTURED:

1. Examples of translated phrases from Caxton's text.
2. A cryptic inscription left by the fifteenth-century owner John White.

Caxton's phrasebook: learning English and French

***Vocabularius* [French and English]**
Westminster: [William Caxton, 1480]
Inc.3.J.1.1[4434]

This is a phrasebook, from which everyone 'may shortly lerne frenssh and englissh'; it is now also seen as an important source for colloquial English in the late fifteenth century. The text seems to have been adapted from a fourteenth- or fifteenth-century work, itself an adaptation of a fourteenth-century school text written in Bruges. This version, as printed by William Caxton, consists of brief, bilingual character sketches of more than 100 people, introduced by their first names, nearly three-quarters of whom are trades- and crafts-men, and women, and it was clearly intended for their use. The sketches include Rogier the feltmaker ('Hath many a good hatte of bever and of felte') and Felice the silkwoman ('maketh so many purses and pauteners [pouches] of silke for she is thereof a maistresse').

The Cambridge University Library copy is one of four complete copies known to survive. It was owned at the end of the fifteenth century by one John White, and was subsequently acquired by Ripon Minster in North Yorkshire, and formed part of its collections until it was sold on behalf of the Dean and Chapter of the cathedral in May 1960 by Sotheby's. It was bought by the New York bookseller, H.P. Kraus (1907–1988), and the Library obtained it by exchange for another Caxton book from its existing holdings. Within the Royal Library collection, given in 1715 by George I, were two copies of the *Recuyell of the historyes of Troye*, printed in Bruges in about 1473–1474. Both copies were incomplete, and before parting with the more incomplete, the Library removed ten leaves from it and bound them into the copy which was to be retained, to supply some of the lacunae. Kraus took the now substantially more incomplete copy in exchange for the *Vocabularius*, its final home being the Yale Center for British Art.

Whilst in the Ripon collection, the *Vocabularius* is known initially to have been bound, in 'melancholy looking forrel, or white sheep skin' according to Dibdin, with a copy of Chaucer's translation of Boethius's *Consolation of philosophy* printed by Caxton in about 1478. However, they were separated in about 1815 and rebound individually by the well-known London bookbinder, Charles Lewis (1786–1836), the binding of the *Vocabularius* being gold-tooled brown morocco.

Alan Coates *is an Assistant Librarian specializing in rare books and printed ephemera, at the Bodleian Libraries, University of Oxford.*

Frensshe	Englissh
La grace de saint esprit	The grace of the holy ghoost
Veul enluminer les cuers	Wylle enlyghte the hertes
De ceulx qui le aprendront	Of them that shall lerne it
Et nous doinst perseuerance.	And vs gyue perseueraunce
En bonnes operacions	In good werkes
Et apres ceste vie transitorie	And after this lyf transitorie
La pardurable ioye & glorie	The euerlastyng ioye and glorie

1

Frenſſhe	Engliſſh
Ce ſont les buuraiges.	Thiſe ben the drynkes
Vin de rin et danſay	Rynyſſh wyn and of elzeter
Vin de beane & de germole.	Wyn of beane and of germole
Vin franſoys et de ſpayne	Frenſſh wyn and of ſpayne
Muſkadel & baſtard	Muſcadel and baſtard
Vin doſoye et de garnate	Wyn of oſeye and of garnade
Vin de gaſcoyne	Wyn of gaſcoyne
Malueſye romenye	Malueſeye romeneye
Vin cuit vin gregois	Wyn ſoden wyn greek
Ypocras & clarey ſont fait	Ypocras and clarey ben made,
De vin & bonnes eſpices	Of wyn and good ſpices
Blanc vin vin vermeil.	White wyn rede wyn.
Miel mies	Hony mede
Seruoiſe dangleterre	Ale of englond
Seruoiſe dalemayne.	Byere of alemayne
Sydre eſt fait de pommes	Syther is made of apples
Boulie eſt faitte	Boulye is made
Diauwe & de leuain.	Of water and of leuayn
Et de tercheul	And of worte
Fontaine boit on bien.	Welle watre drynke me well
Liauwe boiuent les beſtes	Watre drynke the beſtes
Sy buc on les toilles	So weſſhe me with all lynnenclothis
d Aultres choſes ſans attendre.	Of othir thinge withoute taryeng.
Endementiers quil me ſouuient	Whiles that I remembre.
Vous veul deuiſer et aprendre	I wyll to you deuiſe and teche
Se vous voules bergaignier	Yf ye wyll bergayne
Draps ou aultres marchandiſſes.	Wullen cloth or othir marchandiſe
Sy alles a le halle	So goo to the halle.
Qui eſt ou marchiet	Whiche is in the market
Sy montes les degretz	So goo vpon the ſteyres
La trouueres les draps.	There ſhall ye fynde the clothes
Draps meſles	Clothes medleyed
Rouge drap ou vert	Red cloth or grene.
Bleu aſuret	Blyew y aſured
Gaune vermeil	Yelow reed.
Entrepers morret	Sad blew morrey
Royet eſquiekeliet	Raye chekeryd
Saye blanche & bleu.	Saye white and blew
Eſcarlate en grain	Scarlet in grayne
Sy poes commencier.	So may ye begynne
Par tele ſalutation	By ſuche gretyng
Côme il eſt en primier chapitle	As it is in the firſt chapitre.

1480

PICTURED:

1. The last page of the *Horae*, showing the forged colophon.
2. The eighteenth-century binding.
3. Another page of the book, showing the genuine fifteenth-century decoration.

'Concerning a Book supposed to have been printed by Coster'

***Horae* [Dutch]**
Delft: [Jacob Jacobszoon van der Meer], 8 April 1480
SSS.19.16

For centuries the Dutch town of Haarlem has been associated with the name Laurens Janszoon Coster, supposed inventor of printing with moveable type around the middle of the fifteenth century. According to the legend, Coster is said to have amused his grandchildren while on a walk in the woods by stamping impressions of letters made from pieces of tree bark. He later experimented with ink and woodblock printing, and eventually developed lead type. A servant named Johannes Faust stole Coster's equipment, however, and fled to Mainz, where his method of printing was refined and perfected. This history of the dawn of printing was widely believed until the nineteenth century and still has its adherents today, but documentary evidence has proved stubbornly elusive.

The Costerian legend has left its mark on this little book, one of two copies the University Library holds of a Dutch book of hours in fact printed in Delft in 1480. In 1756 the duke of Marlborough heard of a book in the possession of 'a gentleman at Harlem' which was apparently printed by Coster in 1450. His secretary had it examined by a local agent, who found it not only bore a colophon naming Coster as the printer but also an inscription telling how it was bought in 1450, shortly after most of Coster's goods had been destroyed in the sack of Haarlem by the Spanish. The secretary was not convinced, but the book was later acquired as a curiosity by Francis Freeling, founder member of the Roxburghe Club, eventually passing into the collection of Samuel Sandars, who bequeathed it to the University Library in 1894.

The 'gentleman at Harlem' was one George Smith, a military captain who later published some books on Freemasonry. In the 1750s he described himself as a reader in mathematics, but seems to have had a side-line as a forger of early books, which he passed off as products of Coster's press at Haarlem and also of that of Frederik Corcellis, founder of an equally legendary business in Oxford in 1468. The inscription and colophon were both added by Smith, the last apparently stamped from a wood block, and then decorated to match the fifteenth-century decoration of the rest of the book. The volume was later given an English binding in red morocco and in its current form is as much a relic of eighteenth-century collecting fashions as of fifteenth-century devotional printing.

William Hale *is Rare Books Specialist at Cambridge University Library.*

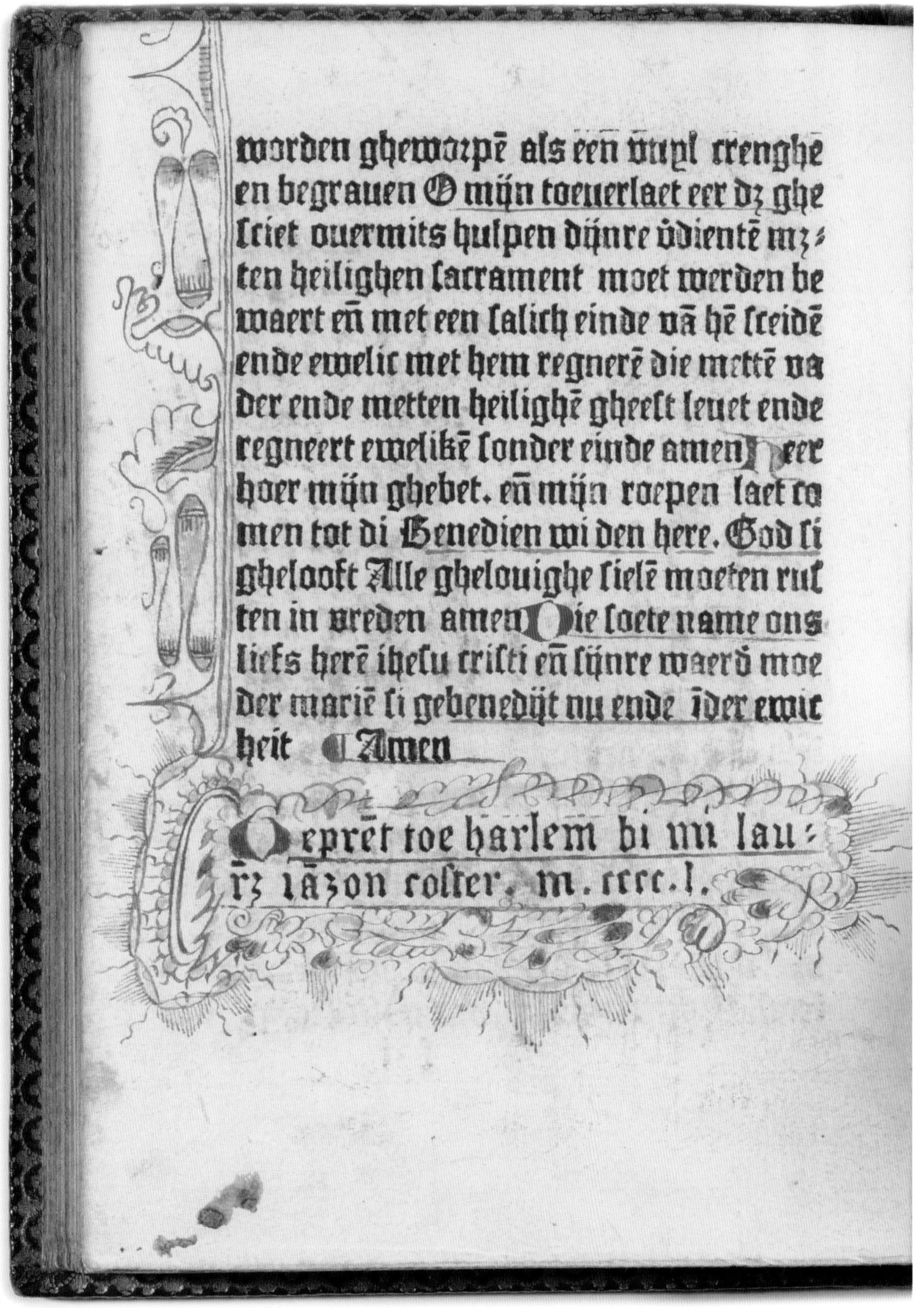
worden ghewarpē als een vuyl crenghe
en begrauen O mijn toeuerlaet eer dz ghe
sciet ouermits hulpen dijnre v̄dientē mz
ten heilighen sacrament moet werden be
waert eñ met een salich einde vā hē sceidē
ende ewelic met hem regnerē die mettē va
der ende metten heilighē gheest leuet ende
regneert ewelikē sonder einde amen Heer
hoer mijn ghebet. eñ mijn roepen laet co
men tot di Genedien wi den here. God si
ghelooft Alle ghelouighe sielē moeten ruſ
ten in vreden amen Die soete name ons
liefs herē ihesu cristi eñ sijnre waerd moe
der mariē si gebenedijt nu ende īder ewic
heit Amen

Gheprēt toe harlem bi mi lau
rz iāzon coster. m.cccc.l.

1

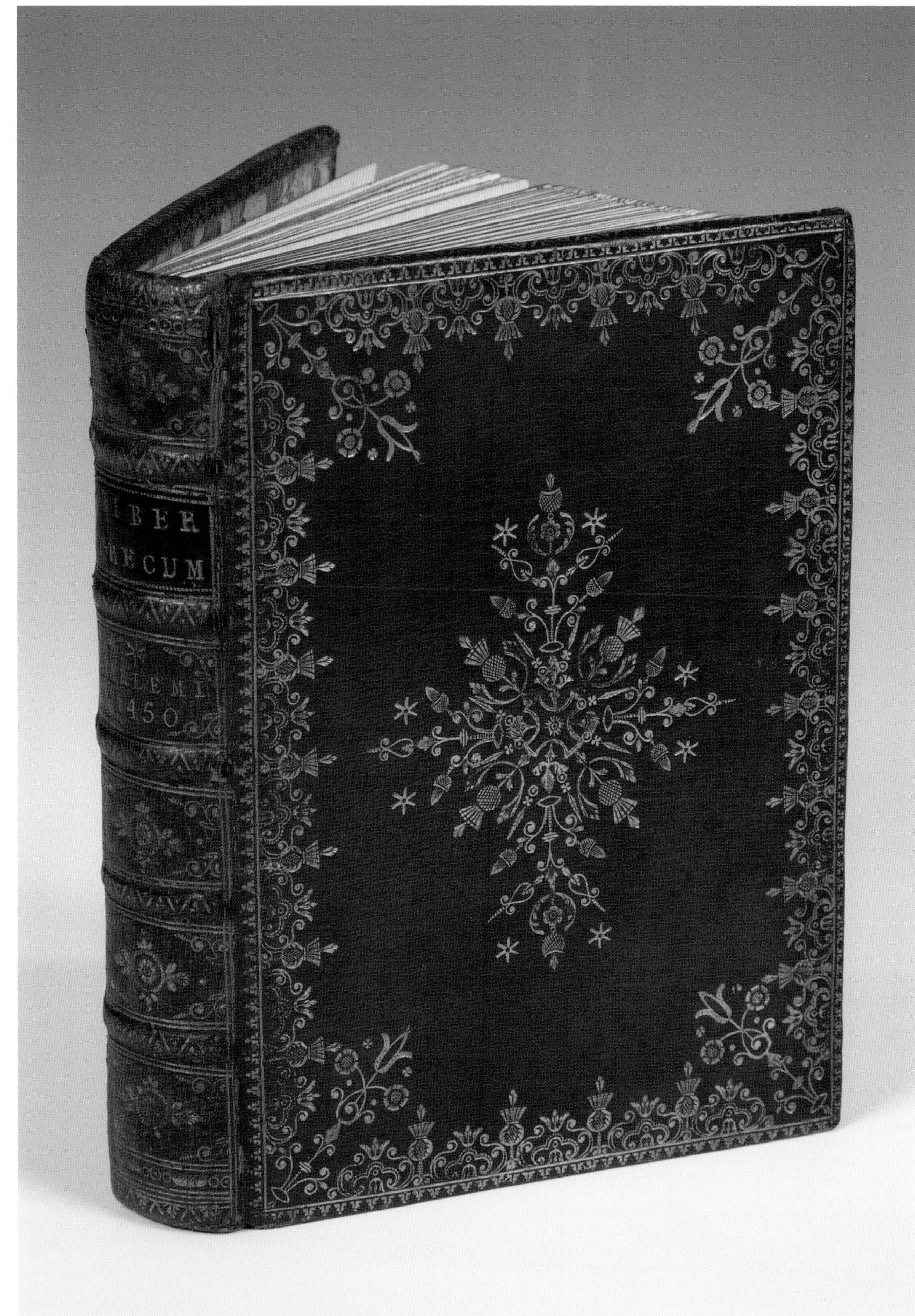

2

glorie Heer maec ghesont dÿn volc eñ be-
nedie dÿn erfnis Eñ berechtse eñ ōhoecht
se van nu tot in ewicheit Alle daghe bñ
dien wi di Eñ wi louen dinē naē eewelic
Ghewaerdighe di heer ons te behoeden
desen dach sonder sonde Ontferme di ō-
ser heer ontferme di onser Dine ontferm
herticheit ghewerde op ons als wi in dÿ
ghehoept hebben In di heer heb ic ghehoept . en laet mi niet scandelic confuust
staē indē ewicheit . ōs. Salicheit der sielē eñ
des lÿfs ghif ōs ihūs cristus die
Od wÿsheit des vads Laudes
wilt dencken in mÿn. Glorie si
den vader Alst was Psalmus
Louet den heer al ghi heiden louet dē
heer alle volc Want sÿn ontfermicheit is
ghestadicht op ons die waerheit des hee-
ren blÿft ewelic Glorie Aūt. Die ewichz
roept inder stratē so wie die wÿsheit mit
die neighe hē tot mi eñ hi selse viden ende

PICTURED:

1. The decorated second leaf, bearing at the foot Sub-Prior Nicolas's faded oath.
2. The nineteenth-century armorial book binding, commissioned by Mark Masterman Sykes of Sledmere.
3– 9. A selection of the charming woodcut illustrations throughout the volume, some embellished by hand with red ink.

A bestseller and a faded oath

Dialogus creaturarum moralisatus
Gouda: Gerard Leeu, 3 June 1480
SSS.40.15

This is the first edition of one of the most charming books printed in the fifteenth century. Its printer, Gerard Leeu, had started his business three years earlier in the small Dutch town of Gouda, and we see him here setting out on a new venture: illustrating his books. The text itself was quite a find, a compilation of 121 amusing discussions between God's creations, each leading to a moral supported by solemn theological works. It was written in or near Milan, probably in the fourteenth century, but was hardly known in northern Europe. A few surviving manuscripts are illustrated in the tradition of bestiaries. Leeu's artist, producing a woodcut for each dialogue, interpreted this model using very simple lines to almost cartoonish effect. In the present copy the rubricator added delicate touches in red to many of the cuts.

The immediate success of the book is evident from the rate with which it was reprinted. Between 1480 and 1482 Leeu published it six times, in Latin, Dutch and French, using the same set of woodcuts. Further reprints, and imitations by others, continued well into the sixteenth century.

Leeu's ambition was to sell his books far beyond Gouda, and indeed, their early owners are recorded in the Low Countries, in France, in the German lands, and in England. The copy shown here was owned early in the sixteenth century by the Sub-Prior of the Dominican friary in Warwick, Nicolas Alexander, who noted that a previous English owner, Robert Compson, had given it to him. Both owners read the book attentively, pen in hand, for in the margins they wrote comments on the text in Latin, often marked with little flags. There is also the faint trace of a different kind of note, written at a later date at the foot of the second leaf. We can still read that it says (in Latin) 'I, Nicolas Alexander, deny the authority of the pope and affirm our king Henry VIII as supreme head of the Anglican Church, and his successors, in perpetuity.'

The friary in Warwick was surrendered to the king in October 1538, whereupon the fabric of the building was stripped out by the citizenry and country folk, leaving a mere shell. This was the background against which Nicolas must have written his declaration in the book he had managed to salvage, leaving us to imagine the precise circumstances.

Lotte Hellinga *retired as Deputy Keeper in the British Library in 1995: among her recent work is the compilation of the* Catalogue of books printed in the XVth century now in the British Library *(2007).*

Prefacio i librū qui dicit᷑ dyalogꝰ creaturarū moralizatꝰ omni materie morali iocūdo et edificatiuo modo applicabilis ¶ Incipit feliciter

Quoniā sicut testa᷑ ysidorus in liͦ de sūmo boͦ liͦ pͦ caͦ quarto dicens ꝙ ex pulchritudine circūscripte nature ostendit nobis deꝰ pulchritudinis sue ptē aliquā· qui circūscribi nequit et intelligi· vt ipsis eisdem vestigijs homo reuertatur ad deū q̄bus auersus est a deo Et q̄ ꝑ amorē pulcritudinis creature· a creatoris forma se abstulit· rursus ꝑ creature decorem· ad creatoris sui pulchritudinē reuertatur Que quidem creature· et si nobis sicut liber iste fingit· dyaletice | voce formata nō loquātur Inclinacione tamē et naturalis institutionis ꝓprietate· nos docere nostrosqꝫ mores corrigere si bene pēsamus· nō desinūt Quod illud gloriosū lumen doctorū Sanctus augustinus optime intelligebat cū dicebat O domine deꝰ ōnes creature tue q̄s fecisti· ad me clamāt· et clamare nō desinūt vt te solū deū creatorem meū sup omnia diligā· ¶ Et ideo auctor libri istius hec rite considerans quosdā dyalogos creaturarum ad sanā et moralem doctrinā applicauit | confinxit et composuit· vt ꝑ creaturarū quasi nobis loquētiū ꝓprietates· simul in moribus erudiamur et tedium audientiū euitemus· et ipsorū audienciū memoriam adiuuemꝰ quod maxime per rerū similitudines procuratur ¶ Saluator enī noster ōniū predicatorū perfecta forma | fabulis· palestinorū more· vsus est· vt rerū similitudine ad viam veritatis homines ꝑduceret Auctor ergo libri presentis iocūdo modo morales doctrinas i exterminiū viciorū et virtutū promocionē introducit· quod

1

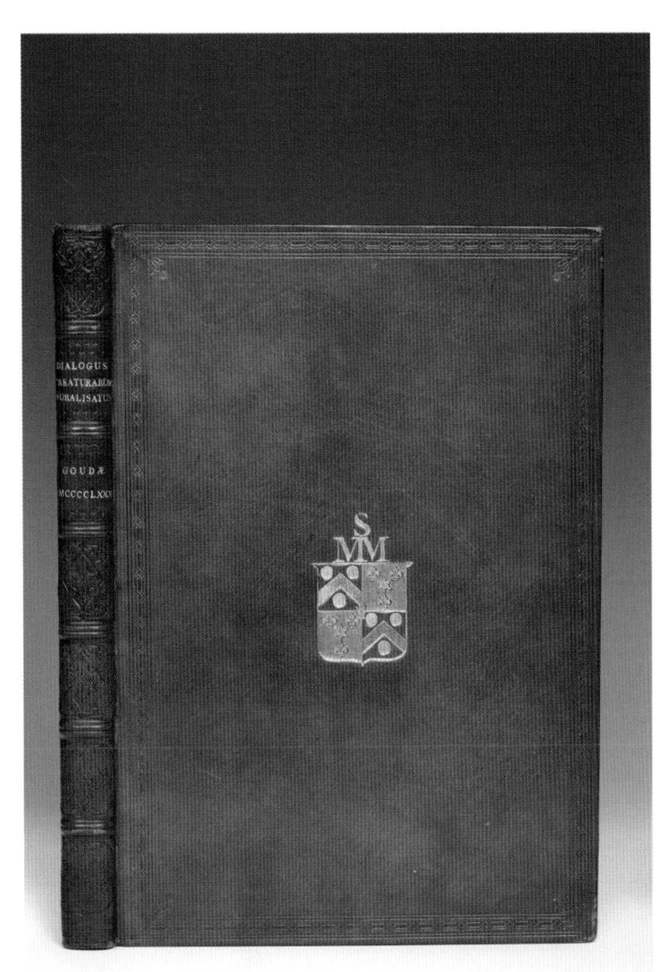

2

3

4

5

6

7

8

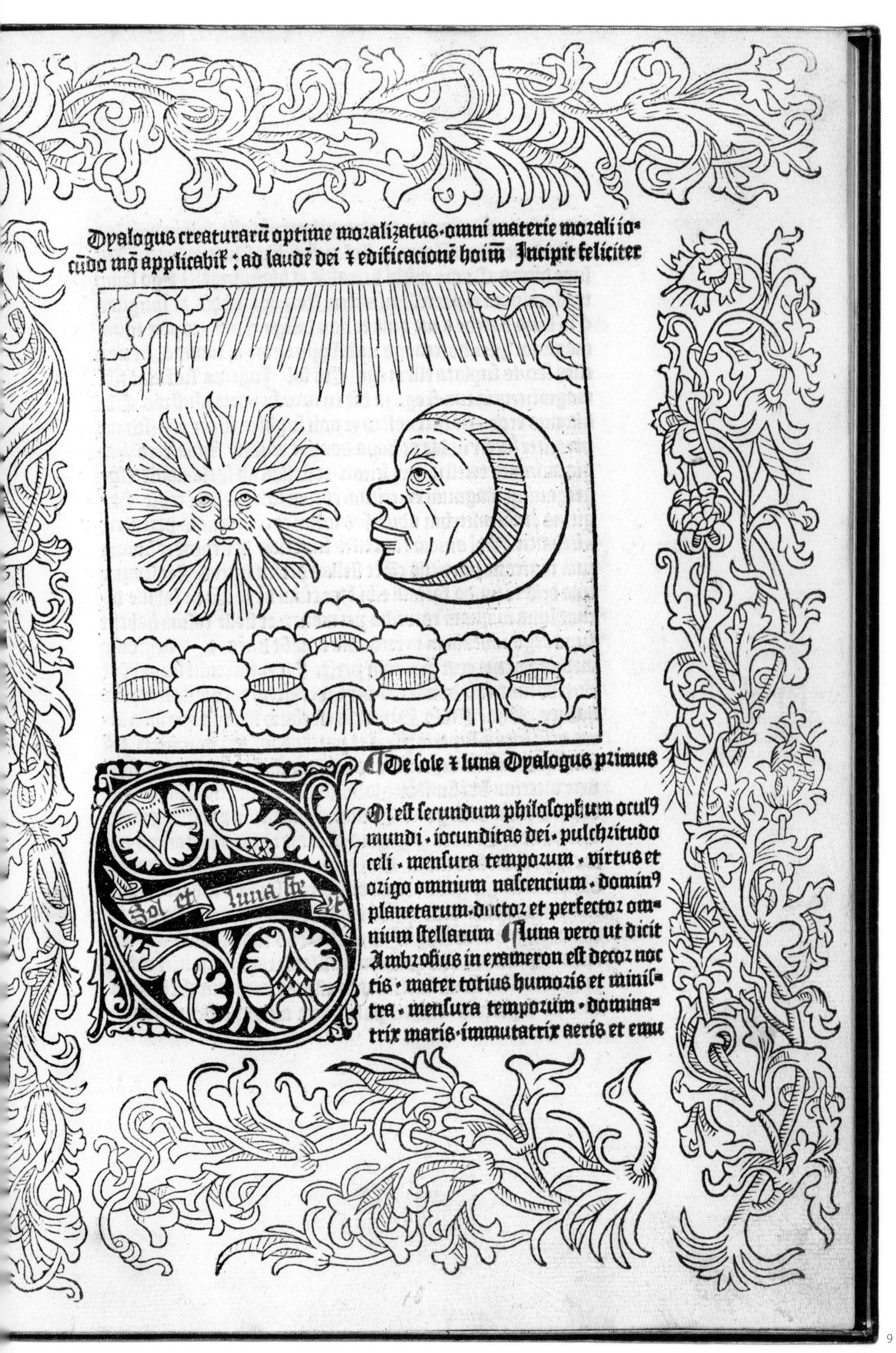

Dyalogus creaturarũ optime moralizatus· omni materie morali iocũdo mõ applicabil: ad laudẽ dei ⁊ edificacionẽ hoim̃ Incipit feliciter

De sole ⁊ luna Dyalogus primus

Ol est secundum philosophum ocul⁹ mundi · iocunditas dei · pulchritudo celi · mensura temporum · virtus et origo omnium nascencium · domin⁹ planetarum · doctor et perfector omnium stellarum ¶Luna vero ut dicit Ambrosius in exameron est decor noctis · mater totius humoris et ministra · mensura temporum · dominatrix maris · immutatrix aeris et emu

9

1481

PICTURED:

1. Only fragments of the original clasps remain.
2. The holes at the upper left corner suggest the book was chained at an early stage.
3. The 1505 bond, utilising a blank leaf stub.
4. A rubbing of the binding showing the unicorn tool.
5. Bowes's discreet annotation.

From one low country to another, to the west country and back

Henricus de Zoemeren (1420–1472)
Epitoma primae partis dialogi de haereticis a Guilielmo de Ockham compositi
Louvain: Johannes de Westfalia, 1481

Bound with:
Ludolf von Sachsen (about 1300–1377)
Vita Christi
[Louvain: Johannes de Westfalia, 1484–1487]

and:
Antonius de Butrio (1338–1408)
Speculum de confessione
Louvain: Johannes de Westfalia, [not before 1483–1485]
Inc.3.F.2.2[3178]

The three items in this volume were all printed in Louvain in the 1480s, but found themselves within a few decades in the hands of a Cambridge graduate living in Somerset. The volume bears annotations by one William Bowes, who in 1479 left Eton College and was admitted as a scholar at the still relatively young King's College, Cambridge. College records show that he was made a Fellow in 1482 and remained thus until 1502, serving several periods as college bursar. He took on the rectorship of Combe St Nicholas in Somerset in November 1502, and presumably took with him this beautiful volume of three theological texts, fundamental reference works for an educated cleric and ones he must have purchased in Cambridge. The stub of the final (blank) leaf of the third item in the volume bears an inscription dated 29 July 1505, stating that William Bowes 'clerke vic[ar] of cumbe seyntnicolas' and two fellow sureties, Henry Bond and Richard Rocetur, promise to pay to the Lord of Bath or his assigns the sum of 40 shillings at the feast of All Saints. Apart from this, and a Biblical quotation in red at the end of the final text signed with his name, Bowes left the text completely without annotation.

The book can be securely placed in late fifteenth-century Cambridge by its binding, of stamped leather over wooden boards with clasps to hold the volume closed on the shelf (the clasps themselves are now lost). The renowned binding scholar Anthony Hobson identified this as the work of the Unicorn binder, so named for his most distinctive tool, a small woodland unicorn. He is known to have bound at least seventy volumes between 1484 and 1505, of which eighteen are in Cambridge libraries (the University Library has one other).

These books need not have remained in Cambridge continuously, of course, and the Library purchased this example from the sale of the great collector E. Gordon Duff in 1925. Its ownership between Bowes and Duff is unknown, though the small holes on the upper board suggest it may have been in one of the chained college libraries early in its life. Many libraries are ever more actively acquiring books with early local provenances, meaning that volumes with the distinctive reddish leather used by Cambridge men such as the Unicorn binder and the prolific Nicolas Spierinck are increasingly coming 'home' once again.

Emily Dourish *is Acting Deputy Head of the Rare Books Department at Cambridge University Library.*

1

Fifteen century binding with small dies and
foliate tools. The reddish dyed leather used for
this binding appears to be confined to bindings
executed in Cambridge.
Inc.3.F.2.2
Scripsit E.Gordon Duff.
Munificentia Tobiae Rustat

2

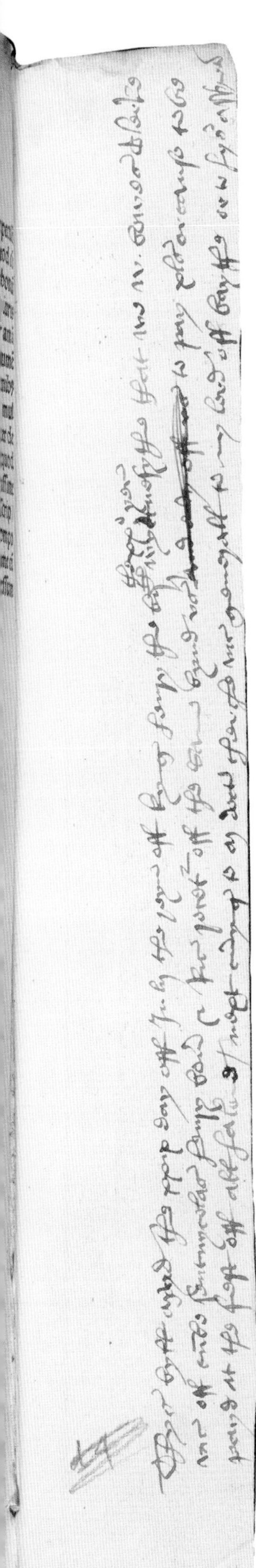

3

4

crederent ꝙ posset contrahi matrimo
nium inter illos q ex vna parte sunt
in secundo vel in tercio ⁊ ex alia sunt
in quinto. Sed planum est quia remo
ta persona extra metam consanguini
tatis est quia ē in quinto gradu. Vn̄
non attinet illi ex quo est vltra quar/
tum gradum.

5

1481

PICTURED:

1. The colophon of the 1481 Dante, emphasizing the Florentine nature of the endeavour.
2. The hand-coloured copper-plate illustration to the opening of the first canto of *La commedia*.

The exile returns …

Dante Alighieri (1265-1321)
La commedia
Florence: Nicolaus Laurentii, Alamanus, 30 August 1481
Inc.1.B.8.4[1933]

Known to Italians as *Il Sommo Poeta*, Dante is considered to be the father of the modern Italian language. Born in Florence around 1265, he became embroiled in the political infighting that dominated the Italian city state in the Middle Ages and was forced to flee the city in 1301. His most important work, *La commedia* (*The divine comedy*) was written in exile. He never returned to his beloved Florence and died in Ravenna in 1321. As his fame grew, Florence came to regret his exile. After a number of printed editions were published in Foligno (see pp. 34–37), Mantua, Venice, Naples and Milan, finally a lavish new edition was planned in Florence. This incorporated a new commentary by the Florentine humanist Cristoforo Landino and an introduction by Marsilio Ficino. The most remarkable features of this edition are its large size and the illustrations planned to accompany the text.

The original design was to include illustrations, based on drawings by Botticelli, at the beginning of each of the 100 chapters, using the technique of printing from engraved copper-plates rather than the usual relief woodblock. The printer, Nicolaus Laurentius *Alamanus*, was a German from Breslau who had produced another book illustrated with engravings, *Monte santo di Dio*, in 1477. The ambitious scheme was never fully realized and only nineteen engravings were finally executed. Most copies, including this one, have just the first two engravings, which were printed directly onto the page. Only about twenty copies are known to contain the other seventeen engravings, which were printed on separate slips and pasted into the spaces provided. This copy is, however, unique as both illustrations have been expertly coloured by hand. It also has extensive evidence of more than one careful early reader. There are manuscript headings summarizing the contents of each chapter and marginal notes by at least three different readers from the sixteenth and seventeenth centuries. Extra pages have also been added with a manuscript list of concordances from the text. In the church of Santa Croce in Florence is an empty tomb, built in 1829 with the inscription '*Onorate l'altissimo poeta*'. Despite its unfinished appearance, this Florentine edition remains as a monument to the Italian poet and to the glory of Florence.

Julianne Simpson *is Rare Books and Maps Manager at The John Rylands Library, Manchester.*

FINE DEL COMENTO DI CHRISTO
PHORO LANDINO FIOREN
TINO SOPRA LA COMEDIA DI DAN
THE POETA EXCELLENTIS
SIMO. ET IMPRESSO IN FIRENZE
PER NICHOLO DI LORENZO
DELLA MAGNA A DI .XXX. DA
GOSTO. M.CCCC. LXXXI.

1

CANTO PRIMO DELLA PRIMA CANTICA O VERO COMEDIA DEL DIVINO POETA FIORENTINO DANTHE ALEGHIERI : CAPITOLO PRIMO :

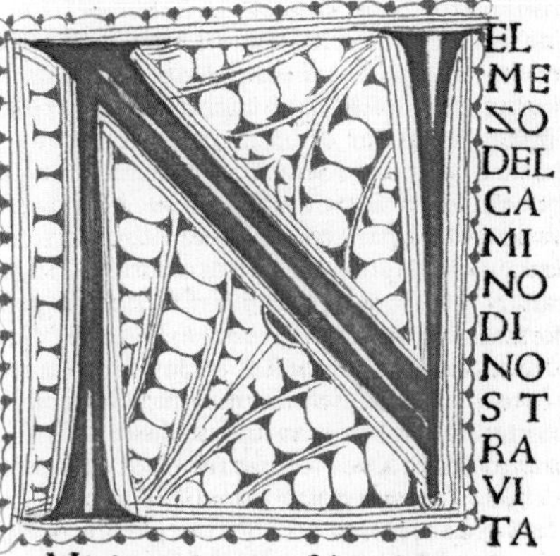

EL
ME
ZO
DEL
CA
MI
NO
DI
NO
S T
RA
VI
TA

Mi ritrouai peruna ſelua obſcura
che la diricta uia era ſmarrita
Et quanto adire quale era e/ coſa dura
eſta ſelua ſeluaggia et aſpra et forte
che nel penſier rinuoua lapaura
Tanto era amara che pocho e piu morte
ma per tractar del ben chio ui trouai
diro dellaltre coſe chio uho ſcorte
I non ſo ben ridire chomio uentrai
tantera pien diſonno inſu quel puncto
che lauerace uia abbandonai
Ma poi chio fui appie dun colle giunto
la oue terminaua quella ualle
che mhauea dipaur elcor compuncto
Guardai inalto et uidi leſue ſpalle
coperte gia deraggi delpianeta
che mena dricto altrui per ogni calle
Allhor fu lapaura un pocho queta
che nellago del chuor mera durata
lanocte chio paſſai con tanta pieta

h abbiamo narrato non ſolamente lauita del
poeta et eltitolo dellibro et che coſa ſia po
eta Ma etiam quãto ſia uetuſta et anticha quãto
nobile et uaria quanto utile et ioconda tal doc
trina. Quanto ſia efficace a muouere lhumane
mẽti; et quãto dilecti ogni liberale ĩgegno. Ne
giudicammo da tacere quanto in ſi diuina diſci
plina ſia ſtata la excellentia dello ingegno del
noſtro poeta. Inche ſiſono ſtato piu brieue che
forſe non ſi conuerebbe; conſideri chi legge che
lanumeroſa et quaſi infinita copia dellecoſe del
le quali e neceſſario tractare miſſforza non uolẽ
do chel uolume creſca ſopra modo; a inculcare
et inuiluppare piutoſto che explicare: et diſtẽ
dere moltecoſe et maxime quelle lequali quãdo
ben taceſſi non pero ne reſtera obſcura la expo
ſitione del teſto. Verremo adunque aquella.
Ma perche ſtimo non eſſer lectore alcuno ne di
ſi baſſo ingegno; ne di ſi pocho giudicio: che ha
uendo inteſo; quanto ſia et laprofondita et ua
rieta della doctrina; et la excellentia et diuinita
dello ingegno delnoſtro toſcano: et fiorentino
poeta: non ſi perſuada che queſto principio
delprimo canto debba per ſublimita et grande
za eſſer pari alla ſtupenda doctrina dellechoſe
che ſeguitano; pero con ogni induſtria in ueſti
gheremo che allegoricho ſenſo arechi ſeco que
ſto mezo delcamino; et che coſa ſia ſelua Diche
ueggio non piccola differentia eſſere ſtata tra
glinterpreti et expoſitori diqueſta cantica. Im
pero che alchuni dicono; che il mezo della uita
humana e el ſonno moſſi; credo dalla ſententia
dariſtotele dicendo lui nellethica neſſuna diffe
rentia eſſere tra felici; et miſeri nella meta della
uita per che lenocti che ſono lameta del tempo
cinducono ſonno; et daquello naſce che ne bene
nemale ſentir poſſiamo. Ilperche uogliono que
ſti; che el poeta pongha el mezo della uita per la
nocte; et lanocte pelſonno; ad notare che queſto
poema non ſia altro che una uiſione che gliap
parue dormẽdo per laquale hebbe cognitiõe del
le coſe dallui deſcripte ĩ queſte tre comedie. Di
cono adũque che lui imita Ioanni euangeliſta el
quale dormẽdo ſopra elpecto di chriſto redemptore hebbe uiſione delle choſe celeſte; oueramẽte
ponghi lanocte dimoſtrando lui hauere cominciato elſuo poema dinocte nella quale raccoglẽdoſi
lanimo inſemedeſimo et abſoluendoſi et liberandoſi da ogni cura meglo intenda. Ma benche tale
ſententia quadri al poeta; nientedimeno leparole non la dimoſtrono ſenon cõ tanto obſcura ambi
guita: che non pare degna della elegantia ditanto poeta Prima perche nonſeguita che benche nelle
reuolutioni deltempo tanto ſpatio occupin lenocti quanto e di; perqueſto dicendo io ſcripſi dinoc
te ſintenda io ſcripſi nel mezo della mia eta; perche et nel principio et nelfine della eta humana ſo
no lenocti chome nel mezo et ſimilmente e di. Il perche per lamedeſima ragione ſi potrebbe fare
tale interpretatione pẽl di chome per lanocte. Altridicono che uolle pelmezo del camino intende
re che nelmezo delleta dette principio alſuo poema. Ma non e unamedſima opinione deltermine
della noſtra eta; per che diuerſi ſcriptori diuerſamente ſentono. Ariſtotile nel ſuo de republica

2

1483

PICTURED:

Caxton's 'explicit', containing his apology for the addition of the concluding twelve lines.

Finishing the unfinished

Geoffrey Chaucer (died 1400)
The book of fame
[Westminster]: William Caxton, [1483]
Inc.3.J.1.1[3506]

A commercial printer needs to produce books that will sell, to a public that has no experience in buying them. When William Caxton set up the first printing press in England in 1476, therefore, he sought texts that would find a ready market: religious and devotional works, and books that readers would already expect to enjoy – not least the works of England's master poet, Geoffrey Chaucer. The *Canterbury tales* was accordingly one of the very first products of his press, and other works of Chaucer followed.

The dream poem now known as *The book of fame* is one of these, but as the displayed page shows, there were problems with it. One is an accident of time: two leaves have been lost before the one shown here. The other is an accident of transmission: the manuscript from which Caxton was working ended sixty lines before the end as found in modern editions, and even that longer version is incomplete, perhaps because Chaucer himself never finished it or because his original ending was itself lost. Caxton makes up for the deficiency by adding twelve lines of his own, signalled in the print by the marginal 'Caxton', which have the dreamer wake and write down his dream. He then explains the problem in his own voice: 'I fynde no more of this werke to fore sayd / For as fer as I can understonde / This noble man Gefferey Chaucer fynysshyd at the sayd conclusion.' He follows that with an encomium of his author, as the one who 'excellyth in myn oppynyon alle other wryters in our Englyssh'.

The book was printed in a standard format that invited binding together with other works. Some took the opportunity to assemble something resembling a 'Works of Chaucer': R. Johnson, who records his purchase of this copy in 1510 for 4d ('iiijd'), bound it with other works including Caxton's translations of the French *Eneidos* and *Godfrey of Boloyne*. The volume came to the University Library as part of the collection of Bishop John Moore, acquired at his death by George I and donated to Cambridge University. It was disassembled into its constituent parts in the late nineteenth century.

Helen Cooper *is Professor of Medieval and Renaissance English at the University of Cambridge.*

They were a chekked bothe two
And neyther of hym myght out goo
And wyth the noyse of them wo   Caxton
I sodeynly awoke anon tho
And remembryd what I had seen
And how hye and ferre I had been
In my ghoost / and had grete wonder
Of that the god of thonder
Had lete me knowen / and began to wryte
Lyke as ye haue herd me endyte
Wherfor to studye and rede alway
I purpose to doo day by day
Thus in dremyng and in game
Endeth thys lytyl book of Fame

Explicit

I fynde nomore of this werke to fore sayd / For as fer as I can understõde / This noble man Gefferey Chaucer fynysshyd at the sayd conclusion of the metyng of lesyng and sothsawe / where as yet they ben chekked and maye not departe / whyche werke as me semeth is craftyly made / and dygne to be wreton & knowen / For he towchyth in it ryght grete wysedom & subtyll understondyng / And so in alle hys werkys he excellyth in myn oppynyon alle other wryters in our Englyssh / For he wrytteth no voyde wordes / but alle hys mater is ful of hye and quycke sentence / to whom ought to be gyuen laude and preysyng for hys noble makyng and wrytyng / For of hym alle other haue borowed syth and taken / in alle theyr wel sayeng and wrytyng / And I humbly beseche & praye yow / emonge your prayers to remembre hys soule / on whyche and on alle crysten soulis I beseche almyghty god to haue mercy Amen

Emprynted by Wylliam Caxton

PICTURED:

1. Bartholomaeus Ghotan's colophon.
2. The hand-coloured woodcut initial which opens this Low German text.

Illuminating the soul – but almost forgotten

Licht der Seelen
Lübeck: Bartholomaeus Ghotan, 1484
Inc.5.A.14.2[1017]

Many of the 300 or so incunabula in the Low German vernacular are very rare, and some of them are now virtually forgotten. Cambridge University Library holds a rich collection of books in Low German, which includes treasures such as the highly decorative Lübeck Bible of 1494, but also lesser-known editions of great historical and literary value, such as the very first book printed in Low German, a translation of the Psalms from about 1474. Another remarkable Low German edition, the *Licht der Seelen* ('Light of the soul'), was until recently largely unknown to scholars. Like many vernacular Lübeck imprints, the *Licht der Seelen* was published anonymously. However, the scattered references to Latin sources indicate that the author was a learned cleric, who also cultivated an emotional and sophisticated writing style. He mentions his source, 'a book of thirty large sexterns' (360 leaves), but this mysterious volume seems to be lost, like so many other medieval books. From this source, he extracted a substantial work, the *Licht der Seelen*, essentially a confessional manual, intended according to the prologue for 'simple folk'.

But was it really? The Cambridge copy, one of only nine extant, was acquired in 1870; its medieval provenance is unknown. Unfortunately, leaf a1 with a woodcut of the Last Judgment is missing, with its image and caption strikingly encapsulating the book's subject: 'Remember the end, and thou shalt never commit sins' (*Memorare nouissima tua et in eternum non peccabis*). For those individuals who have failed in this regard, the author offers spiritual advice on all matters relating to sin, confession, and salvation. Like the *Dance of death*, also printed in Lübeck, the *Licht* addresses almost every class, rank and profession of medieval society, from kings and noblemen down to beggars and peasants. Conspicuously, it does not address clerics, but tries to make up for this by adding a Latin appendix, the devotional treatise *Corona beatae Mariae virginis* ('Crown of the Blessed Virgin Mary'). Moreover, the table of contents announces a final chapter on the subject of the Mass, which is in fact not present in the printed work. It seems that the author of the *Licht der Seelen* intended to create a universally applicable manual for all the different groups of late medieval society, thus bringing into being a mixture of Latin erudition and lay devotion that is unique in fifteenth-century printing.

Falk Eisermann *is Director of the Gesamtkatalog der Wiegendrucke (Union Catalogue of Incunabula) at the Staatsbibliothek zu Berlin.*

1

Hoc opus arte mei impres-
sum Bartholomei.
Ghotan | degentis et in vrbe
Lubeck residentis.

Jt bock is ghemaket vm̄e der entuoldigen/vn̄ simpel mynschen willen vth deme latine/vn̄ lereren der billigen schryfft/vn̄ de bewysinge der lerere synt hyr doch selden gheset To dem̄ ersten male vm̄e korte willen. To dem̄ anderen male/aff yemant predekede sulke materie. vnde bewysede dat mit den lereren/dat nemāt dorste spreken. De predeket vth dudeschen boken. Unde also worde vorsmat dat wort godes. Jtem dit bok ys ghemaket hastliken. Vynt yemant wat dat he beterē kan/na vthwysinge vn̄ inholdende der billigē schrifft dat mach he don/mit sodane bescheyde/dat de syn des bokes blyue. Jtē dit bok holt wol in sik in dē latine. xxx. grote sexternē vn̄ mer/darūme ys dat nicht mogelik mit kortē wordē vele to schriuen de/vn̄ vele to bewysende. ¶ Van souen namē desses bokes/sunder de erste name schal blyuen.

¶ De erste name de het de ieger/alszo eyn gut ieger soket dat wilt in dē wolde/vn̄ in dem̄ wolde hoch vn̄ syde/vn̄ allē endē wor he menet wilt to vindē de Also schal ok de sunder iaghen/vn̄ sokē van grūde synes herten/wan he wol vnde alle syne sūde bichten wil. vn̄ wo he got den heren vortornet heft mit synen gedanken/in synē herten/mit synen worden.

PICTURED:

1–3. Examples of the woodcuts illustrating Caxton's first edition of the *Myrroure*, later reused both by Caxton and his successor, Wynkyn de Worde.

Reflecting fifteenth-century hearts and seventeenth-century minds

Meditationes vitae Christi **[English]**
[Westminster: William Caxton, about 1484]
Inc.3.J.1.1[3517]

The myrroure of the blessyd lyf of Jhesu Cryste is an early fifteenth-century English translation of pseudo-Bonaventure's *Meditationes vitae Christi*, a Latin text of meditations on the narrative of the life of Christ. This translation, with extensive rewriting and additions, was prepared by Nicholas Love (active 1410), a Carthusian monk of Mount Grace in Yorkshire. It was completed by 1410 and licensed for reading by Thomas Arundel, Archbishop of Canterbury, who issued the 'Constitution' in 1409 as part of his campaign against Lollardy, to regulate preaching, forbid the circulation of translation of the Scriptures and suppress unorthodox texts.

As an approved text, the *Myrroure* gained immense popularity and has survived in more manuscripts than any other religious prose of the fifteenth century. At least nine editions were published by William Caxton and his successors by 1530, including four incunables, and all editions are extant in very few copies. The copy shown here is the only known to survive of Caxton's first edition; besides this, a fragment alone is recorded in Lambeth Palace Library.

1

Caxton's first edition is undated, but recent analyses of paper stock and type successfully assigned its printing date to about 1484. The text is accompanied by running titles and marginalia, both printed in Latin. It is also adorned with charming woodcut illustrations which vividly depict the life of Christ. It is said that Caxton imported the woodblocks from the continent, and they were possibly northern French in origin. This series was not only reused by Caxton in his second edition, but also recycled by his successor Wynkyn de Worde.

The Cambridge copy belonged to the library of John Moore, Bishop of Ely and a great book collector. On his death, George I purchased the collection and donated it to Cambridge University Library in 1715. On the front free endpaper are extensive notes in a seventeenth-century hand, and the same hand transcribed four pages of index and wrote: 'This was coverd wth boards wch were worm eaten and almost worn out.'

Satoko Tokunaga *is Associate Professor at Keio University, Japan; her current research topic is the reception of medieval literature in English print culture.*

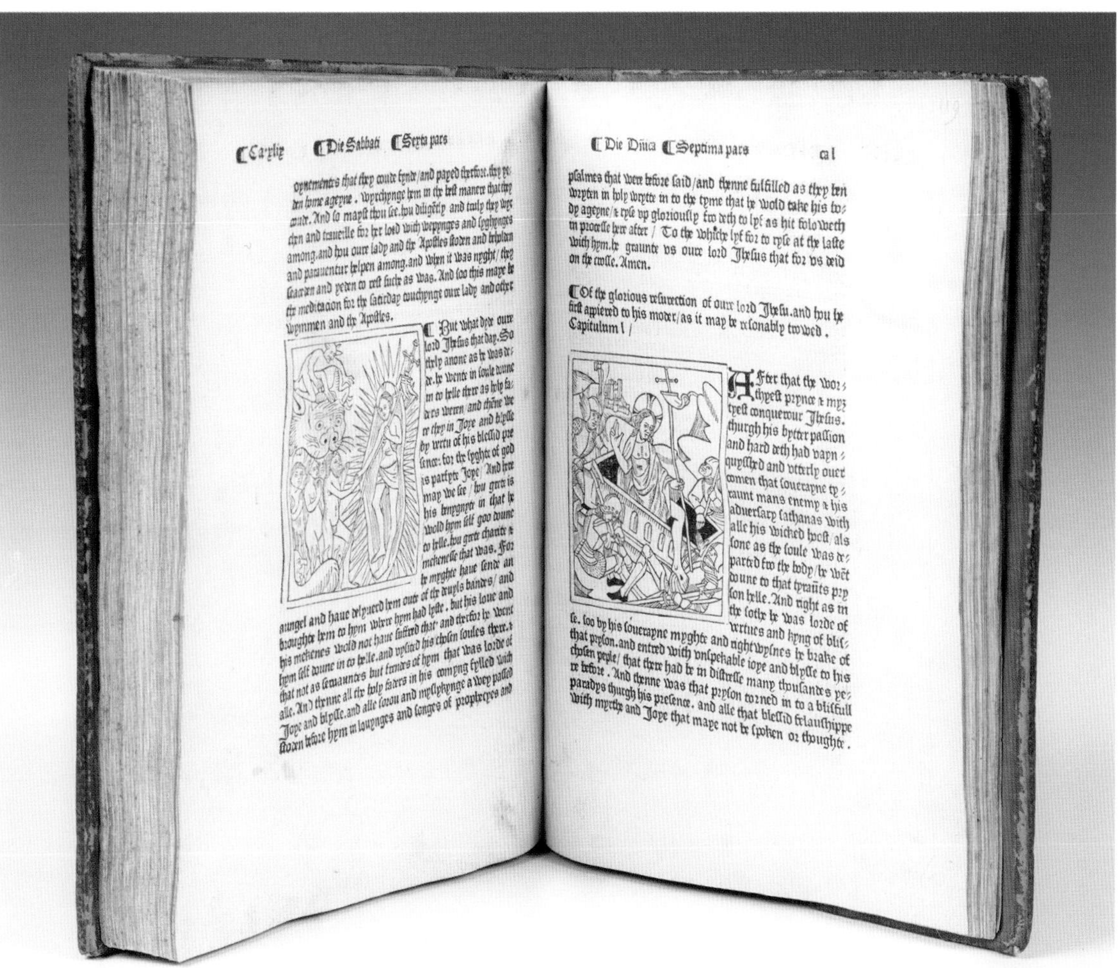

2

How Jhesus came to Jherusalem vpon Palm̄sondaye/

Capitulum xxxvij

The sonday after erly vpon the morowe oure lord Jhesus disposed hym as he had said to go in to Jherusalem in a newe maner & an vncouthe otherwise than euer he did before. but to fulfille the prophecye of zacharye the prophete said to that purpos/ And when he with that lytyl but blessid cõpany cam to a place in myddes the wey that was cleped bethfage/ he sente two of his discyples in to Jherusalē.

3

PICTURED:

1. "A sup[er]fluyte of nunnys"
2. "Here begynnyth the blasyng of armys"
3. The colophon, with the 1612 annotations of William Burton.

4–9. Examples of the colour-printed armorial devices found throughout the book.

10. "The propretees of a goode hors".

A medieval gentleman's manual

Book of hawking, hunting and heraldry
St Albans: [Schoolmaster Printer, not before 1486]
Inc.3.J.4.1[3636]

The *Book of hawking, hunting and heraldry*, also known as the *Book of St Albans*, by the mysterious Schoolmaster Printer is unique: the first English book on sport, the first English printed armorial, the first English book with popular rhymes, and the first book with colour-printed woodcut illustrations in England, in red, blue, and occasionally gold. During the Middle Ages St Albans had a flourishing monastery, with a scriptorium where chroniclers had been at work since the thirteenth century. Subsequently, some of St Albans' monks – probably after studying the art of printing under Caxton at Westminster – founded a print shop, active from 1480 to 1486, producing eight books, of which the *Book of hawking, hunting and heraldry* was the last and most ambitious.

The text was based on various sources and served as a manual for gentlemen seeking information on a variety of subjects. The essay on hawking was not intended as a full practical guide, but to introduce technical terms, and to describe the feeding of birds of prey and their illnesses. The treatise on hunting is attributed to Dame Juliana Berners (born 1388), the Prioress of Sopwell Priory near St Albans. It contains a list of special collective nouns for animals, a tradition still used in modern English. 'A superfluity of nuns', however, may have been coined as a joke, and had already appeared in a unique copy of John Lydgate's *The horse, the sheep and the goose*, printed ten years before by Caxton (see pp. 50–51). The treatise on heraldry, with coloured representations of coats of arms, is admirably arranged. It contains a section on the use of heraldic terms, recounting contemporary discussions on the relationship between gentility and heraldic practice.

The Cambridge copy, imperfect like most, was formerly owned by William Burton (1575–1645) and Bishop John Moore (1646–1714). Burton was an antiquary, famous for *The description of Leicestershire* (1622); one of the annotations in his hand on folio 4 recto cites John Leland and John Bale.

The *Book of St Albans* proved popular. Wynkyn de Worde reprinted it in 1496 with the addition of an essay on fishing, and again with omissions in 1518; later editions by other printers followed. There is a manuscript copy of the treatise on heraldry based on de Worde's edition of 1496 in the Takamiya Collection, Tokyo (MS 86), now on deposit at Yale University's Beinecke Library.

Toshiyuki Takamiya *is Professor Emeritus of Keio University, and holds honorary Doctor of Letters degrees from the Universities of Sheffield and Glasgow.*

1

1

Here begynnyth the blasyng of armys

I Haue shewyd to yow in thys booke a fore how gentilmē began. and how the law of armys was first ordant. and how mony colowris ther be in cootarmuris. and the difference of cootarmuris with mony other thyngis that here nedis not to be rehersed. Now I intende to procede of signys in armys and of the blasyng of all armys. Bot for to reherce all the signys that be borne in armys as Pecok Pye Bacc Dragon Lyon & Dolfyn and flowris and leevys it war to longe a taryyng. ner I can not do hit: ther be so mony. Bot here shall shortli be shewyd to blase all armys if ye entende diligentli to youre ru; lys. And be cause the cros is the moost worthi signe emong al signys in armys: at the cros I will begynne. in the wich thys nobull and myghti prynce kyng Arthure hadde grete trust so that he lefte his armys that he bare of .iij. Dragonys. and ou that an other shelde of .iij. crownys. and toke to his armys a crosse of Siluer in a felde of verte and on the right side an ymage of owre blessid lady with hir sone in hir arme. and wt that signe of the cros he dyd mony maruelis after. as hit is wrytyn in the bokis of cronyclis of his dedys Also I haue red thys signe of the cros to be sende from god to that blessid man Marcuri as vincencius sayth. in speculo historiali. of the mar; uellis deth of Julian thappostita Emproure. li°. xv°. he saythe thangele brought vn to the foresayd Mercuri all armure necessari with a shelde of asure and a cros fluri with .iiij. rosis of golde. as here i this And I fonde neuer that euer any armys war sende from heuyn bot in theym was the sygne of the cros. Excepted in tharmys of the kyng of fr; aunce the wiche armys certanli war sende bi an awngell from he; uyn that is to say .iij. flowris in maner of Swerdis in a felde

c i

2

¶ Explicit .

finis huius Libri / finis /

¶ Here in thys boke afore ar contenyt the bokys of haukyng and huntyng with other plesuris dyuerse as in the boke apperis and also of Cootarmuris a nobull werke . And here now endyth the boke of blasyng of armys translatyt and compylyt togedyr at Seynt albons the yere from thincarnacion of owre lorde Ihu Crist . M . CCCC . lxxx vi . 2: H:7:

Liber Willmi Burton Lindliaci Leicestrensis, morantis apud Fald in com. Staff: ex dono consanguinei mei charissimi Thomae Purefey de Barwell iuxta Lindley in com: Leicest: armig: 1612:

3

exemple .

erit as here now
they be calde ar;

io et auro . Et
Anglice sic .

4

e shelde .

most comyn wey
thys stockyn it ap

nendo loco . Et
dor . Et a gli;
s of golde .

5

s mych as ther
rupibus in tyme
r i his armys . iij
s it is dowtit .
m : that he bare

He berith Sable

6

7

8

in tharmys of the
flocyon apperis · &
e floriſchyt contrari

9

The proprietees of a goode hors .

A Goode hors ſhulde haue . xv . ꝓpretees . and condicions . Yt is to wit . iij . of a man . iij . of a woman . iij . of a fox iij . of an haare and . iij . of an aſſe .
Off a man boolde prowde and hardy .
Off a woman fayre breſtid faire of here & eſy to lip vppon .
Off a fox a faire tayle ſhort eris with a goode trot .
Off an hare a grete eygh a dry hede . and well rennyng
Off an aſſe a bigge chyne a flatte lege . and goode houe .

10

1487

PICTURED:

1–6. The best-preserved of the seven surviving leaves.

Reynard the fox: catch as catch can

Historie van Reynaert die vos

[Antwerp: Gerard Leeu, 1487-1490]

Inc.4.F.6.2[3367]

'The moment I saw these fragments I recognised them at once as printed in Antwerp by Gerard Leeu in 1487, and as such they have a particular interest', wrote Henry Bradshaw in 1875. No one then or since has had that combination of exact vision and visual memory that made Bradshaw, University Librarian from 1867 to 1886, venerated by all who knew him. The moment had come entirely by chance. He had gone to view Sotheby's sale of the books of Senator Friedrich Culemann of Hanover on 7–10 February 1870, hoping to buy one or more of the four Wycliffe bibles offered. Bernard Quaritch, intent on buying them for the *Bibliotheca Lindesiana*, dissuaded him. His eye turned to the Reynaert fragments, which Quaritch bought on his behalf for eight guineas.

None knew better than Bradshaw the complexity of medieval texts, as well as early printing types. The 'cunning fox' legend originated in north-west Europe, its earliest known version in Latin verse in the tenth century, followed about 1180 by the Middle High German *Reinhart Fuchs* and the French *Roman de Renart*. In Flanders a verse translation was made about 1250 (*Reinaert I*), and enlarged about 1375 (*Reinaert II*). This was the ancestor of the verse text (with prose glosses by Henric van Alckmaer) of which the 'Reynaert fragments' are the sole witness, and they in turn are the source for a Low-German *Reynke de Vos*, printed at Lübeck in 1498. William Caxton's 1481 *Reynard the fox* derives from the 1479 Gouda prose *Reinaert II*, but somewhere between the verse *Reinaert II* and *Reynke de Vos* was a link: these fragments. Senator Culemann, who bought them about 1853–1854, planned an edition of his discovery, but allowed Hoffmann von Fallersleben to publish them in 1862. Bradshaw subsequently corresponded with the Dutch incunabulist M.F.A.G. Campbell about the fragments, and about Friedrich Prien's forthcoming edition thereof, finally published in 1887, just after Bradshaw's death.

Besides the text, Leeu's edition had striking woodcut illustrations, four of which appear in the fragments. The blocks were not reprinted, but were copied independently, in the 1498 Lübeck *Reynke de Vos*, and for a now lost English *Reynard*; Wynkyn de Worde used them about 1495–1500 in three editions of Lydgate's *The horse, the sheep, and the goose* (for an earlier edition see pp. 50–51). Those blocks had a long life, used again in a later Wynkyn de Worde *Reynard* of about 1525 (known only by two leaves in Cambridge University Library), and six more surviving editions printed between 1550 and 1640.

Nicolas Barker *was admitted to Cambridge University Library as a reader in 1944: he has been editor of* The Book Collector *since 1965.*

1

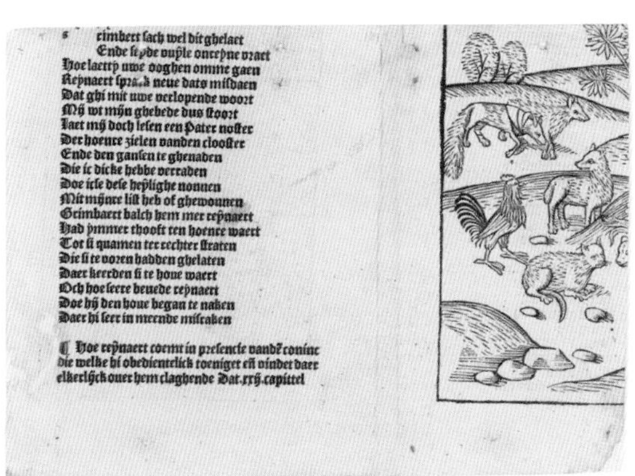

2

Bÿlode soude ic des ontghelden
Soe mostick mÿn gheluc wel schelden
Niet daer bÿ her coninck lyon
Wat ghi wilt dat moechdÿ doen
Ende ghebieden ouer mÿ
Hoe goet hoe claer mÿn sake sÿ
Ghi moecht mÿ vromen ende scaden
Wildÿ mÿ sieden ofte braden
Ofte hanghen ofte blenden
Ic en mach v niet ontwenden
Wÿ sÿn alle in uwen bedwanck
Ghi sÿt starck ende ic bin cranck
Mÿn hulp is cleyn die uwe is groot
Voerwaer al sloechdi mÿ doot
Dat waer v eene crancke wrake
Recht in deser seluer sprake
Spranck op bellÿn den ram
Ende sÿn moeye die mit hem quam
Dat was dame olewÿ
Bellÿn sprack nv toe gaen wÿ
Alle voert mit onser claghen
Brune spranck op mit sinen maghen
Ende tybert sÿn gheselle
Ende ysegrim die snelle
Die haze ende dat euerzwÿn
Elck wilde in die claghe sÿn
Panthel die kemel ende bruneel
Die gans dat wezel ende tlampreel
Boudwin den ezel borreel den stier

3

Ouer al in heren houen
Dat sÿ soe verre comen bouen
Die schalcke sÿn in dien gheboren
Dat sÿ den goeden beraden toren
Dat wreke god an haer leuen
Ende moet hem sulck loon gheuen
Als sÿ van rechte wel sÿn waert
Die coninck sprack an reynaert
Oncreÿne vuÿle lose druut
Hoe wel coendÿ uwen saluut
Maer ten baet v niet een kaf
Coemt uwes smeekens af
Ic en worde bÿ smeeken niet v vrient
Dat ghi mÿ dicke wel hebt ghedient
Dat wort v nv te rechte ghegouden
Ghi hebt oec wel den vrede ghehouden
Dien ic gheboot ende hebbe gheswoꝛen
O wÿ wat heb ic al verloren
Sprack cantecleer aldaer hÿ stont
Die coninck sprack hout uwen mont
Her cantecleer ende laet mÿ spreken
Ic moet antwoerden sine treken

¶ Hoe dat die coninck reÿnaert zeere confu selÿck eñ wredelÿck toe spreect om der groo ter quade felle daden daer hÿ of beclaecht is/ eñ hoe dat hem reÿnaert weder verantwoert soe hi best kan Dat.xxiÿ.capittel

4

Dat hermel die wesel waren oeck hier
Cantecler ende sÿn kinder
Claechden seer haren hinder
Ende maecten groot wederslach
Dat troeseel een cleen beiach
Liep oeck mede in deser scare
Alle dese ghinghen openbare
Voer haren heere den conick staen
Ende deden den vos reÿnaert vaen

¶ Hoe die coninck te recht sittet ende gheeft die sentencie datmen reÿnaert vanghen sou de eñ bÿder kelen hanghẽ Dat.xxiiÿ.capittel.

5

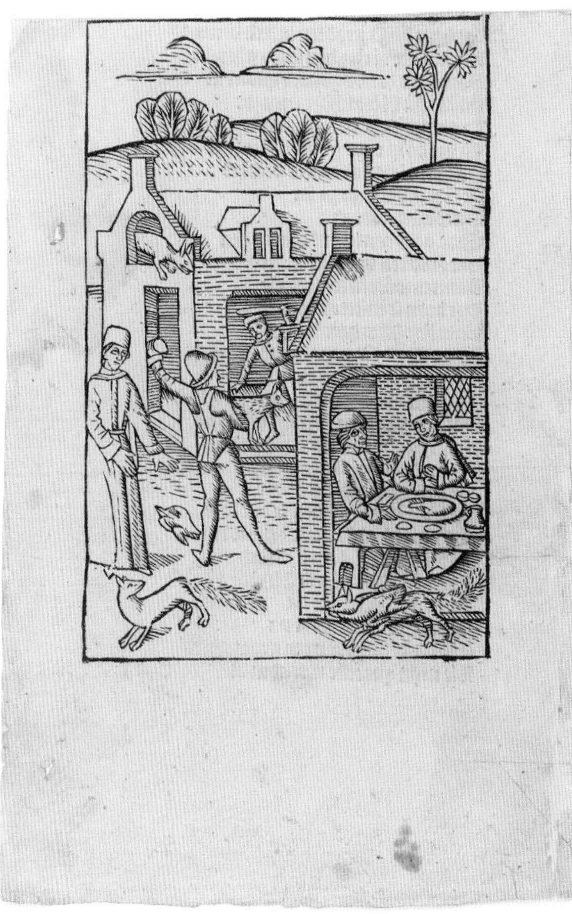

6

1487

PICTURED:

1. The opening leaf, with the Cornaro family arms, held aloft by a triton and putto.

2–8. A selection of the Pico Master's extraordinary initials.

Maestro of the capitals

Sabellico (1436?–1506)
Decades rerum Venetarum
Venice: Andreas Torresanus, de Asula, 21 May 1487
SSS.2.3

I have to confess there is something both tantalising and frustrating in having a history of Venice placed in front of me, only to find that it is written in Latin so that I cannot read it. The ultimate compensation, however, is that I can give the whole of my attention to its physical presence – and what a presence that is. There is immense pleasure to be found in the richness of the illumination; here we are in a different world, breathing a different air, and the printed page before us is suddenly calm, lucid, confident.

The opening page makes the most significant bow to decoration, with the arms of the Cornaro family, to whom this book belonged, supported by a triton with a winged putto and decorative cornucopia. The book's power lies in the disposition and balance of the classical typeface on the page: it is as though graphic design appeared, fully formed, overnight. The crisp typography is enhanced by the beautifully decorated capitals at the opening of each section, capitals which echo the book's precursor, the illuminated manuscript. These small pen drawings, detailed, refined and witty, yet simultaneously restrained and elegant, are by the Maestro di Pico.

The characters who inhabit his tiny canvasses wear scarcely a scrap of clothing between them, and their proportions are unworldly, as though specially designed to inhabit their small but complex world of capital letters. A nude figure seated on an urn rests on the upper opening of a letter B, as though on a window. A bearded man playing a string-less violin (or is it a cheese board?) leans his cornucopia gently against the letter F. One of two figures populating the interstices of a letter M holds a sheep by the back leg, which hangs down into the margin, whilst a cloven-footed figure behind the letter A lifts into his margin the wonderful curving gesture of his trumpet.

These miniature scenes hark back to illuminated capitals, but are more restrained in their technique of neat pen drawing, and simple coloured background. I have no doubt that these are restraints that are chosen, not imposed, so in looking at them I cannot avoid the sense that these drawings also look forwards, to the detailed full-colour illustration that contemporary printing makes a commonplace of today.

Quentin Blake *was knighted for services to illustration in 2013, read English at Downing College, Cambridge, and also holds an honorary doctorate of the University.*

PRIMAE DECADIS LIBER PRIMVS

M. ANTONII SABELLICI RERVM VENETARVM AB VRBE CONDITA AD MARCVM BARBADICVM SERENISS. VENETIARVM PRINCIPEM ET SENATVM LIBER PRIMVS PRIMAE DECADIS FOELICITER INCIPIT.

VONIAM IGITVR SATIS CONstat priſcos Venetos & urbis & Imperii de quo hæc ſcripturi ſumus conditores fuiſſe. nihil ab re fore exiſtimaui quando de origine gentis inter ueteres auctores parum conſtare uideo: priuſq̃ urbis primordia aperiantur: de illorum uetuſtate aliquid breuiter referre. Fuerunt itaq; priſci Veneti non Italiæ indigenæ: ſed ut quidam tradiderunt a Venetis Gallis oceani accolis oriundi. Neq; hi nomen tantum ſecuti uidentur: Sed quia rei maritimæ ſtudium & gloriam: qui Adriatici ſinus oram tenuerunt: ut illi nunq̃ neglexerint: Eſſentq; iis qui in Gallia ſunt ſi non lingua: moribus tamen & ornatu corporis: ut Polybius ait per q̃ſimiles: Alii uero eos e Paphlagonia profectos affirmant: in quibus eſt Liuius: Is Pylæmene Duce ad Troiam amiſſo: cum Antenore in Italiam ueniſſe tradit: quod ipſum ſecutus Cato Troiana ſtirpe Venetos procreatos credidit: Cornelius nepos & ipſe ex Henetis qui Cromnam oppidum circa Paphlagoniam tenuerunt: Venetos eorum cognomines in Italia ortos exiſtimauit: Quidam Cappadocibus eam gentem finitimam tradiderunt: ac cum Cimeriis militaſſe: poſteaq; Adriam perueniſſe: Alii uicum non longe ab Amaſtri tenuiſſe arbitrati ſunt: Requirebantq; interim tota regione Henetos quaſi nuſq̃ oſtenderentur. Sed inter omnes fere conſtat hanc de qua loquimur Paphlagonum eſſe gentem: quod Xenodotus non ſolum credidit: ſed Amyſum quoq; oppidum id eſſe exiſtimauit: quod in ea terra poſtea Henetia dicta ſit: Cæterum qui ita eſſe autumant: præcipuam utriuſq; gentis in equis muliſq; alendis induſtriam in argumentum adducunt Homeri uſi teſtimonio cuius illud eſt: Mularum genus ex Henetis quæ robore præſtent: quum de Aſiaticis interim ſummus poeta loqueretur. Strabo uetuſtatis auctor diligentiſſimus nobiliſſimam equarum progeniem uſq; ferme ad ſua tempora in his Venetis qui Adriatici maris partem accolunt perueniſſe ſcribit: quarum fama ob eximiam pernicitatem ualde celebris fuiſſet. Hæc certe atq; alia multa faciunt ut eorum ſim ſententiæ: qui cum Antenore Henetos in Italiam ueniſſe tradunt: ac mutata littera deinde Venetos appellatos. Antenoris aduentum in intimum maris Adriatici ſinum non ſolum Veneti teſtantur qui eius comites fuere: Sed q; locus in quem primum egreſſi ſunt Troia eſt dicta: quodq; Troiano deinde Pago nomen manſit. Ii primo pulſis ſuis ſedibus Euganeis qui eius terræ oram: quæ eſt inter mare & alpes incolebant: Patauium condiderunt: Procedente deinde

Vet° de Venetorum origine opinio

Vera Venetorum origo

Troia Pagus in Venetis

a iii

M.ANTO.
COND
ea urbe Veneti
Syriæ recæpta
2

VRBE CON
numerus ſit expletus :
4

M.ANTON
BE CON
ſum ex Hetruria
6

M.ANTONII
BE COND
continuo cogitare
3

M . ANTON
VRBE CON
let ut recentem
5

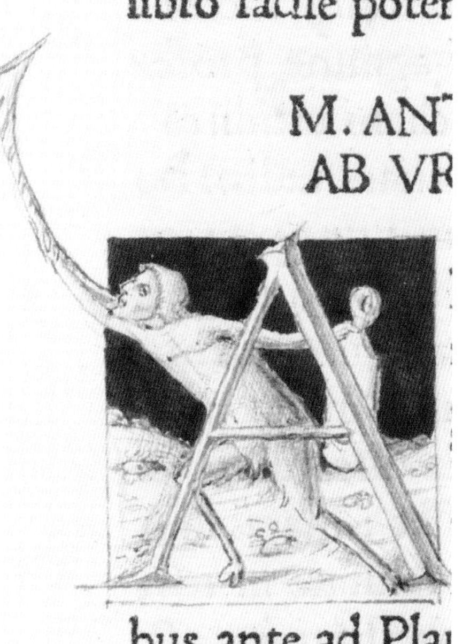
libro facile poter
M.ANT
AB VR
bus ante ad Pla
7

67

M.ANTONII SABELLICI RERVM VENETARVM AB VR
BE CONDITA LIBER PRIMVS SECVNDAE DECADIS

MVLTA NOBIS RES VENETAS SCRIBENTI/
bus occurrunt : quæ tam Romanis similia sunt : ut
consilio : laboribus : fortunæ uarietate : euentu
ipso nihil uideri possit similius : Sed horum omni
um quæ non pauca sunt ut dixi : Bella quæ Vene
ti cum Genuensibus gessere : simillimam uidentur
mihi habere speciem : cum iis quæ Romanus popu
lus cum Carthaginensibus olim gessit : neq; enim
locorum uicinitate (ut sæpe fit) inter illos æmulatio:neq; bellum ortum ui
deri potuit : quippe qui tantum inter se distabant quantum Tyrheni pe/
lagi Libyciq; inter Italiam atq; Aphricam spaciatur amplitudo: Distabant il
li multum inter se : Sed ne hi quidem sibi uicini : Quin siquis Italiæ lati/
tudinem consideret tam uterq; populus ab altero recedit : ut nisi relicta Ita
lia amplius recedere non possit : Est enim Italia ut Strabo ait promontori/
um ab alpibus: quarum altitudine quasi uallo quodam a septentrione muni
tur ad meridiem excurrens : alluiturq; ab occasu Ligustico Tyrhenoq; mari:
Ab ortu Hadriatico & Ionio : Insinuant se se hinc pelagi fluctus : nitun/
turq; ut Italiam tutiorem reddant alpes perstringere : Sed id ipsum non cõ
sequuntur : In hoc intimo sinu inclytæ Venetiæ resident: Illinc Ligusticum
mare satagit Apennini radicibus hærere : quod pene efficit : In hoc quoq;
recessu Genua illa Veneti imperii æmula sita est : quo fit ut pene contra:
ne quod eminentissimus poeta longe dicam : diuersis Italiæ finibus sibi re/
spondeant : Opposuit illis ad internitionẽ quandoq; concursuris prudens na
tura ingentem maris uastitatem : ut essent obices quibus immensa utriusq;
populi odia : immensæq; frænarentur iræ : His uero non solum Italiæ am
plitudinem : sed alta quoq; Apennini iuga ab alpibus in Liguriam primo:
inde Anconem usq; procurrentia : unde occursu maris suo impetu auersa
ad Garganum montem inclinant : Mox quasi pelagus reformidantia extre/
mum Italiæ cornu petunt : tanq̃ uim fluctibus quos totiens effugerant illa
tura : Sed illorum iras tanta aquarum uastitas non coercuit : Nec horum
quidem alpium asperitas : Ab Ilio Romani oriundi : Ab Ilio & Veneti: Mix
tæ Phœnicibus Libycæ gentes : Mixti & Phœnicibus Ligures: Gestarum re/
rum æmulatio primo illos : inde imperii cupiditas accendit : His quoq; hæc
duo non aliud bellorum causam præbuerunt : Illi de Siciliæ possessione :Hi
ut dixi de Ptolemaide certare cœperunt : Fuerunt Romani qui uicerunt quã
doq; propiores periculo pœnis qui postea uicti sunt : Fuerunt & Veneti
qui Ligusticas uires pœnitus frægerunt : Centum & amplius annos paribus
odiis sæpe etiam uiribus inde bellatum : Hinc quoq; tam diuturni & ali/
quanto longiores fuerunt labores : ut ab illis ita quoq; ab his arma quan/
doq; posita : odia uero nunq̃ : Euentus si non idem : non tamen omnino
diuersus : Excidit Carthago illa ingens : Superba Genua abiectis armis
quia plus non potuit uictoribus Venetis perpetuo cessit : De his igitur bel
lis dicere pergam : quæ Veneti cum ferocissimo populo deinceps gessere : Si
pauca adhuc illis prætulerimus : quæ iccirco præferenda crediderim : quia
in quibusdam annalibus prius relata reperio : Alioquin enim ipsa tempo℞

Breuis Ita/
liæ descri/
ptio

Attende re
rum gesta/
rum com/
paratiõe

I

1488

PICTURED:

1. The coronation of Ladislas I, King of Hungary, later sanctified.
2. The initial opening, with hand-coloured woodcuts and the 1542 annotations of Stephan Rodtacker, a member of the University of Heidelberg.

The first printed 'Chronicle of the Hungarians'

János Thuróczy (about 1435–1488/9)
Chronica Hungarorum
Augsburg: Erhard Ratdolt, for Theobaldus Feger, 3 June 1488
Inc.5.A.6.18[829]

The *Chronica Hungarorum*, the most extensive fifteenth-century account of the history of Hungary, was written by János Thuróczy, Protonotary at the court of royal appeals in Buda under the Chancellor Thomas de Drag (died 1490/1). When the first printed edition was published in Brno (Moravia) on 20 March 1488, it opened with a preface addressed to Drag in which Thuróczy described the intentions of his work. Even though Thuróczy meant to rectify the shortcomings of older chronicles, his book is still largely a compilation from earlier sources. The mythical origin of the Huns and Magyars, who were thought to descend from the Scythians, is covered in great detail. Benefiting from access to royal charters and other documentary sources, Thuróczy placed particular focus on the events of the preceding hundred years, which had not been recorded systematically. He accorded a more cursory treatment, however, to the reign of King Matthias Corvinus (reigned 1458–1490), under whom Thuróczy served.

In order to satisfy the demand for copies of Thuróczy's chronicle, a second edition of the work appeared less than three months after the first. The reprint was commissioned by Theobald Feger, a bookseller of Buda, and produced by Erhard Ratdolt in Augsburg, who had only recently returned to Germany after a prolonged stay in Venice. Ratdolt was famous for the outstanding quality of his books, and his far-reaching trade network guaranteed their quick and wide distribution. In order to adapt the book to the expectations of different audiences, he produced three variants. Two dedication copies survive in Budapest in which the preface to Drag is printed in gold letters on parchment. The version intended for Hungarian readers concludes with the recent military successes of King Matthias Corvinus: the conquests of Vienna in 1485 and of Wiener Neustadt on 17 August 1487. As these events were potentially controversial, they were omitted in the third issue, targeted primarily at the German market. The Cambridge copy belongs to the latter group and attests the long-standing and Europe-wide interest in Thuróczy's chronicle. The volume moved through the hands of at least four owners within a century: a member of the University of Heidelberg in the 1540s, a pastor in Latvia and a British diplomat and envoy to Russia, from whom the book passed on to the Master of Emmanuel College, who bequeathed it to the University of Cambridge.

Bettina Wagner *is Head of Manuscript Cataloguing and Curator of Incunabula at the Bayerische Staatsbibliothek in Munich, Germany.*

De coronatione sancti regis Ladislai primi: fratris Geyse filij Bele similiter primi: 7 de exercitijs eiusdem.

Audita vo morte regis magni: ꝯuenit vniuersa multitudo nobiliū hungarie ad fratrē eius Ladislaum Et eū cōmuni cōsensu parili voto 7 cōsona volūtate ad suscipiēdū regni gubernacula cōcorditer elegerūt: īmo fere magis affectuosissimis ꝑcib9 cōpulerūt. Oēs eni nouerāt ipsum esse vestitū ꝯsumatiōe

1

Chronica Regum Hungarorum

Hystoria sancti
ladislai.

1488

PICTURED:

1. The dramatic opening woodcut initial.
2. The gold binding stamps of Fabri de Peiresc, a cipher of his initials.

3–5. Images of readers and their books in the fifteenth century.

6. A genealogical tree for the kings of France.

Six ages in two volumes

Rudimentum novitiorum* [French] *(La mer des histoires)
Paris: Pierre Le Rouge for Vincent Commin, 1488–1489
SSS.3.10–11

'In this book which may be called the Flower or Sea of histories, we tell in order from degree to degree the largest part of the stories and the great things worthy of memory that have happened in this world from the Creation to the present' – although, to make them easier to learn and to stave off boredom, 'they are only touched in brief'. This is the mission statement of the massive *Mer des histoires,* a universal history in two volumes first published in 1488, probably the most elaborate illustrated book produced in Paris during the incunable period. Translated from a Latin work entitled *Rudimentum novitiorum*, published at Lübeck in 1475, the *Mer* renders the six ages of human history visually spectacular by adding enormous historiated letters, decorative marginal panels full of birds, beasts and grotesques, and numerous illustrated woodcuts which are recycled at many points across the volumes. There are also many full-page and fold-out illustrations, including maps, genealogies and chronologies, which allow the reader to view the world and to gain a comparative understanding of the unfolding histories of peoples and empires.

The *Mer* was printed by Pierre Le Rouge, who was (according to the colophon) 'imprimeur du Roy'. The Cambridge copy cannot compete with the illuminated copy printed on vellum for presentation to Charles VIII, now in the Bibliothèque nationale de France, but it is still a magnificent book with a distinguished provenance. It was owned in the early seventeenth century by the antiquary Nicolas-Claude Fabri de Peiresc (1580–1637), who had his ingenious cipher stamped onto the red morocco binding and the title pages, and who made several annotations in the margins. By the eighteenth century it had passed into the library of Jean-Baptiste Denis Guyon, Seigneur de Sardière, '*Ancien Capitaine au Régiment du Roi*', and it was item 1407 (out of 2550) in the sale catalogue of his library at his death in 1759. The book came to the University Library in the remarkable 1894 bequest of Samuel Sandars of Trinity College.

Although it would be eclipsed in the 1490s by the mighty *Nuremberg chronicle*, the *Mer des histoires* is a reminder of the extraordinary ambition of publishers in this period. Many an early printed book strove to gather the whole world between its covers. Although their contents now seem quaint, the energy and beauty of the results are palpable.

Jason Scott-Warren *is a Reader in the Faculty of English at the University of Cambridge, and Director of the Centre for Material Texts.*

1

2

3

4

5

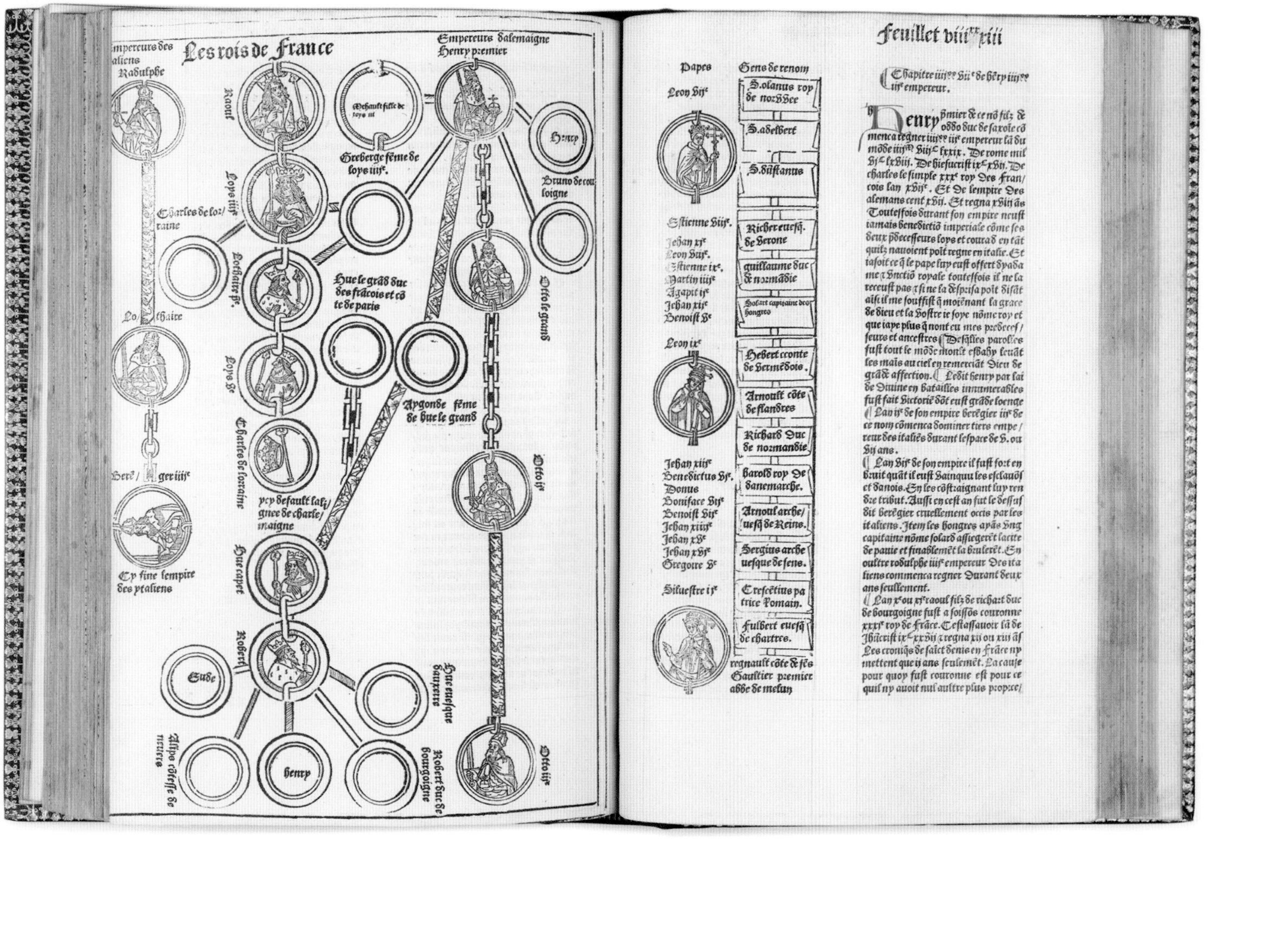

6

PICTURED:

1. The indulgence *in situ*, upside-down on the blank leaf at the end of a Low Countries pamphlet.
2. The ghostly trial impression – the only surviving evidence for this indulgence.

Passport to paradise or printer's waste paper?

Image of pity
[Westminster: William Caxton, about 1490]

Trial impression on the final blank page of:
Jacobus de Guytrode
Colloquium peccatoris et crucifixi Jesu Christi
[Antwerp: Mathias van der Goes, 1487–1490]
Inc.5.F.6.3[3409]

Images of pity were among the most widely reproduced texts in late medieval Europe. Reflecting the intensity of Christocentric devotion at this time, the print depicts Jesus as the Man of Sorrows, surrounded by the instruments of his Passion. Beneath the image is an indulgence: a promise of partial release from the years of punishment in purgatory people believed they would suffer for the sins they had committed during their lives. Indulgences were originally bestowed upon those who participated in the Crusades or undertook an arduous pilgrimage to the Holy Land. But the yearning desire of the laity for assurance of their salvation, combined with the advent of mechanized printing, fuelled a process of inflation and commodification. By the fifteenth century, simply meditating upon an icon or reciting a series of short prayers was enough. The offer (as here) of 32,755 years of remission in exchange for repeating five *Pater Nosters*, five *Ave Marias* and the Creed exposed indulgences to the mockery of contemporary satirists, and in 1517 they were the target of the provocative protest by Martin Luther that precipitated the Protestant Reformation.

1

Of the vast number of indulgences printed in pre-Reformation England, only 27 survive. Most were swept up in the iconoclastic storm launched by the Henrician reformers; those that escaped have often been deliberately defaced or obliterated. This incunable is thus a rare survival. It is also a bibliographical curiosity in two other respects. It is not a carefully produced print, intended for distribution or sale at a cathedral or shrine: rather it is a trial impression roughly printed on the final blank page of another book, as if the typographer had picked up the closest piece of paper to hand to test the effect of the woodblock, creating a print that is faint, smudged, and imperfect. Secondly, this image of pity was once part of the library of Richard Holdsworth, Master of Emmanuel College, Cambridge, bequeathed to the University at his death in 1649. Another indulgence from his collection was unscrupulously stolen by a reader in the eighteenth century and sold, eventually passing into the possession of George III and thence into the British Museum. Many English incunables paradoxically owe their survival to early modern Protestant scholars who collected them less as typographical antiquities than as emblems of the triumph of the Reformation over a dark era of ignorance and 'popish superstition'.

Alexandra Walsham *is Professor of Modern History at the University of Cambridge.*

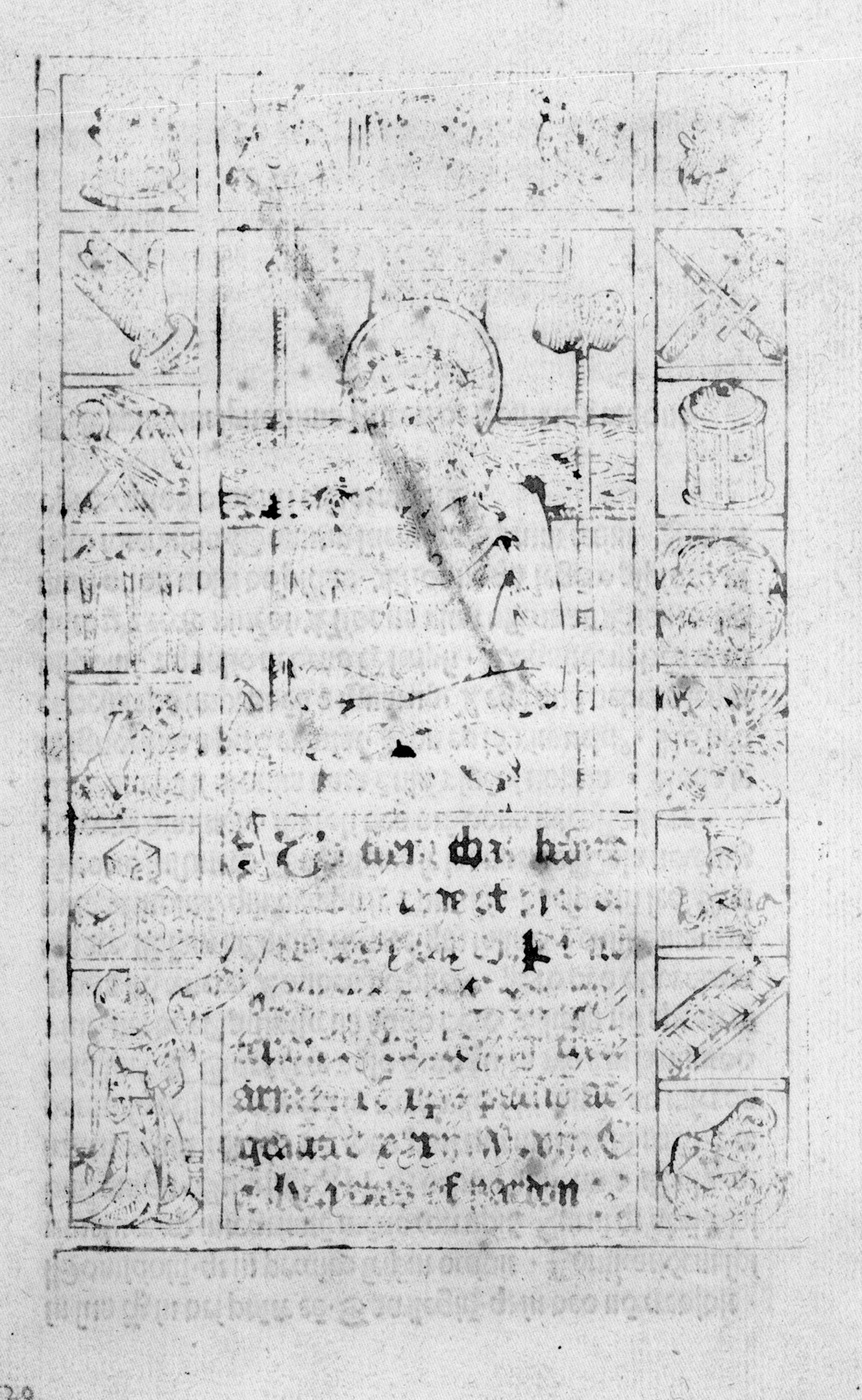

2

1490

PICTURED:

1. The Empress falsely accuses the Prince of attempted rape.
2. The Prince and the Seven Sages consult the stars to discover the Prince's fate.

Wicked women and wise counsellors

Historia calumnie nouercalis que septem sapientum inscribitur
Antwerp: Gerard Leeu, 6 November 1490
SSS.15.17

This phenomenally successful tale collection is little known today, but was one of the most popular works of medieval literature in both manuscript and print, with versions in nearly every European language. Generally known as *The Seven Sages of Rome*, its origins go beyond medieval Europe to *The book of Sindbād*, a work of perhaps the fifth century BC, and most likely Persian, Hebrew or Indian in origin.

The stories are told to the Emperor of Rome by the Empress and the Seven Sages in order, respectively, to justify and refute the false charge of attempted rape brought by the Empress against her stepson the Prince. The fifteenth tale is told by the Prince himself, whereafter he is exonerated. There are thirty-three printed editions recorded before 1501 and it remained in print in Britain from the Richard Pynson edition of about 1493 right through to at least the 1830s.

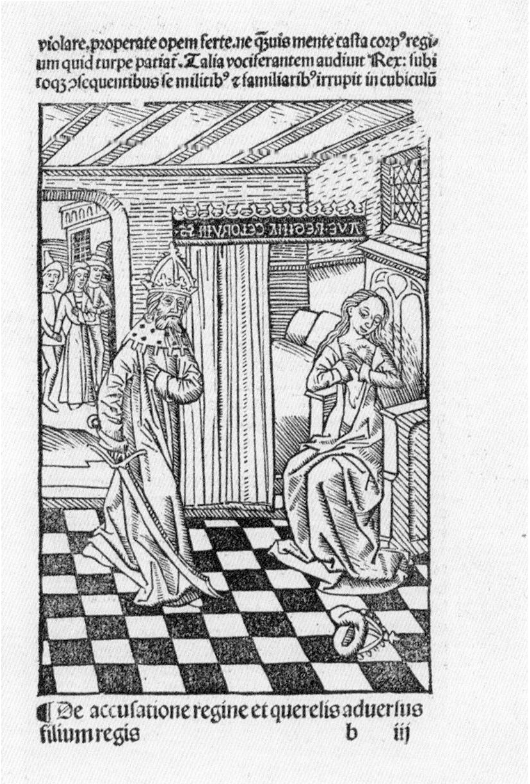

1

This copy of Gerard Leeu's 1490 edition is part of Cambridge University Library's fine holdings of Low Countries' incunabula. Leeu first printed a Dutch version in 1479, followed by one in Latin some time before 3 June 1480. This 1490 edition is a different version of the story, illustrated with twenty-three woodcuts also used for the 1488 Dutch edition printed at Antwerp by Gerard Leeu's brother Claes and the 1490 Latin edition printed in Cologne by Johann Koelhoff the Elder. Interestingly, the woodcuts illustrate the frame tale, not the embedded stories, and twelve are repeats, functioning as visual aids to mark the beginnings of new tales.

The Library's copy wants the last eight leaves, and therein lies a mystery. The first missing leaf is headed 'De contione quadam apud regem et optimates super futuro statu regni per filium regis', and in the catalogue of the Harley library compiled in the 1740s this is erroneously listed as a separate work, along with a separate entry for an undated *Historia calumniæ novercalis* (undated perhaps because it was missing the last eight leaves containing the imprint). Of the surviving copies of *Historia calumniæ novercalis*, one at the Bodleian Library consists of only the last eight leaves (Douce Fragm. f.36), and it is tempting to think that this and the University Library's may be those described in the Harley catalogue, perhaps at one time forming a complete copy, but at some stage in their history disbound and treated as separate works.

Jill Whitelock *is Head of Special Collections at Cambridge University Library.*

¶ De profectione septem sapientum cum filio regis ad patrem consultis prius astris

2

PICTURED:

1. Ornamental borders containing flowers, foliage, birds and animals occur on many pages of the book.
2. Mary and Joseph adoring the newborn child at the opening of Terce of the Hours of the Virgin.
3. The Meeting of the Three Living and the Three Dead as a memento mori precedes the Office of the Dead.

An illustrated Parisian book of hours

***Horae ad usum Romanum* [French and Latin]**
Paris: Pierre Le Rouge, for Vincent Commin, 9 May 1491
Inc.5.D.1.19[2530]

This Book of Hours, printed on vellum, containing as its main texts the Offices of the Virgin Mary and of the Dead, is illustrated by 28 full-page wood or metal cuts, all of which have been illuminated. It is one of only two extant copies of this edition: the other, also on vellum and illuminated, is in the Bibliothèque nationale de France. The Cambridge copy ends with an illuminated manuscript supplement with the text of the Passion according to St John headed by a miniature of the Mocking of Christ, and at the end a painted image of a *memento mori* skull and a penitential text. It is one of the most beautifully illuminated printed books surviving in Cambridge.

The printer, Pierre Le Rouge 'libraire du roy', was working in Paris from about 1485 and died in 1493. The period of his time there coincides with the rise of the luxury printed Book of Hours illustrated by many wood or metal cuts, often illuminated, and clearly an attempt by printers to compete with the market of illuminated Books of Hours, still predominant in the 1480s. The first illustrated Book of Hours printed in Paris by Anthoine Vérard had appeared in 1486, but with woodcuts of rather poor quality. In 1488 and 1489 Jean du Pré produced two much finer illustrated Hours, some of whose woodcuts were used in Pierre Le Rouge's 1491 Hours. Vérard's Hours of 1490 contained better quality wood or metal cuts, but still not as good as those used by Jean du Pré and Pierre Le Rouge, who seem to have collaborated with the same artists who designed a series of images of the life of Christ and the Virgin Mary, the Fall of the Rebel Angels, the Parable of Dives and Lazarus, and the Three Living and the Three Dead. Jean du Pré used an almost identical set in his 1495 Hours of the use of Besançon.

The artist who created the original set of images in the late 1480s is known as the Master of the Apocalypse Rose, because he made cartoons for the rose window of the Apocalypse in the Sainte Chapelle in Paris. In addition, Pierre Le Rouge in his 1491 Hours introduces images by a different artist of the sibyls set between prophets and apostles, which face the biblical images. An inscription of ownership records that in 1565 this Hours belonged to Jeanne Pettre living at Nancy.

Nigel Morgan *is Emeritus Honorary Professor of the History of Art, University of Cambridge.*

1

Deus in adiu/
torium meum
intende Dñe
ad adiuuandum me fe
stina Gloria patri ⁊ fi
lio et spiritui sancto

2

Cy apres se en
suinēt Vigiles de
Placebo domino

Ilexi quoniā
exaudiet dñs
oıōis mee uia
iclinauit aurē suā michi
et ī diebus meis inuoca
bo Circūdederunt me

1491

PICTURED:

1. Two physicians on the banks of a river, opening the section on fish.
2. Three scholars in a zoological garden, opening the section on mammals.

3–8. Woodcuts depicting minerals, fish, insects and other beasts.

A garden of earthly delights

Hortus sanitatis

Mainz: Jacob Meydenbach, 23 June 1491

Inc.3.A.1.8[37]

This is the first natural history encyclopaedia. Today we consult such works to discover more about wonders of the world we live in, but readers at the end of the fifteenth century had more practical concerns. They believed that the natural world had been created by God to be of use to humanity and that animals and plants were there to provide cures for diseases. So this encyclopaedia is entitled *Hortus sanitatis*, 'The garden of health'.

Two earlier such books had dealt with plants, but this one, compiled by Jacob Meydenbach, adds sections on mammals, fish, birds, and rocks, and concludes with a description of the diagnostic qualities of urine, presumably so that readers might discover the sources of the remedies they needed.

Many of the plants Meydenbach describes are immediately recognisable, but there are some where fantasy has taken over. The mandrake, in truth, has a near magical ability to relieve pain. Its wrinkled forked root, however, was believed to represent a man. Furthermore, if it was pulled up it would emit a shriek so appalling that it would kill the collector. Meydenbach provides the solution: the collector should take a dog with him and tie its lead to the plant. Then, after stopping his ears to shut out the lethal shriek, he should beat the dog so that it flees and so pulls up the root.

Hortus sanitatis describes familiar animals too, but adds details of which readers might be ignorant: bile from gall bladders, for example, could be used to treat infected wounds. It also includes descriptions of exotic creatures which few, if any, of its readers could have seen. The crocodile was of interest because, perhaps paradoxically, ointments made from its body parts would cure wrinkled skin. Even dragons appear amongst Meydenbach's descriptions, as does the unicorn, which he recommends as a fertility aid for those struggling to conceive.

The University's copy of this book belonged to John Moore, who was Bishop of Ely in the early eighteenth century. He would have had no difficulty, of course, in reading the Latin. For most of us, however, the charm of this wonderful book rests in its woodcut illustrations. Many of the plants, while delightfully stylized, are easily recognizable. But it is the human figures, surrounded by birds or standing by rivers containing not only fish but mermaids, that take us back most vividly to the birth of scientific natural history.

David Attenborough *has spent his working life making natural history documentaries for television; his interests in the natural world, however, extend not only to its present condition but to the way in which naturalists have learned about the other creatures with which they share the planet.*

1

2

3

4

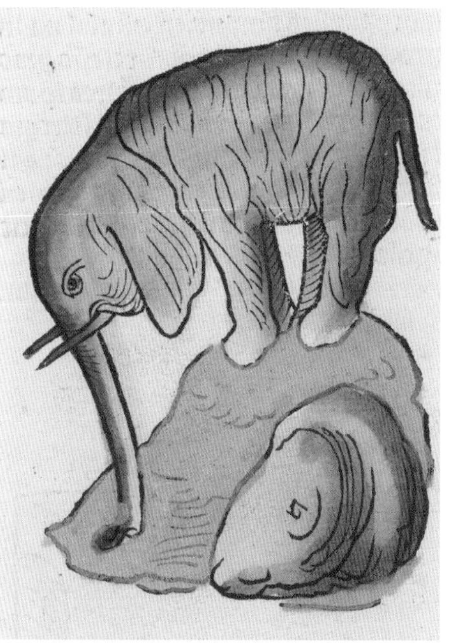
5

6

7

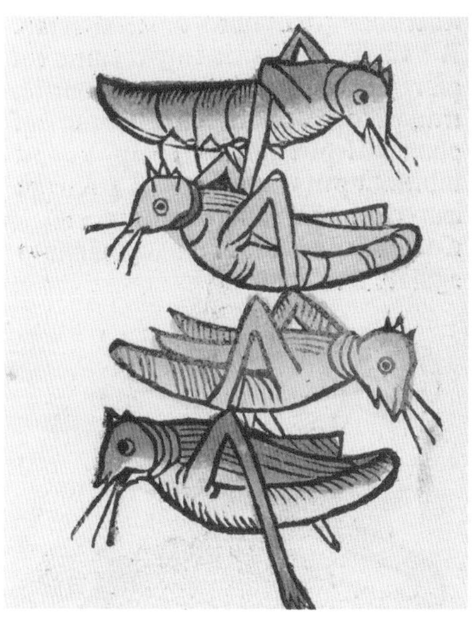
8

1493

PICTURED:

1. Katherine Parr's faded inscription below a prayer to St. Katherine of Alexandria.
2. Maud Parr's inscription below the Crucifixion.

Piety and peril in the Tudor court

Horae ad usum Sarum

[Westminster]: Wynkyn de Worde, [about 1493]

Inc.4.J.1.2[3570]

This 1493 *Horae* by Wynkyn de Worde is the first printed book of hours for the English market to have survived more or less complete. Medieval *Horae* were often fashionable devotional accessories, public tokens of piety, power and prosperity. Printing ultimately brought such books within the reach of people of modest means, but this is a luxury item, printed on vellum, with hand-coloured initials. In addition to the usual Latin psalms, litanies and prayers, it includes many English prayers, like the popular Passion devotions, the 'Fifteen Oes', published in 1491 by William Caxton under the royal patronage of the Lady Margaret Beaufort.

Horae were often given to friends, dependents and patrons, with inscriptions commemorating these intimate exchanges. This book belonged first to the Henrician courtier Sir Thomas Parr, but after his early death in 1517, his widow gave the book to her brother-in-law, William, future Baron Parr of Horton. At the foot of the finest picture in the book, a crucifixion scene, she reminded William of his duty to his extended family:

> Brother et es another saying
> that owt of syt owt of mynd
> but I troste in yow
> I chall not fynd et trew
> Mawd Parre.

Maud's three children added their own less pointed endearments. Katherine Parr, destined to be Henry VIII's last queen, placed hers appropriately under a prayer to her name-saint, Katherine of Alexandria:

> Oncle wan you do on thys loke
> I pray you remember wo wrote thys in your boke
> your louuvynge nys Katheryn parr.

William remained close to Katherine, and when she became queen served as her chamberlain. But in October 1530 he presented this family heirloom to the teenage Earl of Surrey, Henry Howard, who had recently joined the household of the King's bastard son and possible heir, Henry Fitzroy, Duke of Richmond. Parr had fought in Scotland under Surrey's father, the third Duke of Norfolk, and the gift, commemorated in four Latin inscriptions, was clearly intended to consolidate William's connections to this influential dynasty.

Katherine and William Parr both became protestants, moving far from the Catholic devotional world represented by books like this: so too would Henry, Earl of Surrey. But Surrey's proud flamboyance proved lethal in the murderous paranoia of the dying Henry's court, and he was executed for treason early in 1547. The book and its inscriptions form a poignant monument to the political perils and religious uncertainties of Henry VIII's England.

Eamon Duffy *is Professor of the History of Christianity at the University of Cambridge, and author of* The stripping of the altars *(1992).*

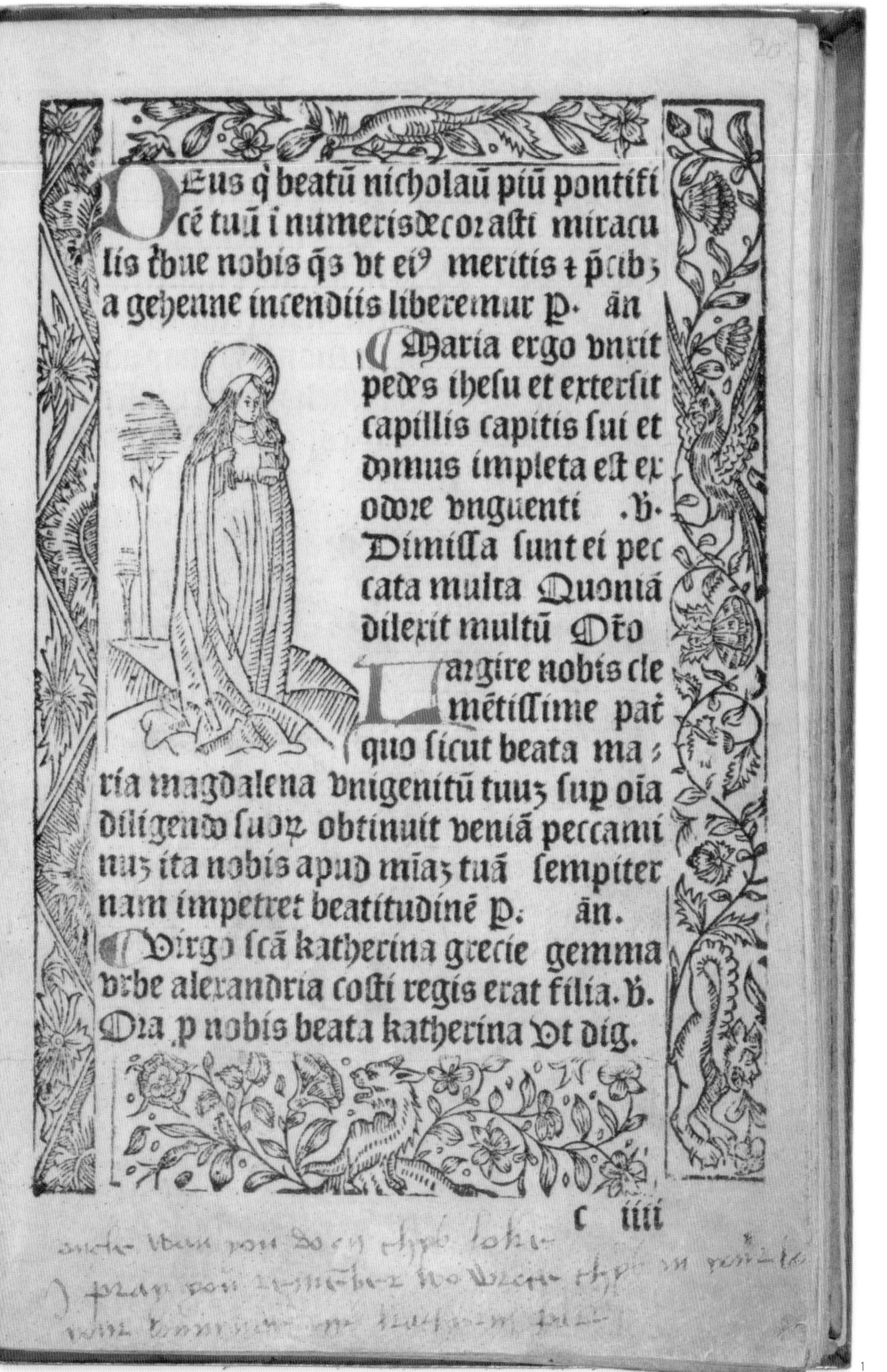

Deus q̄ beatū nicholaū piū pontifi
cē tuū ī numeris decorasti miracu
lis tribue nobis q̄s vt ei⁹ meritis ⁊ p̄cib;
a gehenne incendiis liberemur P. ān

Maria ergo vnxit
pedes ihesu et extersit
capillis capitis sui et
domus impleta est ex
odore vnguenti .V.
Dimissa sunt ei pec
cata multa Quoniā
dilexit multū Oro

Largire nobis cle
mētissime pat
quo sicut beata ma-
ria magdalena vnigenitū tuū sup oīa
diligendo suoꝝ obtinuit veniā peccami
nū ita nobis apud miaꝫ tuā sempiter
nam impetret beatitudinē P. ān.

Virgo scā katherina grecie gemma
vrbe alexandria costi regis erat filia. V.
Ora p nobis beata katherina Vt dig.

c iiii

1

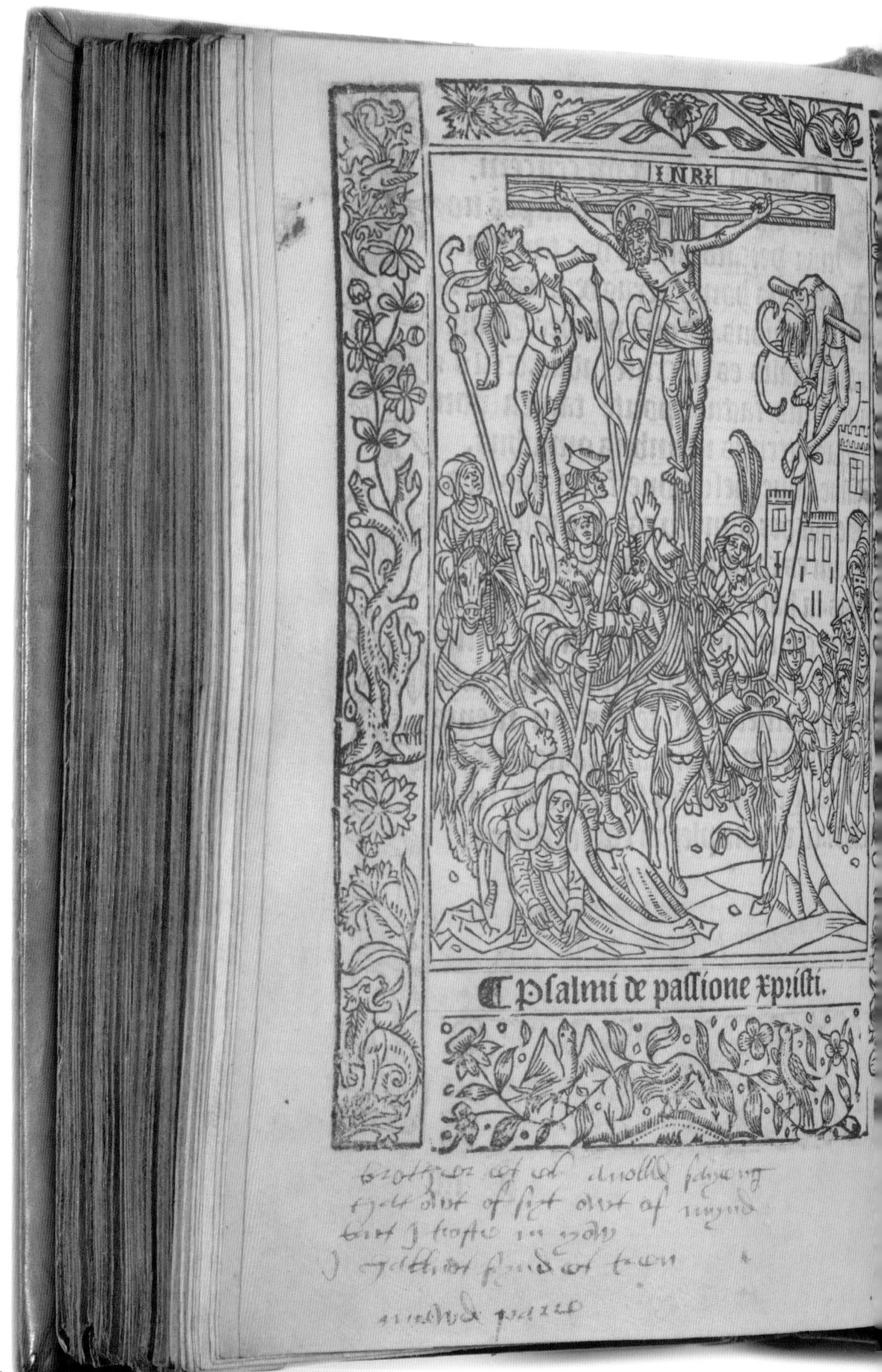

2

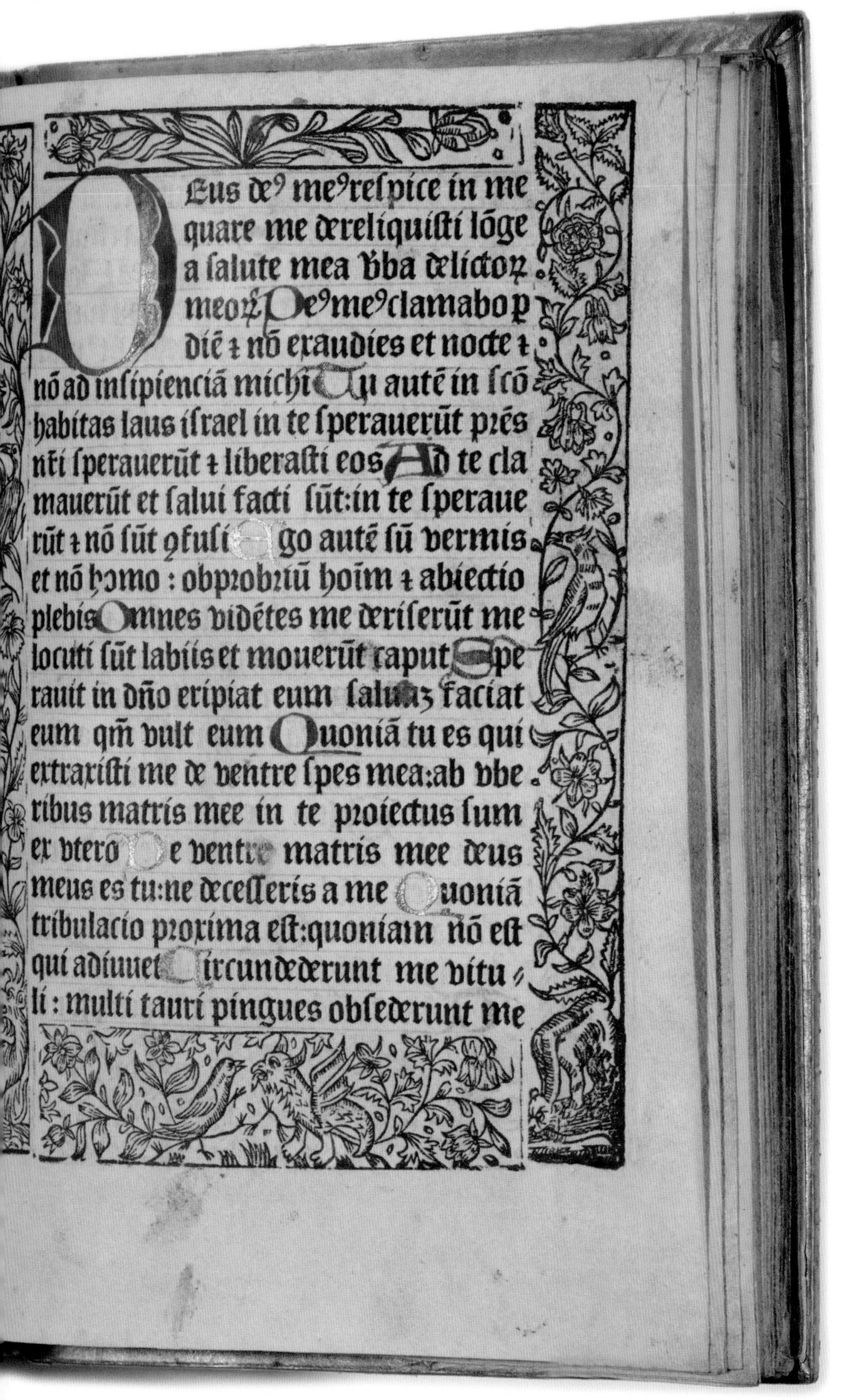

Deus de⁹ me⁹ respice in me
quare me dereliquisti lõge
a salute mea vba delictoꝝ
meoꝝ. Deus me⁹ clamabo p
diē ⁊ nõ exaudies et nocte ⁊
nõ ad insipienciā michi. Tu autē in scõ
habitas laus israel in te sperauerūt pr̄es
nr̄i sperauerūt ⁊ liberasti eos. Ad te cla
mauerūt et salui facti sūt: in te speraue
rūt ⁊ nõ sūt ꝯfusi. Ego autē sū vermis
et nõ homo: obprobriū hoim ⁊ abiectio
plebis. Omnes vidētes me deriserūt me
locuti sūt labiis et mouerūt caput. Spe
rauit in dño eripiat eum saluū faciat
eum qm̄ vult eum. Quoniā tu es qui
extraxisti me de ventre spes mea: ab vbe
ribus matris mee in te proiectus sum
ex vtero. De ventre matris mee deus
meus es tu: ne decesseris a me. Quoniā
tribulacio proxima est: quoniam nõ est
qui adiuuet. Circundederunt me vitu
li: multi tauri pingues obsederunt me

PICTURED:

1. The armorial device at the foot of the title page.
2. and 3. Ornate penwork initials highlighting the parallel columns of text in Latin and Spanish.

Aid to an easier read

***Meditationes vitae Christi* [Spanish and Latin]**
[Barcelona: Peter Michael, about 1493]
Inc.3.H.5.3[4138]

No one has yet attempted a history of the parallel text, its whys and wherefores and the variety of forms it takes, whether epigraphic, manuscript or printed. One early trilingual example is the Rosetta Stone: today's reader may think of the Loeb Classical Library. Bilingual textbooks were appearing by the third century AD and about the year 1000 in England Abbot Aelfric produced a Latin grammar in Anglo-Saxon. It is against this background that one may look at the unique Cambridge copy of the Pseudo-Bonaventure *Meditationes*. On a single day, 16 July 1493, the Barcelona printer Peter Michael signed and issued simultaneous editions in the original Latin and the Spanish vernacular. What we have here, be it the predecessor or successor of these two editions, is a single-volume amalgam of the two texts, printed in parallel columns employing the same type-setting. It presumably served an educational purpose, whether as teaching aid or for the benefit of an ill-read clergy. Whatever the answer, it is a remarkable demonstration of how two independent texts were merged into a single unit for bilingual presentation.

First printed in Augsburg in 1468, the *Meditationes* appeared in a succession of editions and translations printed in Italy, France, Spain and England. The date of around 1493 for the present edition reminds us that it was this genre of devotional tract that the Spanish were quick to export to equip missionaries in the New World, where an accompanying vernacular version would have added value. Something of the same thinking lay behind another Spanish bilingual venture, the first printed Arabic grammar, intended as a missionary tool for the conversion of the Moors in Islamic Spain and including parallel Arabic and vernacular versions of the Lord's Prayer and the Ten Commandments. Within a matter of years Spain was also to embark on the first of the polyglot Bibles, the so-called 'Complutensian Polyglot' (Alcalá, 1514–1517) with combined texts in Hebrew, Aramaic, Greek, and Latin. The title page of the *Meditationes* celebrates its origins, with a decorative woodcut panel containing symbols representing the joint rule of Ferdinand and Isabella, and the union of Aragon and Castile.

Nicholas Poole-Wilson *is a former Managing Director of Bernard Quaritch Ltd.*

1

2

3

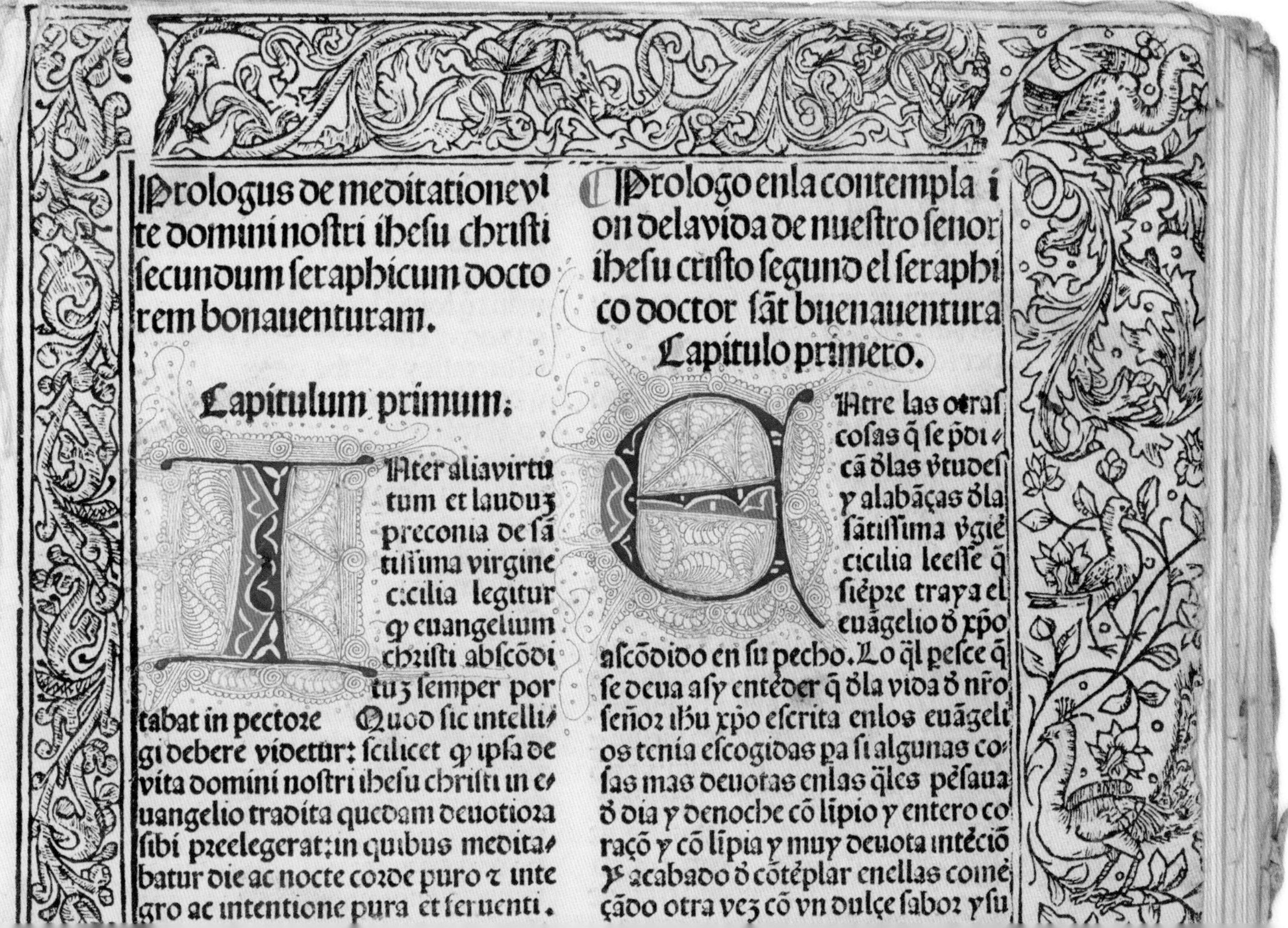
Prologus de meditatione vi te domini nostri ihesu christi secundum seraphicum docto rem bonauenturam.

Capitulum primum.

Inter alia virtu tum et laudū preconia de sā tissima virgine cecilia legitur ꝙ euangelium christi abscōdi tū semper por tabat in pectore Quod sic intelli gi debere videtur: scilicet ꝙ ipsa de vita domini nostri ihesu christi in e uangelio tradita quedam deuotiora sibi preelegerat: in quibus medita batur die ac nocte corde puro ⁊ inte gro ac intentione pura et feruenti.

Prologo enla contempla cion dela vida de nuestro señor ihesu cristo segund el seraphi co doctor sāt buenauentura

Capitulo primero.

Entre las otras cosas q̄ se pdi cā dlas virtudes y alabāças dla sātissima vgiē cicilia leesse q̄ siēpre traya el euāgelio đ xpo ascōdido en su pecho. Lo q̄l pesce q̄ se deua asy entēder q̄ dla vida đ nr̄o señor ihū xpo escrita enlos euāgeli os tenia escogidas pa si algunas co sas mas deuotas enlas q̄les pēsaua đ dia y denoche cō lipio y entero co raçō y cō lipia y muy deuota intēciō y acabado đ cōtēplar enellas comē çādo otra vez cō vn dulçe sabor y su

1493

PICTURED:

1. Verardus's hand-written dedication, alongside the illuminated opening leaf, dateable to between 7 and 27 March 1493.
2. 'Bearer type', the un-inked impression of type used to fill empty space within a printer's forme, here the concluding lines of the *Historia Baetica*.
3. A song praising Ferdinand and Isabella, the lyrics added by hand.

A deluxe presentation copy of contemporary secular drama

Carolus Verardus (1440–1500)
Historia Baetica
and
Marcellinus Verardus (15th century)
Elegiae et carmina
Rome: Eucharius Silber, 7 March 1493

bound with:
Marcellinus Verardus (15th century)
Fernandus servatus
[Rome: Eucharius Silber, between 7 and 27 March 1493]
Inc.4.B.2.27[1283]

As ambassador to the Vatican of the Spanish monarchs Ferdinand and Isabella, Juan Ruiz de Medina, Bishop of Astorga (died 1507) was closely connected with the subject of the two plays in this volume, which commemorate significant events in Spanish history. *Historia Baetica* celebrates the capture of Granada in 1492, a battle which completed the *Reconquista* under Ferdinand and Isabella and ended Islamic rule on the Iberian peninsula, while *Fernandus servatus* commemorates the recuperation of the king from a near-fatal assassination attempt by a madman at Barcelona in December of that year. This deluxe volume, printed on vellum, was illuminated and presented to Ruiz de Medina by the author, Carolus Verardus, who also added marginal annotations in red highlighting Ferdinand's virtues, authority, goodness and other regal qualities.

The performance of *Historia Baetica* included a song in Italian with four voice parts in praise of Ferdinand and Isabella. The music is printed here in woodcut and constitutes the earliest printed music for theatre and the first secular polyphonic music printed in Italy. The verses in this copy are elegantly written in by hand.

Not only are the authors closely related (Carolus was the uncle and patron of Marcellinus) but their works in this volume are too. The editions are printed by the same printer with the same types, in the same format, and they survive most often as companions. The first work has a colophon dated 7 March 1493 and, although the second work is undated, the Cambridge copy allows its production to be placed within a three-week period, from 7 to 27 March 1493. On the first page of *Fernandus servatus* is a blind impression of 4 lines of bearer type, which are the last 4 lines of the *Historia Baetica*, showing that the second work followed on immediately from the first. Reinforcing this evidence is the fact that the two editions share the same paper stock in another, paper, copy of these works at Cambridge. Ruiz de Medina became Bishop of Badajoz on 27 March 1493 and yet both in the printed text of the *Historia Baetica* and in Verardus's presentation inscription here, he is named still as Bishop of Astorga. We may therefore date not only the printing of *Fernandus servatus* but also the illumination and presentation of this volume to between 7 and 27 March.

Only one other copy printed on vellum is recorded, and it is the dedication copy of *Historia Baetica*, finely illuminated for Cardinal Raffaele Riario (1424–1521) in whose house at Rimini the play was performed on 22 April 1492.

Margaret Lane Ford *is International Head of Group, Books and Manuscripts, at Christie's.*

1

Reueren. in xpo patri Domino Io. Medinae epo Astoricen. illmorum Regum hispaniae apud Pont. Max. oratori Carolus Verardus Cesenas Sal. P.D. Regio oratori nimirum Regia dona debentur. Quid autem tam Regium: q. ea scripta quibus Regia dicta ac facta celebrantur? Ego igitur historiam quam de urbe Granata singulari virtute felicibusq. auspicijs Fernandi et Hellisabes hispaniarum Regis ac Reginae quorum vices Romae geris: Recepta: nuper composui: muneris loco tibi Venerande Presul iure mitto: obsecrans ut eam ab inuidorum morsibus calumnijsq. improborum tuo patrocinio et autoritate tuearis. In quo principibus tuis ut debes magnopere inseruies: et immortali beneficio me tibi perpetuo deuincies. Vale ac me per humanitatem tuam rogatus Regiae illorum Maiestati plurimum comenda.

Caroli Verardi Cæsenatis Cubicularii Pontificii in historiam Bæticam ad R. P. Raphaelem Riarium. S. Georgii Diaconum Cardinalem: Præfatio:

CVm felix ille uenerãde præsul: & iam pridẽ ab uniuerso christiano orbe mille uotis exoptatus nuntius Romã peruenisset: quo cognitum est urbem Granatam cũ omni eius regno: quod per octingentos fere annos impio Magmedis dominatu oppressum fuerat: iugo seruitutis excusso in christi libertatem erectum nunc tandem in potestatẽ ac ditionem Fernandi & Hellisabes christianissimorum Inuictissimorũq; Hispaniæ Regis ac Reginæ deuenisse: memet continere non potui: quin arrepto calamo summam saltem huius rei litteris mãdarem: præsertim cum ob eam causam Pontifex ipse Maximus: Senatus apostolicus: Populusq; Romanus tanta uictoria exultans: quibuscunq; posset modis: lætitiæ suæ signa mõstraret. Templis omnibus sacra fierent: Supplicationes per dies complures ad cuncta puluinaria constituerentur: Gratiæ deo Immortali ac diuo Iacobo hispaniaæ patrono ad aras omnis agerentur: Vrbe tota longissimus sacerdotum ordo diuinis hym

2

FERNANDVS: SER
VATVS:

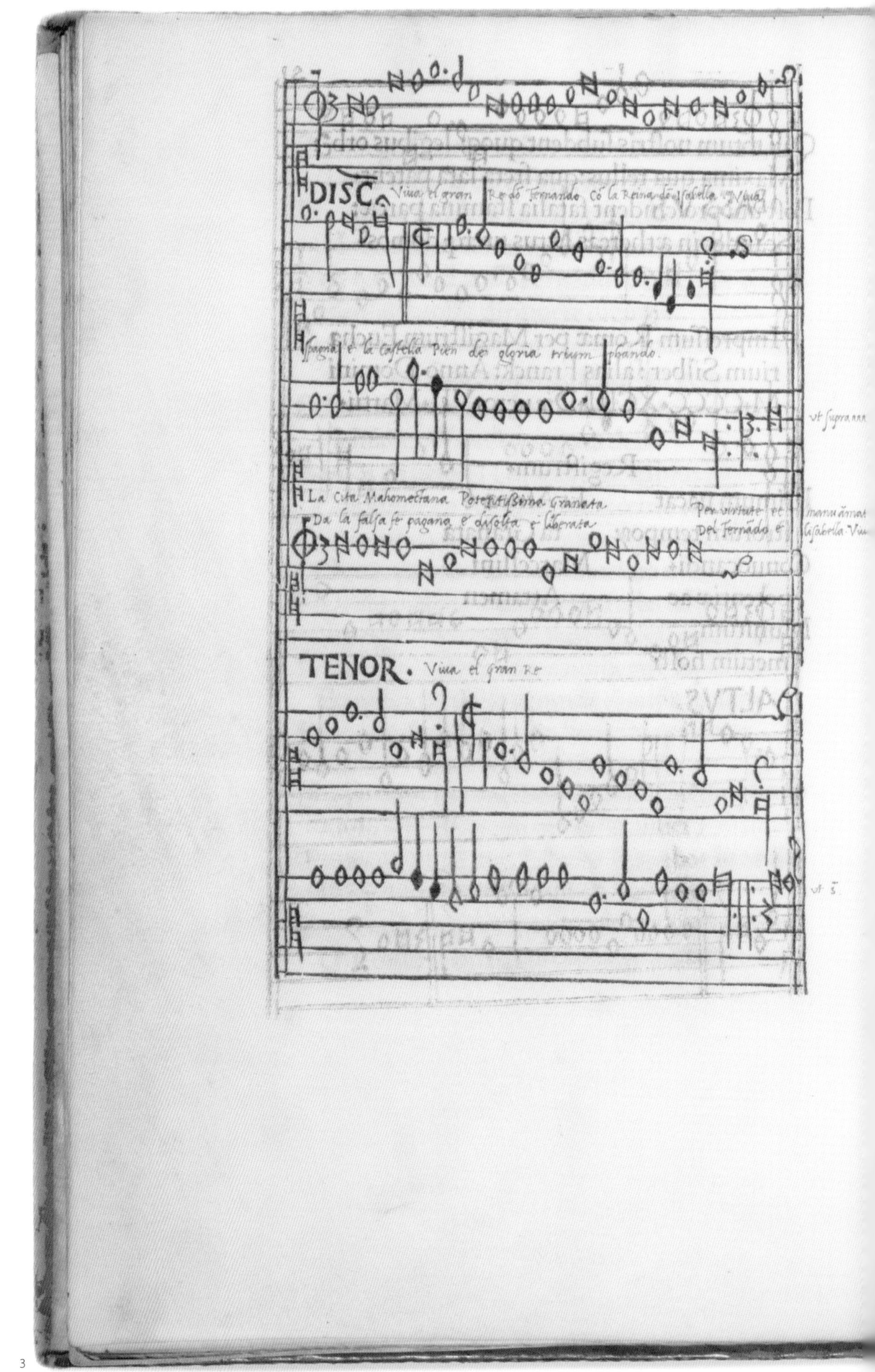
DISC
Viua el gran Re dō Fernando cō la Reina de Ysabella Viua
Ispagna e la Castella Pien de gloria trium phando
La Cita Mahometana Potentissima Granata
Da la falsa fe pagana e disolta e liberata
TENOR.
Viua el gran Re

3

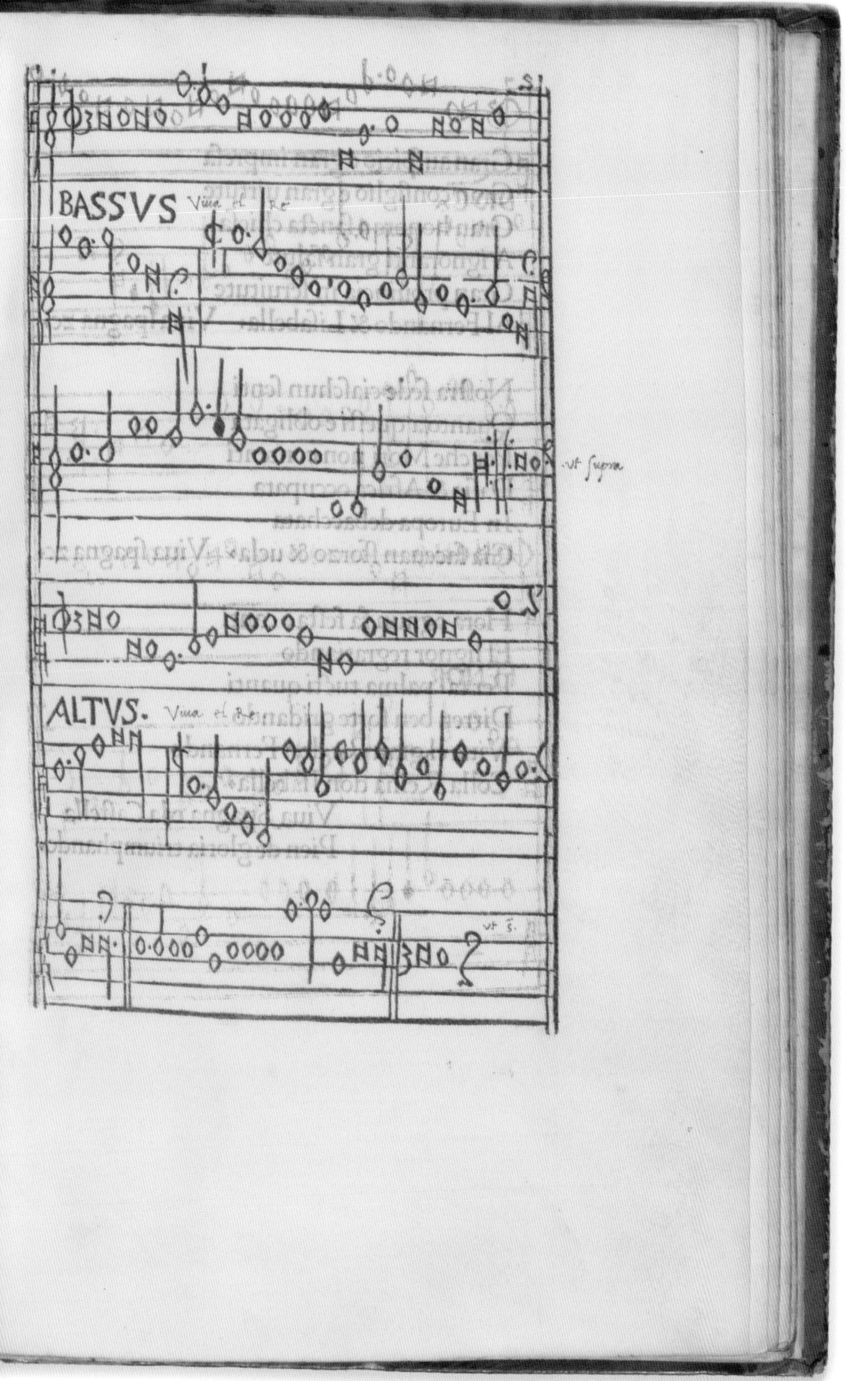
BASSVS
ALTVS.

1493

PICTURED:

1. The inscription recording Parker's donation to the University of 1574.
2. Events of the early 1490s recorded in the 1493 *Chronicle*.
3. The fall of Sodom and Gomorrah, with Lot's wife.

The *Nuremberg Chronicle*

Hartmann Schedel (1440–1514)
Liber chronicarum
Nuremberg: Anton Koberger, for Sebald Schreyer and Sebastian Kammermeister, 12 July 1493
Inc.0.A.7.2[888]

The celebrated *Nuremberg Chronicle* is not a rare book, but it is an extraordinarily interesting one. More than 1,200 copies still survive, and there are no fewer than four in Cambridge University Library. It is a history of the whole world, in Latin, from the Creation to the Last Judgment (with a few blank pages so that owners could fill in any events between the book's publication and the end of the world, for total comprehensiveness). The author was the Nuremberg physician and book collector Hartmann Schedel. The book was printed by Anton Koberger (died 1513), a goldsmith who had set up a flourishing printing shop in Nuremberg in 1470. The *Chronicle* includes the astonishing total of over 1,800 vivid woodcuts, some of great complexity, printed from approximately 645 different blocks designed and cut for the purpose by the Nuremberg artists, Michael Wolgemut (about 1434/36–1519) and Wilhelm Pleydenwurff (about 1450–1494). In this copy they are coloured by hand. The young Albrecht Dürer (1471–1528) had been an apprentice in Wolgemut's workshop and was the godson of Koberger, and it is an old question whether he too was in some way involved in this mammoth artistic and patriotic enterprise.

This glorious copy was given in 1574 to the University Library by Matthew Parker (1504–1575), Master of Corpus Christi College 1544–1553, Vice-Chancellor in 1545 and 1548, and Archbishop of Canterbury from 1559 to 1575. Parker assembled a vast private library of books and medieval manuscripts, some of extreme age and value, which in 1574 he entrusted into the care of his former college in Cambridge, where they remain in what is still known as the Parker Library. He especially sought chronicles and texts touching on the origins and antiquity of the English church. Parker was also, very unusually for his time, interested in the history of printing. In a unique Caxton (now Parker Library EP H.6) he jotted down different opinions on the date of its invention, including '*Cronica magna testatur inventam fuisse Anno Domini 1440*.' That *Chronica magna*, 'Great chronicle', is this copy. The reference to printing having been invented in 1440 occurs on folio 252 verso, where it is marked by Parker with one of his distinctive symbols of three dots and a flourish.

Christopher de Hamel *is Fellow Librarian of Corpus Christi College, Cambridge.*

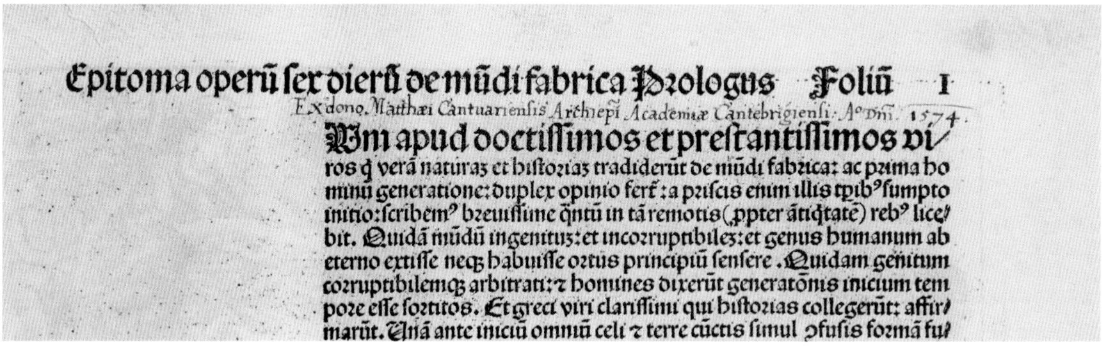
Epitoma operũ sex dierũ de mũdi fabrica Prologus Foliũ I
Ex dono Matthaei Cantuariensis Archiepi Academiae Cantebrigiensi. Ao Dni. 1574
Cum apud doctissimos et prestantissimos vi-
ros q verã naturaz et historiaz tradiderũt de mũdi fabrica: ac prima ho
minũ generatione: duplex opinio ferẽ: a priscis enim illis tpib⁹ sumpto
initio: scribem⁹ breuissime q̃ntũ in tã remotis (ppter ãtiqtatẽ) reb⁹ lice-
bit. Quidã mũdũ ingenituz: et incorruptibilez: et genus humanum ab
eterno extisse neq3 habuisse ortus principiũ sensere. Quidam genitum
corruptibilemq3 arbitrati: 7 homines dixerũt generatõnis inicium tem
pore esse sortitos. Et greci viri clarissimi qui historias collegerũt: affir-
marũt. Unã ante iniciũ omniũ celi 7 terre cũctis simul ɔfusis formã fu-

1

TEmpestas ingens prius inaudita. anno salutis. 1490. die. 12. mēs iulij. in regia vrbe ↄstātinopolitana admodū deseuit. Supioꝝ em̄ triū sydeꝝ ignes. q̄ decidui ad terras fulminū nomē hn̄t. cū ↄtagiū nimij hūoris ex supiore circulo atq̄ʒ ardoris e sbiecto p hūc modū egerāt. Turbato itaq̄ʒ aere cū collectus humoꝝ habūdantiā stimulabat. seu graui sideꝝ ptu. Et cuʒ ī nube luctabaꝉ flat⁹ aut vapoꝛ. primo ingētia tonitrua audita. Exin fulmīa ardētia visa. ⁊ longiore tractu fulgetra. Et quāq̄ʒ a saturni sidere ,pficisci ista ↄsectati sunt. sicut crementia a martis. Qualiter cū vulsinis oppidū thuscoꝝ opulētissimū totū crematum ē fulmīe. In ea vrbe p̄clarissima hec gesta. xp̄iani id diuine ,puidētie attribuūt. Ubi antiq̄ colūna ymaginē ↄstatini impatoris hēbat. fulgur ⁊ horrid⁹ impet⁹ ue dū ptē ei⁹ deiecit. Uerū vt veridici narrarūt negociatores veneti ⁊ alij. octīgētos domos ignis reꝝ edax ↄsūpsit. Et hoīm tria milia. vt nec lignū nec forma edificioꝝ r̄māsit. Ea forma vt circ il⁹ deuastatōis īfra oñdit. iō hāc figurā ī laudabilē rei mēoriā adiūxim⁹.

CUm varia reꝝ miracl'a effluxis tpib⁹. vt oñdim⁹ euenert. Uisa ei horrēda oñta corona trabes telluꝝ hyat⁹ sanguine⁹ pol⁹. ardētes clipei ⁊ alia. Lac pluere e celo visū. ⁊ lanā. carnē ⁊ cruorē descēdē. visi ↄcurrētes mōtes. Et lūa solq̄ʒ triplex. cruce sigtus lapis excidit tpib⁹ friderici scdi ipatoꝝ (vti p̄missū ē) Nouissime āno. 1492. vij. yd⁹ nouēbris. ī meridie sb friderico. iij. ipatore. ad agros ei⁹ ,pprios. cū crepuit p aera fulmē. igēs lapis cōcidit. cui forma delte. aciesq̄ʒ triāgula fuit. missus ab obliq̄. hūc senserat Enſheim. Sūt gaudia q̄ʒ sensit. Cū illic ī agros desiluit depopulat⁹ humū. in ptes distract⁹. pōd⁹ tñ gue adhuc hʒ. ⁊ ad oñtationē obsuatur. tanq̄ʒ futuꝝ omen.

BElla p h̄ tpa inter regē maximilianū. ⁊ regeʒ frācie. ob ducissam britānie. p mltas clades gesta fuerūt. Et adhuc sub dubio marte vigent.

Nachor vo octo de melcha genuit filios e qbus batuel tercius fuit q genuit rebeccam filiaz et laba
filiū. Iste nachaor scd̄us filius thare. vxor eius melcha. Hus primus filius nachor. Job filius bu
Bus scd̄s filius nachor habuitq duos filios videlicet beor primus. balaaz scd̄us. Batuel ter
filius nachor filiū habuit vnū laban et vnā filiā rebeccā. s. Laban filius batuel duas habuit filias qs p
seruitiū. 14. ānor iacob filio rebecce sororis sue in vxores tradidit. Lya pria filia laban primaq vxor.
cob lippa oculis genuit sex filios et vnā filiā. Scd̄a filia laban rachel vxor iacob. diu sterilis tandē ge
it duos filios et mortua in partu. sepelitur pe bethleē. Rebecca vxor ysaac. Istā rebeccā duxit ysaac
lius abrahā in vxorem quā helieser seruus abraham abduxit de aram mesopotamie in terrā chanaan. q
annuente inoleuit vt desponsanda prius requiratur de cōsensu. Camuel quartus filius nachor. Caseth
tus filius. Aran sextus filius. Pheldas septimus filius. Bela octauus filius.

3

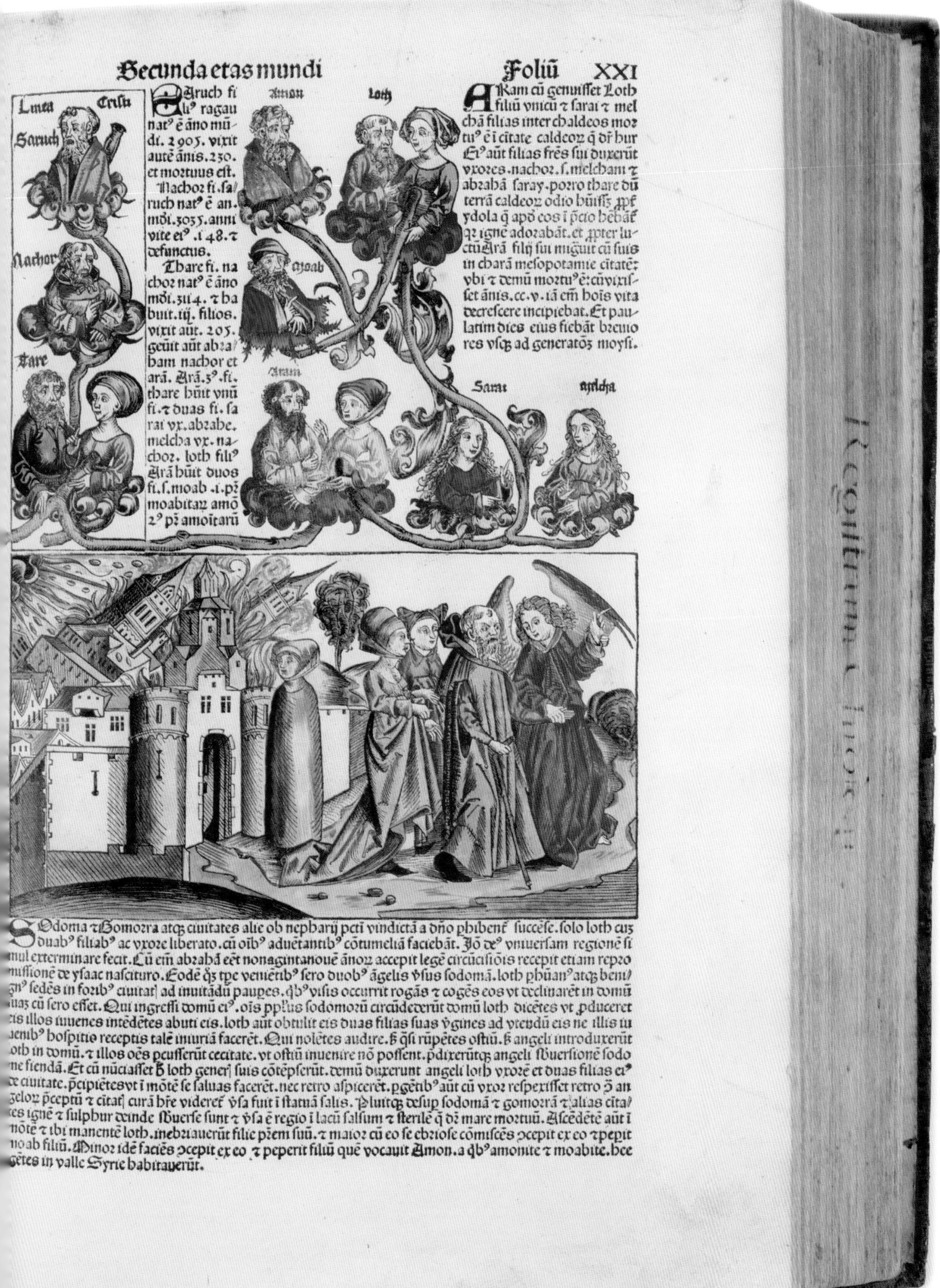

Linea Cristi

Saruch

Nachor

Tare

Saruch fi
lius ragau
nat⁹ ē āno mū-
di. 2905. vixit
autē ānis. 230.
et mortuus est.

Nachor fi. sa/
ruch nat⁹ ē an.
mūdi. 3035. anni
vite ei⁹ . 148. ꝛ
defunctus.

Thare fi. na
chor nat⁹ ē āno
mūdi. 3114. ꝛ ha
buit. iij. filios.
vixit aūt. 205.
genuit aūt abra/
ham nachor et
arā. Arā. 3⁹. fi.
thare hūit vnū
fi. ꝛ duas fi. sa
rai vx. abrahe.
melcha vx. na-
chor. loth fili⁹
Arā hūit duos
fi. s. moab. i. pr̄
moabitaꝝ amō
2⁹ pr̄ amoītarū

Amon

Loth

Moab

Aram

Sarai

Melcha

Aram cū genuisset Loth
filiū vnicū ꝛ sarai ꝛ mel
chā filias inter chaldeos mor
tu⁹ ē ī citate caldeoꝝ q̄ dr̄ hur
Ei⁹ aūt filias frēs sui duxerūt
vxores. nachor. s. melcham ꝛ
abrahā saray. porro thare dū
terrā caldeoꝝ odio hūisꝫ ꝑꝑt
ydola q̄ apō eos ī p̄cio hēbāt
q꞉ ignē adorabāt. et ꝓpter luctū Arā filij sui migrāuit cū suis
in charā mesopotamie citatē:
vbi ꝛ demū mortu⁹ ē: cū vixis-
set ānis. cc. v. iā eīn hoīs vita
decrescere incipiebat. Et pau/
latim dies eius fiebāt breuio
res vsqꝫ ad generatōꝫ moysi.

Sodoma ꝛ Gomorra atqꝫ ciuitates alie ob nephariȷ pctī vindictā a dn̄o phibent̄ succēse. solo loth cuꝫ duab⁹ filiab⁹ ac vxore liberato. cū oīb⁹ aduētantib⁹ cōtumeliā faciebāt. Jō de⁹ vniuersam regionē simul exterminare fecit. Cū eīn abrahā eēt nonagintanouē ānoꝝ accepit legē circūcisiōis recepit etiam repromissionē de ysaac nascituro. Eodē qꝫ tpe venietib⁹ sero duob⁹ āgelis v̄sus sodomā. loth phūan⁹ atqꝫ benign⁹ sedēs in forib⁹ ciuitatꝭ ad inuitādū paupes. qb⁹ visis occurrit rogās ꝛ cogēs eos vt declinarēt in domū suaꝫ cū sero esset. Qui ingressi domū ei⁹. oīs pplus sodomorū circūdederūt domū loth dicētes vt pduceret eis illos iuuenes intēdētes abuti eis. loth aūt obtulit eis duas filias suas v̄gines ad vtēdū eis ne illis iuuenib⁹ hospitio receptis talē iniuriā facerēt. Qui nolētes audire. ꝭ q̄si rūpētes ostiū. ꝭ angeli introduxerūt loth in domū. ꝛ illos oēs pcusserūt cecitate. vt ostiū inuenire nō possent. pdixerūtqꝫ angeli sbuersionē sodome fiendā. Et cū nūciasset ꝭ loth generꝭ suis cōtēpserūt. demū duxerunt angeli loth vxorē et duas filias ei⁹ de ciuitate. p̄cipiētes vt ī mōtē se saluas facerēt. nec retro aspicerēt. pgētib⁹ aūt cū vxor respexisset retro ꝯ angeloꝝ p̄ceptū ꝛ citatꝭ curā hr̄e videret v̄sa fuit ī statuā salis. Pluitqꝫ desup sodomā ꝛ gomorrā ꝛ alias citates ignē ꝛ sulphur deinde sbuerse sunt ꝛ v̄sa ē regio ī lacū salsum ꝛ sterilē q̄ dr̄ mare mortuū. Ascēdētē aūt ī mōtē ꝛ ibi manentē loth. inebriauerūt filie prēm suū. ꝛ maior cū eo se ebriose cōmiscēs ꝯcepit ex eo ꝛ pepit moab filiū. Minor idē faciēs ꝯcepit ex eo ꝛ peperit filiū quē vocauit Amon. a qb⁹ amonite ꝛ moabite. hee gētes in valle Syrie habitauerūt.

PICTURED:

1. The hand-coloured Crucifixion in the British Library's *Missale Frisingense*. © The British Library Board, IB.6727 sig. P3 verso.
2. Ratdolt's colour-printed Crucifixion.

Print wins the day

Missale Brixinense
Augsburg: Erhard Ratdolt, 17 August 1493
Inc.2.A.6.18[837]

I chose this scene of the Crucifixion because it is a significant image in a theme that greatly interests me, the history of colour printing. Erhard Ratdolt, a printer in Augsburg, made in 1485 a brave and very successful attempt to achieve a new and difficult task: using relief printing, introduced to Europe by Gutenberg about thirty years earlier, to create an edition of a realistic image in which all the colour is printed. He used black for the linear image, adding to it patches of yellow, dark olive-brown and red. This meant that he had to print four successive impressions on the sheet of paper, each with a different wood block inked in a single colour. This required very precise registration of the new block for each impression, together with the skill of judging which colours to use and in which parts of the print. The image was a tactful one, being a portrait of the bishop who had commissioned the book, the *Breviarium Ratisbonense*. It must immediately have become the bishop's favourite breviary.

1

The work must also have been time-consuming, however, and expensive for Ratdolt. Five years later he printed a missal, the *Missale Frisingense*, including another image of the Crucifixion. This time he got his prints hand-coloured, certainly because it was cheaper and possibly because he expected it to be more reliable. He was clearly disappointed by the result, and with good reason judging from the copy in the British Library. When he used the same image three years later, seen here in the copy of the *Missale Brixinense* in the University Library, he reverted to his earlier technique and used entirely printed colour; red, olive, fawn, and a new colour, the blue-grey of the Virgin's robe. This clear and confident print shows up the amateurishness and inadequacy of the hand-coloured version, in which the thick red gouache of the saint's cloak almost entirely obscures the black defining lines of the image, while whoever was slopping on the green paint has obliterated the crown of thorns.

Ratdolt had conclusively proved a principle that over the centuries would gradually become evident: that in a commercial undertaking, where realism and consistent accuracy are important, colour printing is far more reliable than the work of many hands using tempera or gouache or watercolour to provide an edition of coloured prints.

Bamber Gascoigne *is an author and television presenter and was Sandars Reader in Bibliography in 1994, lecturing on the development of colour printing: he presented 'University Challenge' for 25 years.*

Ut famulū tuum ep̄um nostrum cum omnibus sibi cōmissis: ab omni aduersitate custodi: et pacem ecclesie tue nostris concede temporibus.

2

1494

PICTURED:

1. The 1546 annotation recording Katherine Palmer's gift to Anthony Bolney, Sub-Prior of the Cluniac monastery in Lewes.
2. The woodcut image of the Virgin and Child from the title page.
3. The printer's device of Wynkyn de Worde, Caxton's successor.

A gift of gratitude

Walter Hilton (died 1396)
***Scala perfectionis* [English]**
[Westminster]: Wynkyn de Worde, 1494
Inc.3.J.1.2[3534]

The *Scala perfectionis*, or 'Ladder of perfection', was written by Walter Hilton in the late fourteenth century. It explores the role of contemplation in religious life and encourages the reader to become closer to God through prayer and meditation. This copy was once owned by Katherine Palmer (died 1576), a Bridgettine nun of Syon Abbey, which was one of the most austere and influential religious foundations in England before the dissolution of the monasteries, and one committed to the contemplative life. The order also placed great importance on reading and study, and there seems to have been no ruling against nuns owning books in the sixteenth century, for almost two dozen nuns wrote their names in books that survive from Syon: Palmer herself also owned a copy of the *Chastising of God's children* and a Latin translation of Johann Tauler's sermons.

Palmer probably entered Syon in the turbulent early 1530s, joining a community of men and women living in strict segregation who strongly resisted Henry VIII's claim of supremacy over the church in England. The abbey refused until the last to surrender its keys. When it was suppressed, Palmer became an important figure in the homeless community, and after 1551 heroically led nine of them to Maria Troon at Termonde in Flanders, where they re-established themselves within the cloisters of another Bridgettine house.

An inscription on the title page of this book records that it was given in 1546 by Palmer to Anthony Bolney, Sub-Prior of the Cluniac monastery in Lewes, Sussex. Like many at Syon, Bolney had also resisted Henry VIII's supremacy, and under pressure from the King's visitors, confessed to treasonously upholding papal authority. He was treated leniently and granted a pension of £7 when Lewes was dissolved. It is unclear where he went after that, but Palmer gave him this book in the same year that the former abbess of Syon, Agnes Jordan, died: it is likely that it was given in gratitude for his early support of the community after Syon's suppression and, perhaps, in recognition of their shared commitment to orthodox faith. This book gives us a glimpse of the friendships that continued, against all the odds, among English religious men and women after the dissolution.

Alexandra da Costa *is a University Lecturer in English at the University of Cambridge, focusing on late medieval religious and political literature.*

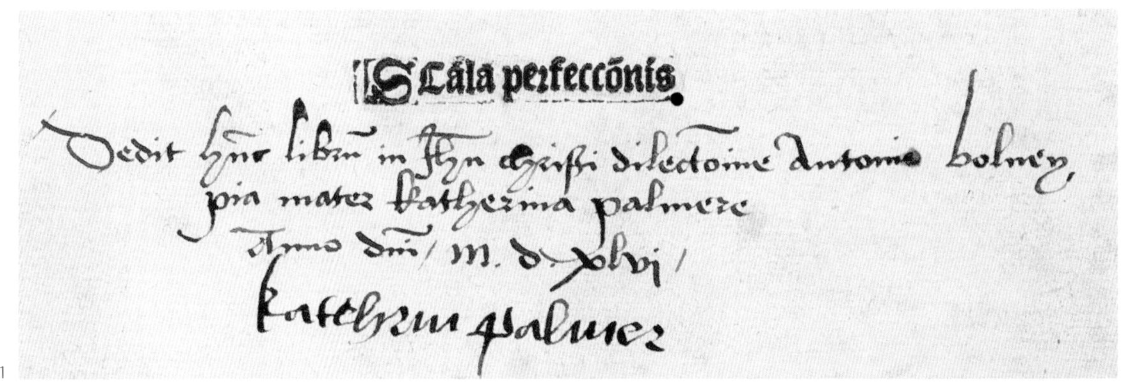

1

2

Caplm xlvi

re afterwarde to the face of Jhesu her spouse / All this louely
dalyaūce of preuy speche bitixe ihū & a soule may be called an
Job.iiii. hidde worde. of the whiche holy wrytt sayth th⁹/ Porro ad me
dcm̄ est vbū absconditū et venas susurrii pcepit auris mea/
Sothli to me is said an hidde worde & the veynes of his row
nynges myn eere hath perceyued/ The Inspyracōn of Jhū is
an hidde worde. for it is preuily hidde fro al louers of the wor
lde & shewed to his louers. thrugh whiche a clene sowle perceyp
ueth redily the veynes of his rownyng þᵗ are specyally shew
enges of his sothfastnes/ For euerych gracyo⁹ knowynge of
sothfastnes felt wyth Inly sauour & ghostly delyte is a preuy
rownyng of Jhū in the ere of a clene soule/ Him behoueth to
haue moche cleñes & mekenes & all other vertues: & to be halfe
deyf to noys of wordly Janglyng þᵗ shold wysely perceyue thi
P. se swete ghostly rownynges þᵗ is the voys of Jhū/ Of þᵗ why
che dauid sayth th⁹/ Vox dñi pparantis ceruos & reuelabit cō
dēsa/ The voys of our lord ihū arayeng hertes & he shal shew
thycke/ That is: the Inspiracōn of Jhū makyth soules lyghte
as hertes þᵗ sterten fro therthe ouer busshes & breres of al worl
dly vanyte. & he sheweth to hem the thicke. þᵗ are his preuitees
þᵗ may not be perceyued but bi sharpe eye. Thise beholdinges
sothfastly groūded in grace & in mekenes maketh a soule wy
se & brēning in desyre to þᵉ face of Jhū/ Thise are þᵉ ghostly thī
ges þᵗ I spake of befor: & they bē called newe gracio⁹ felinges
& I doo but touche hē a litill for wyllyng of þᵉ soule/ For a sou
le that is clene stired by grace to vse of this werkyng may see
more in an hour of suche ghostly matere thā myȝte be wrytē
in a grete boke /

¶ Thus fynysshith this present boke whiche expowneth
many notable doctrynes in contemplacyon / whiche as me se
myth right exspedyēt to those that setten theyr felicyte in ocu
pyenge theimself specyally for theyr soule helthe/

Lenuoye

Infynite laude wyth thankynges many folde
I yelde to god me socouryng wyth his grace
This boke to finysshe whiche that ye beholde
Scale of perfeccion calde in euery place
Wherof thauctor Walter Hilton was
And Wynkyn de worde this hath sett in prynt
In William Caxstons hows so fyll the case
God rest his soule. In Joy ther mot it stynt

This heuenly boke more precyous than golde
Was late direct wyth great humylyte
For godly plesur. theron to beholde
Unto the right noble Margaret as ye see
The kyngis moder of excellent bounte
Herry the seuenth that Jhū hym preserue
This myghty pryncesse hath cōmaunded me
Temprynt this boke her grace for to deserue

Finit felicit̄ liber intitulatus
Scala perfeccionis inpressus
año salutis. M.cccc.lxxxxiiii.

3

PICTURED:

One of only three surviving copies of this broadside almanac.

Bloodletting – when, where and how

Johann Muntz (active fifteenth century)
Tabula minutionum super meridiano Budensi Mccccxcv
Vienna: Johann Winterburg, [before 1495]
Inc.Broadsides.0[4100]

Bloodletting was used prophylactically to maintain health and therapeutically to treat established disease. Following the Hippocratic theory of the ancient Greeks, in medieval Europe it was believed that many illnesses were a consequence of imbalance of the four humours – black bile, yellow bile, blood and phlegm – and bloodletting was a method believed to remove excess humours and return the balance to normal. It was also used to try and stop bleeding from a wound, as bloodletting from the opposite side of the body was thought to reverse the flow of blood away from the injury.

In Europe until the twelfth century it was performed by general medical practitioners known in Latin as *medici*. After that time specialist bloodletters (*minutores*) performed the task along with barbers (*barberi*), leaving the more educated doctors (*physici* and *cyrurgici*) to make the diagnosis and decide the treatment plan. Bloodletting was performed most commonly by opening a vein at the front of the elbow, but it was permissible to use any of over thirty specified veins in the head, arms or legs. After undergoing bloodletting, the patient was strengthened with a nourishing diet for one or two days.

The complex medieval rules for safe bloodletting included never bleeding children or the very weak, and bleeding the elderly only if plethoric. The new moon was thought to be a time when the body was weak, so lunar calendars could be consulted to help decide the safest time for the procedure. The amount of blood removed depended upon the strength of the patient, and the appearance of the blood produced. Medieval manuscripts show how bloodletting at the wrong time after the onset of a fever was believed to lead to deterioration or death.

Broadside almanacs were produced with a limited lifespan, by their very nature; the example here gives the user suitable dates for bloodletting and other forms of purging for the year 1495 in Budapest. After the year had passed, there was no pragmatic reason for the owner to keep it, so of the some 500 broadside almanac editions known to have been printed, most survive in only a few copies. The user would need to obtain another calendar the following year, and one specific to their geographic location, to ensure the most accurate information and thus the greatest chance of safe treatment.

Piers D. Mitchell *is a lecturer in Biological Anthropology at the University of Cambridge.*

Tabula Minutionū super meridiano Budensi Anno dñi M cccc xcv.

Gloriosus deus ⁊ sublimis. qui oĩa verbo creauit. terrã in celi medio collocauit. vt corpora celestia receptaculū inuenirent. cui virtutū suaꝝ (quas a suo creatore ⁊ ordinatore acceperant) effectus imprimerent Vt aũt dñs seculoꝝ mundanis rebus quas sub lunari globo posuit: instabiles et caducas impressiones faciat per indiuidua superiora stabilia ⁊ ꝑpetua. que a luna sursum celi noĩe designant. Solus ille ignorat qui mẽte obstinatus aut mollicie carnalis vite delicatus. opera supioꝝ ⁊ passiones inferiorum non ꝯsiderat et obseruat. Hec Leopoldus ducatus austrie. Qu[illegible]re anno presenti a natali Cristi 1495 currente condñator Mars indicatur. qui homines ad iniurias. rapinas. bella. ⁊ belloꝝ instrumenta ꝯstruenda ⁊ res alias marciales mouebit cum festinatione. et quia fortis in domo sua. signat fortitudinem regis ⁊ victoriã sup inimicos suos ac magnitudinem cordis sui. Hec Albumasar vnde pro eodem anno: tertio post bisextū generales quasdam electiones cõsignare institui Cuius ¶ Aureus numerus 14 ¶ Littera dñicalis D [Nu]merus inditionis 13 ¶ Ciclus solaris 20 ¶ Interuallum a natiuitate Cristi ad Esto mihi 9 ebdomade 3 dies concurrentes ¶ Septuagesima Dominica post [...]ani ¶ Quadragesima Dominica post Perpetue virginis ¶ Pasca Dominica post Tiburcij ¶ Rogationes Dñica ante Vrbani ¶ Ascensio dñi Quita feria post [...] ¶ Penthecoste Dñca post Bonifacij ¶ Septimãe a festo trinitatꝭ ad Aduentũ dñi 24 ¶ Aduẽtus d. Dñica añ Andree ¶ Residuū ad natal'd. 3 ebd. 5 dies.

[Co]niunctões ⁊ oppositões luminariū cū dispositõe aerꝭ ꝭm corundẽ veꝝ motū sup meridião Budẽsi tpib⁹ eqtꝭ verissime calculate.

	¶ Coniunctiones	ho.	mi.	Meridie		¶ Oppositiones.	ho.	mi.	meri.
[Ian]uarij	Feria scda post ꝯuersiõis s. pau. hũida vẽtosa aliqualiter frigida	3	38	post	¶ Januarij	Dominica post epiphanie domini Tẽperata instabilis ventosa	2	19	ante
[Febr]uarij	Feria q̃rta post Mathie apli. niuosa hũida frigida instabil' aura	5	27	ante	¶ Februarij	Die scẽ Appollonie vgi. Hũida siue niuosa ventosa q̃nꝫ serena	3	26	post
[Apr]ilis	Feria quĩta p⁹ annũctiatõis Ma. Instabilis ⁊ tpata cum ventis	4	30	post	¶ Marcij	Feria q̃rta añ Gregorij ppe Hũida ĩstabil' pluries serena cũ fri.	5	57	ante
[Ma]ij	In die sctĩ Marci ewñ. Multuꝫ hũida tpata in frigore p martẽ	1	12	ante	¶ Aprilis	Quita fe. post Ambrosij. Varia ĩ calidis locꝭ tonitruosa hũida	9	10	post
[Iun]ij	Dñica rogatõnuꝫ. Hũida vẽtosa q̃nꝫ serena p iouẽ instabil' ⁊ fri.	8	19	ante	¶ Maij	Dñica post Jo. añ portã lati. Instabil' tpata q̃nꝫ serena p solem	0	30	post
[Iul]ij	Feria scda añ Joãnis bap. Calida ⁊ sicca cũ tõitruis q̃nꝫ trãquilla	2	54	post	¶ Junij	Scda feria post Bonifacij ppe. Instabilis ventosa q̃nꝫ nubosa	3	24	ante
[Au]gusti	Tertia feria añ Marie magd. Tẽpestuosa p martẽ hũida cũ tõi.	10	20	post	¶ Julij	Tertia fe. p⁹ visitatõis Ma. Serena calida q̃nꝫ vẽtus cũ hũidi.	5	46	post
[Sep]tẽbrꝭ	Quita fe. p⁹ assumpcõis Ma. mutabilis cum ventis q̃nꝫ serena	7	44	ante	¶ Augusti	In die Sixti ppe. Instabil' miscue nubosa ⁊ serena aliq̃lr hũid.	7	35	ante
[Oc]tobris	Sexta fe. añ mathei appli. Frigida instabil' p nubes ⁊ pluuias	7	54	post	¶ Septẽbrꝭ	Sexta fe. post Egidij. Frigida et humida cũ pluuijs et nebulis	8	49	post
[Nou]ẽbrꝭ	Dñica post Galli. Hũida vẽtosa pluries serena instabil' cuꝫ tpie	11	5	ante	¶ Octobris	In die Francisci. Vẽtosa tẽpestuosa nõ frigida sicca q̃nꝫ pluuie	9	15	ante
[De]cẽbris	Tertia fe. añ Elizabeth. Hũida niuosa ĩ mõtanis frig. cũ ĩstabi	4	41	ante	¶ Nouẽbrꝭ	Scda fe. post oĩm sctõꝝ. Tpata hũida cũ pluuijs pluries serena.	8	36	post
[Ia]nuarij	Feria q̃rta p⁹ Lucie. Niuosa ĩ calidis locꝭ pluuiosa cũ vẽtꝭ ⁊ cal.	11	43	post	¶ Decẽbris	Feria q̃rta post Andree appli Tempestuosa vẽtosa cũ hũiditate	7	0	ante
					Embolismal	Die Siluestri. Serena tpata nõ excellens frigida q̃nꝫ cũ pluuijs	5	2	post

Tempora ⁊ dies pro fleubotomia scdm verũ cursum lune sub signis zodiaci. fortunatos qꝫ alioꝝ planetaꝝ ad ipsam aspectus in ordine ad etates ⁊ cõplexiones hominũ. membrorumqꝫ qualitatem ydonei non ex necessitate. sed oportunitate.

¶ Januarius

[D]ie Circumcisionis dñi mane bona colerico iuuenili preter pedes — Pisces

[S]exta feria ante Antonij. melancolico virili preter lumbos. — Libra

[Di]e sancti Sebastiani ante meridiem bona flegmatico senili preter coxas. — Sagitt⁹

[S]exta feria et sabatho post ꝯuersionis scti Pauli bona fleg. iuue. p̃ter caput. — Aries

¶ Februarius

[Q]uinta et sexta ferijs post purificationis electa colerico virili p̃ter pectus. — Cancer

[Q]uinta et sexta ferijs post Appollonie bona vi. ⁊ se. melan. p̃ter lumbos — Libra

[Q]uinta et sexta ferijs post Mathie bona iuuenili fleg. preter caput — Aries

¶ Marcius

[Q]uinta et sexta ferijs ante Gregorij optima colerico virili preter pectus. — Cancer

[Di]e sancti Benedicti electa melancolico senili preter crura. — Aq̃rius

[S]exta fe. post ãnunctiatõis sero circa q̃rtaꝫ aut q̃ntaꝫ boñ fleg. iu. p̃ter ca. — Aries

¶ Aprilis

[Q]uarta feria post Ambrosij melancolico virili electa preter lumbos — Libra

[Se]cunda feria ante Tiburtij ante meridiem optĩa fleg. virili preter coxas — Sagitt⁹

[Q]uinta feria ante Georgij electa flegmatico senili preter caput — Aries

[Q]uarta feria post Georgij optima colerico iuuenili preter pectus. — Cancer

¶ Maius

[T]ertia feria post [illegible] optima melancolico virili preter lumbos. — Libra

[illegible] ante portã la. nõ mane bona fleg. virili p̃ter coxas. — Sagitt⁹

[Q]uarta feria post Sophie electa flegmatico senili preter caput. — Aries

[T]ertia feria post Vrbani et q̃rta mane optima colerico iuueni p̃ter pectus. — Cancer

¶ Junius

[S]abatho post Bonifacij optima flegmatico virili preter coxas — Sagitt⁹

[S]abatho ante Viti añ meridiem melancolico virili preter crura. — Aq̃rius

[Q]uarta feria post Viti non sero bona flegmatico senili preter caput. — Aries

¶ Julius

¶ Sexta feria ⁊ sabatho post visitatiõis Marie optima fleg. viri. p̃ter coxas — Sagitt⁹

¶ Tertia feria post Margarethe mane añ sextã bona fleg. senili preter caput. — Aries

¶ Secũda feria añ Marie magdalene bona colerico senili p̃ter pectus — Cancer

¶ Sexta feria post Jacobi optima flegmatico virili ⁊ iuuenili preter coxas — Sagitt⁹

¶ Augustus

¶ Die sancti Laurentij electa flegmatico virili preter caput — Aries

¶ Secunda feria post assumptõis Marie optima colerico senili p̃ter pectus — Cancer

¶ September

¶ Die Egidij et sequenti optima melancolico virili preter crura. — Aq̃rius

¶ Dominica et secunda feria ante natalis Marie bona flegmatico p̃ter caput. — Aries

¶ Dominica post natalis Marie electa colerico senili preter pectus — Cancer

¶ Quarta feria post Mathei bona flegmatico iuuenili preter coxas. — Sagitt⁹

¶ In profesto et festo Michaelis optima melancolico virili preter crura — Aq̃rius

¶ October

¶ Die vndecim milium virginum mane bona fleg. iuuenili preter coxas. — Sagitt⁹

¶ Sexta fe. añ oĩꝫ sctõꝝ p⁹ tertiã vl sabato mane añ sextã bo. fleg. p̃ter caput — Aries

¶ Nouember

¶ Die sancti Leonardi optima colerico virili preter pectus. — Cancer

¶ Quinta feria post Martini bona melancolico senili preter lumbos — Libra

¶ Sexta feria et sabatho post Katherine electa flegmatico virili preter caput. — Aries

¶ December

¶ Quinta et sexta ferijs ante Nicolai optima colerico virili preter pectus. — Cancer

¶ Quinta feria post conceptõis Marie mane melancolico senili p̃ter lumbos — Libra

¶ Sabatho et dñica añ Thome appli electa melancolico iuueni p̃ter crura — Aq̃rius

Quãquam a medietate Julij vsqꝫ ad medietatem augusti suspecte sint Flebothomie Farmacieqꝫ molestie Nihilominus aliqui dies electi dicuntur preter consuetudinem

¶ Dies pro farmacia electi scdm medicinas dandas

[Ian]uarij Die 1 mane in pillul' ꝓ flegmate purg. 9 ĩ elect. ꝓ colera purg. 19 in pociõe ꝓ col. purg.

[Febr]uarij Die 6 in electuarijs ꝓ flegmate purgando 14 circa octauã vel nonã in pocõe ꝓ fleg. pur.

[Mar]cij Die 5. 6 in electua. ꝓ fleg. ⁊ colera purgãdis 14 in pocõe ꝓ quocũqꝫ humore purgando.

[Apr]ilis Die 10 sero in pocione indifferenter 29 in electuarijs pro melancolia ⁊ colera purgandis

[Ma]ij Die 7 nõ mane nec sero in pocione 26 27 in electuarijs pro melancolia purganda.

[Iun]ij Die 2 ꝓ clisteri 5 in potõe ꝓ melã. purgã. 17 ꝓ vomitu 23 sero in elect. ꝓ melã. purg.

[Iul]ij Die 2 sero in pocõe pro fleg. purg. 20 nõ mane nec sero ĩ elect. ꝓ fleg. purg. 27 ꝓ clisteri

[Au]gusti Die 16 sero et 17 in elect. pro fleg. purg. 24 sero et 25 26 in pociõe ꝓ fleg. purganda

[Sep]tẽbris Die 1. 2 pro confortatõe 13 sero ĩ elect. ꝓ flegmate purg. 21 22 in potõe ꝓ col. purg.

[Oc]tobris Die 5. 6 pro solutione ventris 19 sero 26 in pocione pro flegmate purgando.

[Nou]ẽbris Die 6 optima in electuarijs pro flegm. purgando 12 et 13 pro clisteri 27 pro vomitu

[De]cẽbris Die 3. 4 in electuarijs pro melancolia pur. 11 sero 12 in pocõe pro flegmate purgãdo

[Die]s electi ad introitũ balnei cũ vẽtos' aut sñ vẽtos' ꝓ varijs corpoꝝ iuuamẽtis

[Ian]uarij Die 3 ꝓ exi. 8 sñ vẽtoß 12 ꝓ vnc. 17 sñ vẽ. 19 ꝓ mol. 22 ꝓ exi. 27 sñ vẽ. 31 ꝓ exi

[Febr]uarij Die 5 ꝓ hume. 7 ꝓ vnc. 12 ꝓ tpamẽto 14 ꝓ hu. 19 ꝓ lipiditate 26 ꝓ paliß sanatõe

[Mar]cij Die 2 sine vẽtoß 5 ꝓ mollifi. 7 ꝓ vnctõe 12 ꝓ tẽperie 14 ꝓ hum. 16 ꝓ exi 21 sñ vẽ

[Apr]ilis Die 1 ꝓ mollificatõe 8 ꝓ huõrib⁹ equãdis 13 ꝓ exi. 23 ꝓ exi. 29 ꝓ hũec. 30 ꝓ vnct.

[Ma]ij Die 5 et 6 ꝓ tpamẽto 7 ꝓ mollificatõe 16 sine vẽtoß 20 ꝓ exica. 26 ꝓ humectatõe

[Iun]ij Die 2 ꝓ tpie 6 ꝓ paliß sa. 13 ꝓ lipiditate 17 ꝓ exi. 20 sñ vẽ. 23 ꝓ hũec. 30 sñ vẽ.

[Iul]ij Die 4 ꝓ paliß sa. 8 sñ vẽ. 14 ꝓ exicatõe 20 ꝓ humectatõe 27 sine vẽ. 28 ꝓ humect.

[Au]gusti Die 5 sine ventosis 12 ꝓ humectatõe 18 ꝓ vnctõe 22 pro temperie 25 ꝓ mollificatiõe

[Sep]tẽbrꝭ Die 2 sñ vẽ. 7 ꝓ exi. 12 ꝓ humec. 15 ꝓ vnc. 22 ꝓ moll. 23 ꝓ paliß sa. 28 sine vẽ.

[Oc]tobris Die 1 ꝓ limpiditate 7 sine ven. 12 ꝓ vnc. 17 sine ven. 19 et 20 ꝓ mol 27 sñ vẽ.

[Nou]ẽbrꝭ Die 5 sine ventosis 12 pro temperamento 28 pro exicatione

[De]cẽbris Die 3 ꝓ hũect. 5 ꝓ vnct. 10 sñ ven. 12 ꝓ mol. 19 sñ vẽtosis 24 ꝓ exic. 30 ꝓ hũec.

¶ Dies bonorũ aspectuũ ꝭm alios fortunati

¶ Januarij	Die	1	5	6	9	11	15	16	19	23	30	31
¶ Februarij	Die	3	6	12	13	14	17	20	22	24		
¶ Marcij	Die	2	5	7	11	16	20	21	28	30		
¶ Aprilis	Die	3	7	12	15	16	17	26	29	30		
¶ Maij.	Die	5	6	13	14	16	19	20	23	27	29	
¶ Junij	Die	1	2	6	10	13	16	19	23	26	28	
¶ Julij	Die	3	4	8	17	19	26	29	31			
¶ Augusti	Die	4	11	14	17	18	23	25	26	30	31	
¶ Septẽbrꝭ	Die	1	9	10	12	13	19	22	24	27	28	
¶ Octobris	Die	5	6	12	14	17	19	22	23	27		
¶ Nouẽbris	Die	3	5	6	10	14	15	19	21	[illegible]	27	
¶ Decẽbris	Die	3	7	9	11	14	19	22	27	30		

¶ Dies maloꝝ aspectuũ ꝭm alios infortunati,

¶ Januarij	Die	2	4	14	18	21	26	28	29		
¶ Februarij	Die	1	4	8	9	10	15	18	23	25	
¶ Marcij	Die	1	3	8	10	15	17	23	24	26	29
¶ Aprilis	Die	9	11	14	19	20	21	25	27		
¶ Maij	Die	1	8	9	11	15	18	22	24	28	31
¶ Junij	Die	4	8	11	14	15	18	21	22	24	29
¶ Julij	Die	1	5	7	9	11	12	16	21	23	25
¶ Augusti	Die	1	6	7	12	13	15	20	21	27	
¶ Septẽbrꝭ	Die	3	4	11	17	18	25	26	30		
¶ Octobrꝭ	Die	2	4	10	15	16	18	24	28	29	
¶ Nouẽbrꝭ	Die	2	4	7	16	18	24	25	30		
¶ Decẽbris	Die	2	6	8	13	15	16	21	23	28	29

[¶] Dies Seminandi ⁊ plantandi

[Mar]cij Die 5 6 12 13 20 21 28

[Apr]ilis Die 2 8 16 25 28 29

[Ma]ij Die 2 12 13 14 16 22 23 26 27

[Sep]tẽbrꝭ Die 2 9 12 19 28

[Oc]tobris Die 1 6 10 23 24 27

Et si anno presenti nulla sit eclipsis futura tamen annorũ ꝑcedentiũ eclipses suos in hunc annũ portendũt effectus Primo eclipsis solis totalis que fuit anno 1485 hoc anno nobis minat' Sil' solis septẽ pũctoꝝ q̃ fuit 1487 Lune vltia ãno ꝑcedẽti Et q: cũ hoc Mercuri⁹ retrog̃dus Joui retrog̃do opposit⁹ ꝑcedẽti ãno ẽ ꝑcat tribulatões ⁊ dissensiões maxĩas clero euẽturas. q̃re ex ꝑdicta eclipsi magna mgr Joannes liechtenberger ĩ hãc iudicauit snãꝫ Anno dñi 1495 veniet fames q̃uis bñ incipiet ann⁹ in inicio ĩ pte septẽtrionali In aquis oĩa chara erũt Vestimẽta boni precij Aer turbulentus Multe pluuie. In occidẽte plima mala cum saguinis effusiõe videbunt' multa mala inter spũales Esurgẽt insidie ꝯtrauersie Pecora in bono foro Tonitrua ⁊ chorusca[ti]õs videbunt in septẽtriõe Et mlieres clamabũt in celũ vidẽtes angustias plurimas maritoꝝ Pisces morient' in aquis Sꝫ terra meridiana stabit ꝯperẽter cum terra orientali. ⁊c

Impressum Wienne Per Joannem Winterburg.

Hec Mynez.

1495

PICTURED:

1. and 2. Bembo's neat variant and correction to the printing of his own text.

3. The substitution of crops ['*fruges*'] with cornfields ['*segetes*'] allows a glimpse into Bembo's literary mind.

Corrections and clarifications

Pietro Bembo (1470–1547)
De aetna dialogus
Venice: Aldus Manutius, February 1495/1496
Inc.4.B.3.134 [4580]

Pietro Bembo's charming and vivid Latin dialogue, *Aetna*, was printed by Aldus Manutius, probably on commission, in February 1496. Francesco Griffo took special care with the Roman font that he designed and cut for this book. His narrow characters, shortened epigraphic capitals and multiple, varied letter forms produced a graceful and lively page. This copy, as handsome as the rest, has led a particularly adventurous life.

In the 1920s, a period of intense interest in earlier types, it was bought by the typographer Stanley Morison, who used it as the basis for the Bembo type cut in 1929 by the Monotype Corporation, which he advised. In 1930, after studying the book again, he persuaded Giovanni Mardersteig to cut another version which did more justice to the variations in the original, and other forms have followed. The font remains very popular, particularly in Europe.

Morison did not know that his copy had already had a complex history when he bought it. In 1951 Curt Bühler showed that a number of copies of the *Aetna* contain not only stop-press corrections, but substantive changes, entered by hand. He argued that Bembo himself must have made these, and that they were entered in Aldus's shop before customers bought them. In 2011, Laura Nuvoloni discovered that Morison's copy contains not only the corrections Bühler had listed, but seven more as well. She also showed that the small neat hand of these notes is Bembo's own: the notes are authorial.

The copy is too clean to be the working text in which Bembo actually worked out his corrections: more likely he corrected it as a gift for an unidentified friend. But one intriguing possibility remains open, and suggests that the book may have had yet another forgotten encounter. Bembo may have noted his slips himself: at one point he evoked Plato and Aristotle teaching in the shade of plane trees, when he meant to name Socrates and Plato. But it is also possible that friends, or the professional correctors in Aldus's shop, called them to his attention. Thus, friends, critics and correctors alerted Angelo Poliziano to the errors in the first edition of his *Miscellanea* (1489), provoking him to circulate both an errata list and instructions for correcting with the pen. Before Morison, before Mardersteig, before Bühler, before Bembo himself, a press professional may already have been working critically on this exquisite little book.

Anthony Grafton *is Henry Putnam University Professor of History at Princeton University.*

quidẽ uideri ſolẽt); uerum nuſq̃ adeo , ac
nobis ~~uidentibus~~ fuere:nam Aetna quan
ta eſt,nemo quidem ſcit,qui non uidet.

1

Nos numerus ſumus , et fruges conſu-
mere nati,
Sponſi Penelopes , nebulones , ~~Anti-~~ Alci-
noíq;
In cute curanda plus aequo operata iu-

2

miores sunt: nunc nudo latere arabiles in plagas extenditur; et saepe usq; ad imũ descendit, frumentis adeo foecundus; ut credita nonnunq̃ in centuplam segetem cultoribus ferat. itáq; prudenter, ut multa, illud etiã prisci uiri; ꝙ nobilissimum templum Cereris in Aetna cõstituêre: ubi eni potius dea segetum coleretur; q̃ ubi ~~fru-ges~~ optime prouenirent: atq; id quidem tantum de segetibus: uerum ab uniuersa Aetnae fertilitate (ut opinor) fabula etiã emanauit, Aristeum giganta eo in monte ita saluum esse, atq; uiuere; ut neq; ab Aetna prematur unq̃, neq; flammis coelestibus inuratur; ꝙ optimi, et uberrimi essent fructus, qui per Aetnae loca nascerẽtur, nullo telluris uitio, nulla aeris offensi malignitate: nã et Aristeos graeci quidẽ illos uocabant, qui uicissent in certaminibus; ~~quod uerbũ ab optimo deductũ ẽ credo~~, ~~quia nisi optimi non uincerẽt~~: et gigantas scimus esse filios telluris appellatos: ita.

PICTURED:

1. "For the brethren of the Dominican Order in Nuremberg"
2. The woodcut *in situ*.

A Nuremberg woodcut with angels

Christ on the Cross with three angels and a donor with an empty shield
[Nuremberg: 1495–1500]

Pasted within:
Missale Bambergense
Bamberg: Johann Pfeyl, 29 May 1499
Inc.1.A.3.3[4187a]

The prototype of this woodcut was published by Georg Stuchs of Nuremberg, and both volumes in which the two known impressions have been found reveal close associations with the city. The Cambridge volume came from the Dominican monastery in Nuremberg, as is attested by the inscription in the initial D on folio 204v: *pro conuentum fratrum ordinis praedicatorum in Nuremberg* (for the brethren of the Dominican Order in Nuremberg). The Munich impression is pasted in a volume from Strasbourg that once formed part of the library of Hartmann Schedel (1440–1514), physician and humanist, and printer in Nuremberg.

This Crucifixion appears to be unique among fifteenth-century prints in depicting a generic donor and providing space for his coat-of-arms. It comes at the end of a series of images that emphasize the Eucharistic significance of the Crucifixion; the woodcut and the Canon of the Mass reference the partaking of Christ's sacrifice through the wine (clergy) and the wafer (congregation). The angels that collect Christ's blood appear in two groups of woodcuts, beginning with what is possibly the largest surviving woodcut of the fifteenth century, an unfortunately damaged *Christ on the Cross* in the National Gallery of Art, Washington, D.C. Of Netherlandish or Lower Rhenish origin, this Crucifixion may very well have derived from the circle of those who designed the first edition of the Apocalypse blockbook, around 1450. In any case, this highly dramatic rendering of the Crucifixion passed down through Upper and Lower Rhine workshops, appearing in an engraving of about 1475 by Martin Schongauer and also in four or five woodcut versions represented by impressions held in Berlin, Colmar, Linz, Mainz, New York, Oxford, and Washington. A most refined echo was used to introduce the Canon of the Mass in the *Missale Coloniense* (Cologne: Conrad Winter, 1481).

1

Other avenues of transmission are suggested by a now-lost woodcut that once adorned the back of the Imhoff family pew in the Nuremberg's Lorenzkirche and by an anonymous Nuremberg painted panel, the *Epitaph of Georg Rayl*, dating from 1494/5, which includes the kneeling donor. The immediate prototype for the present woodcut was one used in several missals printed by Georg Stuchs. Its popularity is attested by the survival of other close variations. It seems possible that somewhere in this chain of forerunners the presence of Mary Magdalene at the foot of the cross was replaced by the donor present in the Cambridge woodcut.

Richard S. Field, *retired Curator of Prints, Drawings, and Photographs at the Yale University Art Gallery, has written widely on woodcuts, from the fifteenth century to the present, and on late nineteenth-century and contemporary printmaking.*

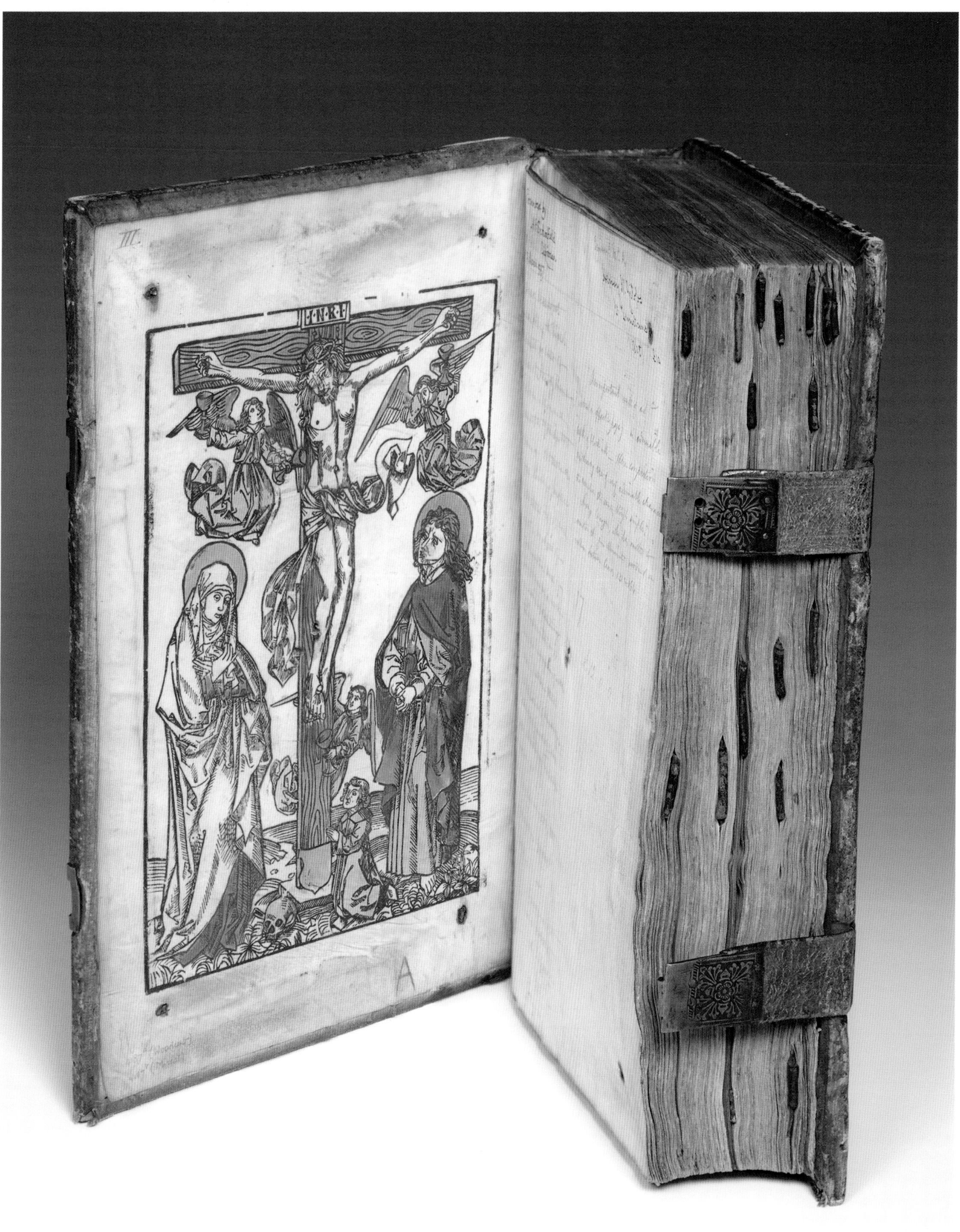

2

PICTURED:

1. The first English printer's device, originally used by William Caxton, later adopted by Wynkyn de Worde, within this monumental volume of nearly 500 leaves.
2. When cymbals are hit together they 'sowneth and ryngeth'.

Musicians and their instruments in a medieval encyclopaedia

Bartholomeus Anglicus (13th century)
***De proprietatibus rerum* [English]**
[Westminster]: Wynkyn de Worde, [about 1496]
Inc. 3.J.1.2[3559]

One of the great historians of medieval books and their contents, C.S. Lewis, often reminded his students that 'not everybody in the Middle Ages lived at the same time'. Sometimes, it seems as if they did. This book contains John Trevisa's fourteenth-century English translation of the *De proprietatibus rerum*, 'On the properties of things', a Latin encyclopaedia completed around 1250 by Bartholomaeus Anglicus, Bartholomew the Englishman. It has been called 'Shakespeare's Encyclopaedia', but much of the material it contains was originally compiled a thousand years before by Isidore, Bishop of Seville, in the last decades of Visigothic Spanish culture. Bartholomaeus makes no secret of his source; on many pages we may see the words 'As Ysidor sayth'.

There are many things in this book to gratify our curiosity: the annoyance caused by fleas, the medicinal uses of sow's milk, the heat in Ethiopia. But I value this text, here so patiently and fully presented, for one particular section: the very last, which concerns music in general and musical instruments in particular. Much of it is indebted to Greek and Latin authors, the former mostly through Latin intermediaries. There is the expected compendium of remarks about the powers of music, for example, which 'abatyth maystry of euyl spyrytes in mankynde'.

1

In the extensive section on instruments Bartholomaeus often leaves Isidore of Seville behind and goes his own way – closely followed by John Trevisa – to provide indispensable information. Here we learn that the best strings of the psaltery, the instrument played by Nicholas in Chaucer's *Miller's tale*, were made of 'laton, or elles those ben goode that ben made of syluer'. That information is unique to this book. Out of nowhere comes the information that the tuning key that harpists used to put their instruments into accord – King David is often shown doing this in medieval art – was called 'wreste' in English, and in Latin *plectrum*. There is also a wonderfully clear statement about the use (or rather the rejection) of musical instruments in church, with only the organ being permitted to accompany 'Proses, sequences and ympnes'. The Church forsakes all kinds of 'mynstralsye', says Bartholomaeus, making us duly cautious about any suggestion that the abundant carvings of angel musicians in medieval churches reveal the sound picture of worship in the English Middle Ages.

Christopher Page *is Professor of Medieval Music and Literature in the University of Cambridge.*

Lyra is sette amonge sterres for loue of Study and praysynge of songe as Ysyder sayth

¶ De Cymbalis. Caplm .C.xlij

Cymbales ben Instrumentes of Musyk and ben smytte togider and sowneth and ryngeth.

¶ De Sistro. Caplm .C.xliij.

Sistrum is an Instrument of Musyk: and hath the name of a lady that firste brought it vp For it is prouyd that Ysis quene of Egypte was the fyrste fynder of Sistrum ¶ And Juuenalis spekyth therof & sayth (Ysis & irato: feriat mea lumina sistro) ¶ And wymmen vsyth this Instrument/ For a woman was the fyrste fynder therof/ Therfore amonge the Amazones the hoste of wymmen is callyd to bataylle wyth the Instrument Sistrū.

¶ De Tintinabulo. .C.xliiij.

Tintinabulū is a belle other ā Camparnole: and hath the name of Tiniendo. tynklynge or ryngynge. Loke tofore. de Vasis. in littera. V. ¶ A belle hath this proprytē. ꝧ whyle he prouffyteth to other in sownynge he is wastyd ofte by smytynge/ Thyse Instrumētes and many other seruyth to Musyk that treatyth of voyce and of sownes/ And knoweth neuerthelesse dysposycōn of kyndly thynges and proporcyon of nombres as Boicius sayth/ And settyth ensample of the nombre of twelue in comparyson to syxe and to other nombres that ben bytwene: And sayth in this wyse. ¶ Here we fyndeth all the accordes of Musyk: from eyghte to syxe nyne to twelue makyth the proporcyon Sexqz tercia/ And makyth togyder the consonancy Dyapente. And twelue to syxe makyth dowble proporcyon and sygnyth the accorde Dyapason. Eyghte to nyne in comparyson ben meane & makyth Epogdonus whyche is callyd Tonus in melody of Musyk/ And is comyn mesure of alle the sownes/ And soo it is to vnderstonde that bytwene Dyatesseron and Dyapente Tonus is dyuersyte of accordes as bytwene the proporcyons. ¶ Sexqz tercia and Sexqz altera only Epogdolis is dyuersyte. Huc vsqz Boicius. in Secundo arismetrice/ Capitulo vltimo. G.

¶ And in the Prologe of the fyrste boke Boicius sayth · that the rather is there vertue of nombres there by it maye be prouyd that those thynges whiche doon stonde by themselfe ben rather in kynde thanne those thynges whyche ben in comparyson to some other thynges:

¶ And the melody of Musyk is nempnyd and callyd by names of the nombres. ¶ Dyatesseron. Dyapente. & Dyapason haue names of the nombres whiche precedeth and gooth tofore in the begynnynge of those sayd names. ¶ And the proporcyon of theyr sownes is founde and had in those same nombres and is not founde nother had in none other nombres.

For ye shall vnderstonde that the sowne and the accorde in Dyapason. of proporcyon of the dowble nombre and the Melodye of Dyatesseron dooth come of

1496

PICTURED:

1. An early sixteenth-century panel-stamped binding from the Low Countries.
2. The Marriage Feast at Cana, a woodcut previously used by Gerard Leeu in Gouda in the early 1480s.

The start of a project

Horae **[Dutch]**
Gouda: Collacie Broeders, 3 October 1496
Inc.5.E.3.10[2890]

This small book recalls several aspects of the work of Henry Bradshaw, Cambridge University Librarian from 1867 until his death in February 1886. It comes from the library of the Enschedé family, auctioned at Haarlem in December 1867.

At the time of the auction, Bradshaw had been Librarian only nine months, and was devoting much of the income from the fund established by Tobias Rustat (1608–1694) to the purchase of incunabula, with a special focus on the Low Countries and Cologne. Now he was his own master, where less than two years earlier he had complained to the Dutch bookseller Martinus Nijhoff that he had to buy early books from his own pocket, while the Library concentrated on those that were 'modern, useful and scientific'. Bidding through Nijhoff, the Library bought extensively at the Enschedé sale, though Bradshaw was disappointed to lose some of the books he most desired. A few more were obtained subsequently.

1

Early liturgical books always intrigued Bradshaw, and he generally preferred books in their original condition. The history of the woodcuts in this devotional volume attracted his particular attention. As the Enschedé catalogue pointed out, they had previously been used by Gerard Leeu at Gouda in the early 1480s. They had been much used by others as well, moving as was common from printer to printer. He discussed the volume in correspondence with J.W. Holtrop of the Royal Library at The Hague, and he worked through it annotating as he went, numbering all the 66 distinct woodcuts (repeated to make a total of 94) and noting some of the textual variations. He did not hesitate to write on a fifteenth-century book if that was the most efficient way of recording information.

Bradshaw never followed up his interest in the migrations of woodcuts among Low Countries printers. Instead, in 1879 he handed the task to a young member of Trinity College, W.M. Conway, training this ready pupil in a few weeks and then sending him on tours of libraries in Britain and abroad: many of Conway's expenses were paid by Bradshaw himself. Within the astonishing space of five years, and guided by Bradshaw, Conway had written and seen published his survey, *The woodcutters of the Netherlands in the fifteenth century* (Cambridge, 1884), a book that remained standard until the appearance of Ina Kok's *Woodcuts in incunabula printed in the Low Countries* in 2013.

David McKitterick *is Librarian and Vice-Master of Trinity College, Cambridge.*

2

1497

PICTURED:

'The Book Fool'.

A visual feast of fools

Sebastian Brant (1458–1521)
Das Narrenschiff* [Latin] *(Stultifera navis)
Basel: Johann Bergmann, de Olpe, 1 August 1497
SSS.15.12

The *Ship of fools* is one of the most influential moral satires ever written. It was composed in German by Sebastian Brant, then a professor of law at Basel University and prolific author of poetry. First published for the carnival period in February 1494, the plot revolves around 109 fools who board a ship to travel to the land of fools, Narragonia. Each of them is introduced through his or her particular obsession or moral failing. We famously find the bespectacled doctor with donkey-ears who collects books he never reads and dusts them with feathers, fearing that too much studying creates confusing fantasies. There are fools who worry too much, others who constantly wish for too much, gothic men of fashion with their long curly hair and pointed shoes, and many others who over-invest in love, eating, the pursuit of wealth and other selfish, un-Christian behaviour.

The whole book is an ode to true wisdom, and Brant states his humanist aim in the first line: to cultivate 'wisdom, reason and good manners' not just among the elites but in everyone. Brant therefore wrote in the vernacular, and his Basel printer engaged a pioneering art team to design an unprecedented number of fine woodcuts to illustrate each fool. The young Albrecht Dürer was among the artists who skilfully drew their interpretation of the fools onto the wooden blocks with ink. They were then cut by specialized craftsmen, the block-cutters. In 1497, Brant's disciple Jacob Locher, a crowned poet laureate, adapted the verse in Latin and added a preface on the classical tradition of moral guidance.

The *Stultifera navis* sailed as one of the first international bestsellers into the early modern world and was soon translated into English, French and Dutch. Its pioneering combination of mottoes, verses and many dynamic, densely contextual images, rooted in recognizable references from everyday life, made it accessible even to those with few literary skills. The Cambridge edition shows what beauty and appeal was achieved by the most ambitious among the first printed books. The typeface is stunningly clear, and the whole look of the book is deeply alluring. This publisher wanted to do something new, combining images with a theme which touched the core of people's lives. Brant held up a mirror to each person to guide him or her poetically into piety and peace.

Ulinka Rublack *is Professor of Early Modern European History at the University of Cambridge, and author of* Dressing up: Cultural identity in Renaissance Europe *(2010).*

De inutilibus libris.

Inter precipuos pars est mihi reddita stultos
Prima: rego docili vastaque vela manu.
En ego possideo multos/quos raro libellos
Perlego: tum lectos negligo: nec sapio:

Inutilitas librorum.

Quod si quis percurrere omnes scriptores cupiat: opprimetur tum librorum multitudine tum diuersa scribentium varietate: vt haud facile verum possit elicere. Distrahit enim librorum multitudo Et faciendi libros plures non est finis.

Primus in excelsa teneo quod naue rudentes
Stultiuagosque sequor comites per flumina vasta:
Non ratione vacat certa: sensuque latenti:
Congestis etenim stultus confido libellis

Diodorus Siculus .li.i.
Ecclesi. xii.

1499

PICTURED:

1–6. A selection of the wonders of the world.

'With many and strange marvels therein' – A well-travelled copy of Mandeville's *Travels*

***Itinerarius* [English]**
Westminster: Wynkyn de Worde, 1499
Inc.5.J.1.2[3556]

The text of Mandeville's *Travels* first circulated in Anglo-Norman French in the 1360s. Immediately popular, it was rapidly translated and propagated across Europe, aided by the arrival of the new technology of print. By 1499, when this pocket edition was printed in London by the émigré printer Wynkyn de Worde, Caxton's successor, the *Travels* was firmly established as one of the most popular pieces of imaginative literature of the medieval period. Irrespective of the fact that its true authorship is still contested, that it plagiarizes numerous earlier sources, that much of its content is utterly spurious and that its author almost certainly never visited any of the places he describes, the *Travels* remains one of the most exotic and exciting travel narratives ever produced.

Mandeville charts the various routes from Europe to the Holy Land and beyond, describing *en route* all he deems extraordinary, monstrous, exotic or bizarre. We learn of natural wonders: ants which make anthills of gold dust, the fountain of youth and valleys of devils. Mandeville's world is populated with cyclopean giants, sustained solely on a diet of raw meat and fish, and pygmies with mouths so small that they have to suck their food through reeds. He describes a land where women dwell entirely without the company of men, a race of fearsome dog-headed cannibals, flat-faced people without noses or mouths, hermaphrodites, headless men with faces in their chests, men with ears hanging to their knees and a race blessed with a single foot so huge it can shield them from the sun.

The Cambridge copy is typical of surviving examples of this popular and enduring text; it has seen heavy use over the centuries and suffered accordingly. It passed through the hands of a succession of English owners in the fifteenth and sixteenth centuries, Walter Bucknell, George English, John Strants, John Sryppe, men who marked the book with their names, but about whom we know nothing more. In the eighteenth century it was acquired by John Watson (1725–1783), the Yorkshire antiquarian, who painstakingly transcribed several leaves by then missing and had the book rebound. From Watson it went first to John Chadwick (1720–1800) of Healey Hall, thence to his son, Charles Chadwick (1753–1829). At some point in the mid-nineteenth century it was snapped up by Cambridge's great benefactor Samuel Sandars, who gifted it to the Library in 1881.

Anne Jarvis *is University Librarian, at the University of Cambridge.*

1

2

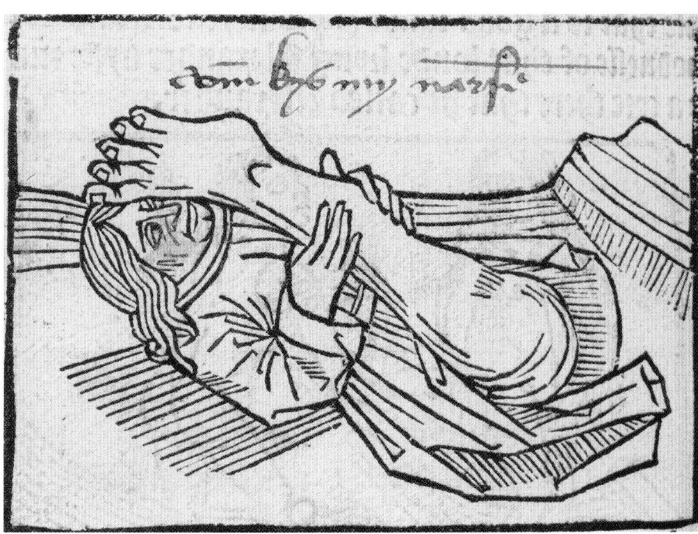
3

4

5

wyues as he wyll a thouſande ⁊ mo/⁊ lyeth neuer
by one of theym but ones. And yͤ londe hath a mer
uayle yͭ is in no other londe. For all maner fyſſhes
of thee cometh there ones a yere one after other ⁊
lyeth theym nere the londe/ſomtyme on yͤ londe ⁊
ſo lye thre dayes ⁊ men of yͤ londe come thyd͛ ⁊ ta
ke of theym what he wyll/⁊ than go thoſe fyſſhes
awaye ⁊ an other maner cometh ⁊ lyeth alſo thre
dayes ⁊ men take of theỹ/⁊ thus do all maner fyſ
ſhes tyll al haue be there ⁊ men haue taken what
they wyll. And men wote not the cauſe why it is.
But they of that coũtree ſaye / that thoſe fyſſhes
come ſo thyder to doo worſhyp to theyr kyng for
they ſaye he is the mooſt worthyeſt kyng of the
worlde/for he hath ſo many wyues and geteth ſo
many childern of theym.

6

And that same kynge hath .xiiij.M. olyfauntes or moo whiche be all tame & they be all fedde of the men of his coũtree for his pleasure by cause ꝥ he may haue theym redy to his honde whan he hath ony warre ayenst ony other kynges or prynces/& than he doth put vpon theyr backes castels & men of warre as the vse is of ꝥ londe / & lyke wyse do other kynges & prynces there about.

¶Of the ylonde called Raso where men be hanged as they are syke. ca.lix.

And fro this yle men go vnto an other yle that men calle Raso / and men of this yle whan that theyr frendes are syke and that they byleue surely that they shall deye/they take theym

PICTURED:

1. and 4. A foetus drawn next to the description of hellebore, which induces abortion.
2. Thomas Lorkyn's distinctive cipher.
3. and 5. Annotations by successive owners, probably Cambridge students of medicine.

Keeping the names of medicines straight

Matteo Silvatico (died about 1342)
Liber pandectarum medicinae
Venice: Bernardinus Stagninus, de Tridino, 27 March 1499
Inc.3.B.3.68[1602]

Learned medicine was mostly written in Latin, but readers of medical books had to cope with an extraordinary variety of technical terms, many originating in other languages. There were Greek, Arabic, Hebrew or Syriac words, transliterated into Latin, and many of these words might refer to the same thing. Working out what a particular medical author meant was vital, especially when it came to prescribing medicines. No surprise then that one of the most valuable books a doctor could own was an alphabetical dictionary of these terms in Latin. The thirteenth-century physician Matteo Silvatico from Mantua was the author of a standard medical dictionary of this kind, the *Opus pandectarum* (literally 'A work of universal knowledge'). His work was incorporated with the *Synonyma medicinae* of Simon of Genoa, physician to Pope Nicholas IV, at the end of the fourteenth century.

This copy of the *Opus pandectarum* was owned by Thomas Lorkyn, the fourth Regius Professor of Physic at the University of Cambridge. When he died in 1591 he bequeathed his extensive medical library to the University with the intention that it should be used by medical teachers and students. The book has his distinctive monogram in it, but before Lorkyn it had at least two previous owners. One was John Holand, who recorded his ownership in 1523, and the other Thomas Southake, Junior, who bought the book in 1534. These two men, otherwise unknown to us, added a remarkable number of notes and drawings to the book. It is quite likely that they too were Cambridge students of medicine.

Most of their notes tell us how to interpret terms in the dictionary. Opposite the entry for *Semissen* (sesame) there is a drawing of the plant, and a note that it grows among grain in England, where the local name for it is 'drawk' (drake). A separate note says in Latin, 'I think this is called darnel.' In fact these two weeds, drake and darnel, are not the same, showing the difficulties doctors had in deciding what was meant by an obscure Latin term. Not all the drawings are of plants or *materia medica*. At two points in the text we find pictures in the margin of a foetus in the womb, in both cases where the text refers to abortifacients – *Abel*, Savin juniper, and *Elleborus*, hellebore.

Peter Murray Jones *is Fellow and Librarian at King's College, Cambridge, and lectures in the Department of History and Philosophy of Science.*

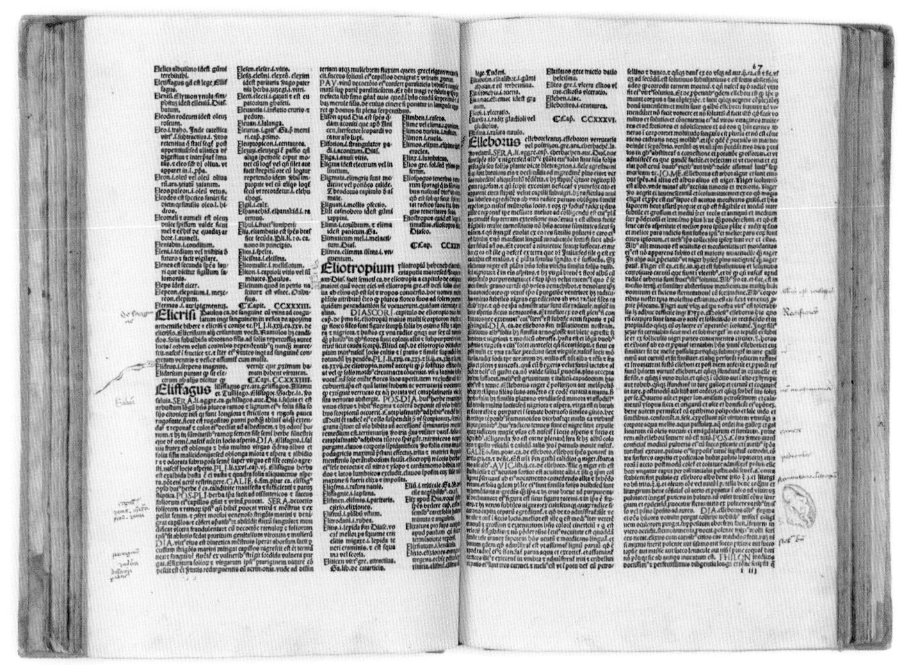

1

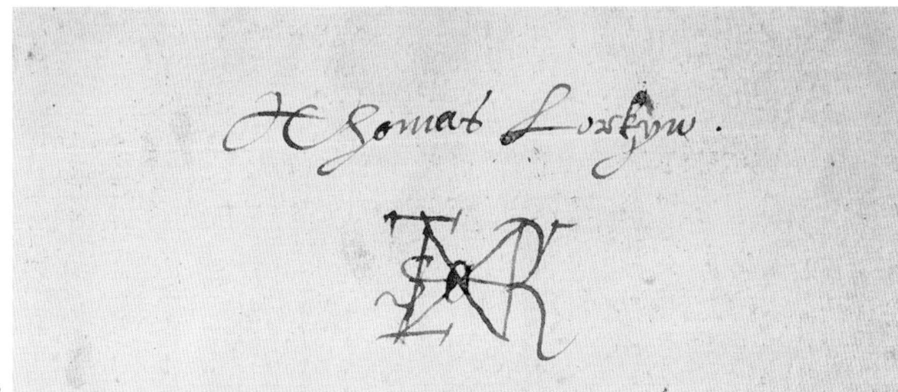

2

a b c d e f g h i k l m n o p q r s t.
Oēs sunt quaterni ꝑter t qui ē qnternꝰ.

Per Bernardinū stagnin de
Tridino mōtisferrati. M.
cccc.lxxxxix. Die ve
ro.xxvij. Marcij
Venetijs.

3

4

5

PICTURED:

1. An unhappy reader's annotation questioning the rendering of stanza 166.
2. The striking title page.

Marking up books in the seventeenth century

Juan de Mena (1411–1456)
Las trescientas sive el labirintho con la glosa de Hernan Nuñez de Toledo
Seville: Compañeros alemanes, Johannes Pegnitzer, Magnus [Herbst], Thomas [Glockner], 28 August 1499
Inc.3.H.4.3b[4208]

Hand-written annotations in books offer an invaluable insight into the personality of their owners. Underlined passages and comments in the margins are also a reminder that books are objects that can travel through time, passing from one hand to another. This edition of Juan de Mena's *Laberinto de fortuna*, also known as *Las trescientas* and composed around 1444, is the first that includes the commentary by the humanist Hernán Núñez (1475–1553). The poem was edited collating both printed and manuscript sources. Despite his care, a previous owner of this copy expressed his dissatisfaction with Nuñéz's rendering of stanza 166, an imitation of Book V of the *Aeneid*. On folio 127 verso the unhappy reader corrected two lines, adding,

> This couplet has to read as I have currently amended it, because otherwise the author would diverge from Virgil whom he is imitating in this couplet.

The word '*rostro*' (face) is changed into '*resto*' (remains), and '*llevó de Messano*' (brought from Messina) into '*loó de más sano*' (was praised as the wisest). These corrections are accurate and have been integrated into later editions. The reader had obviously compared this volume with another, perhaps a second edition of Núñez's commentary (1505), where he also introduced these two amendments. The reason behind these changes was the identification of what he believed to be Mena's Virgilian source for '*resto troyano*', '*reliquias Danaum*' (I. 30) – although this is actually '*reliquias Troiae*' (V. 787). These are the same criteria followed by the owner of this copy.

We do not know who this reader was. There are many annotations from different hands in this volume of Mena, ranging from the sixteenth to the eighteenth centuries. There is a hand-written note at the start of the book bearing the date 1626, which could be in the hand of our reader, a hand which can be dated to the seventeenth century.

What we do know is that the annotator was a conscientious humanist who took the business of reading *Laberinto* very seriously. The annotations also confirm the reputation that Mena still enjoyed two centuries after his poem was first published. Both the owner of this copy and Hernán Núñez recognize the author's erudition and his indebtedness to classical models. This volume is thus both an archive and an intellectual playground. The voices of Virgil, Mena, Hernán Núñez and generations of readers can still be heard sharing ideas and occasionally quarrelling over the interpretation of a verse.

Rodrigo Cacho *is a Reader in Spanish Golden Age and Colonial Studies at the University of Cambridge.*

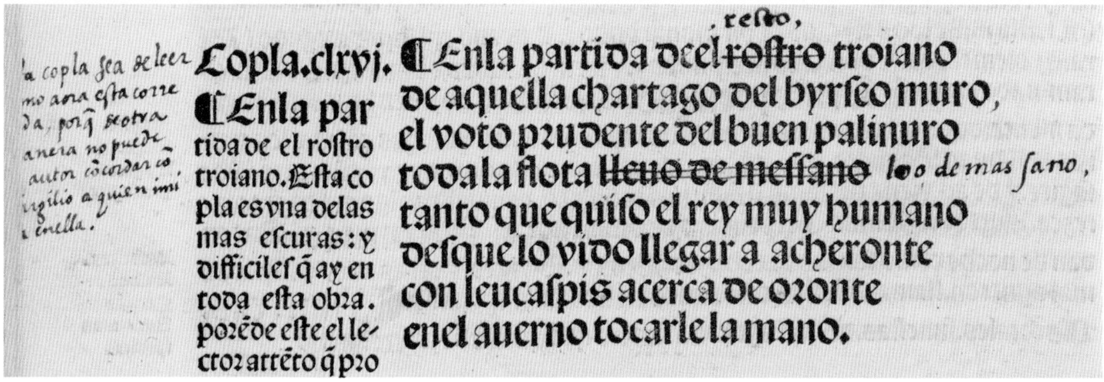
Copla.clxvj.
Enla partida de el rostro troiano. Esta copla es vna delas mas escuras: y difficiles q̃ ay en toda esta obra. porẽde este el lector atẽto q̃ pro

Enla partida del ~~rostro~~ resto troiano
de aquella chartago del byrseo muro,
el voto prudente del buen palinuro
toda la flota ~~lleuo de messano~~ loo de mas sano,
tanto que quiso el rey muy humano
desque lo vido llegar a acheronte
con leucaspis acerca de oronte
enel auerno tocarle la mano.

1

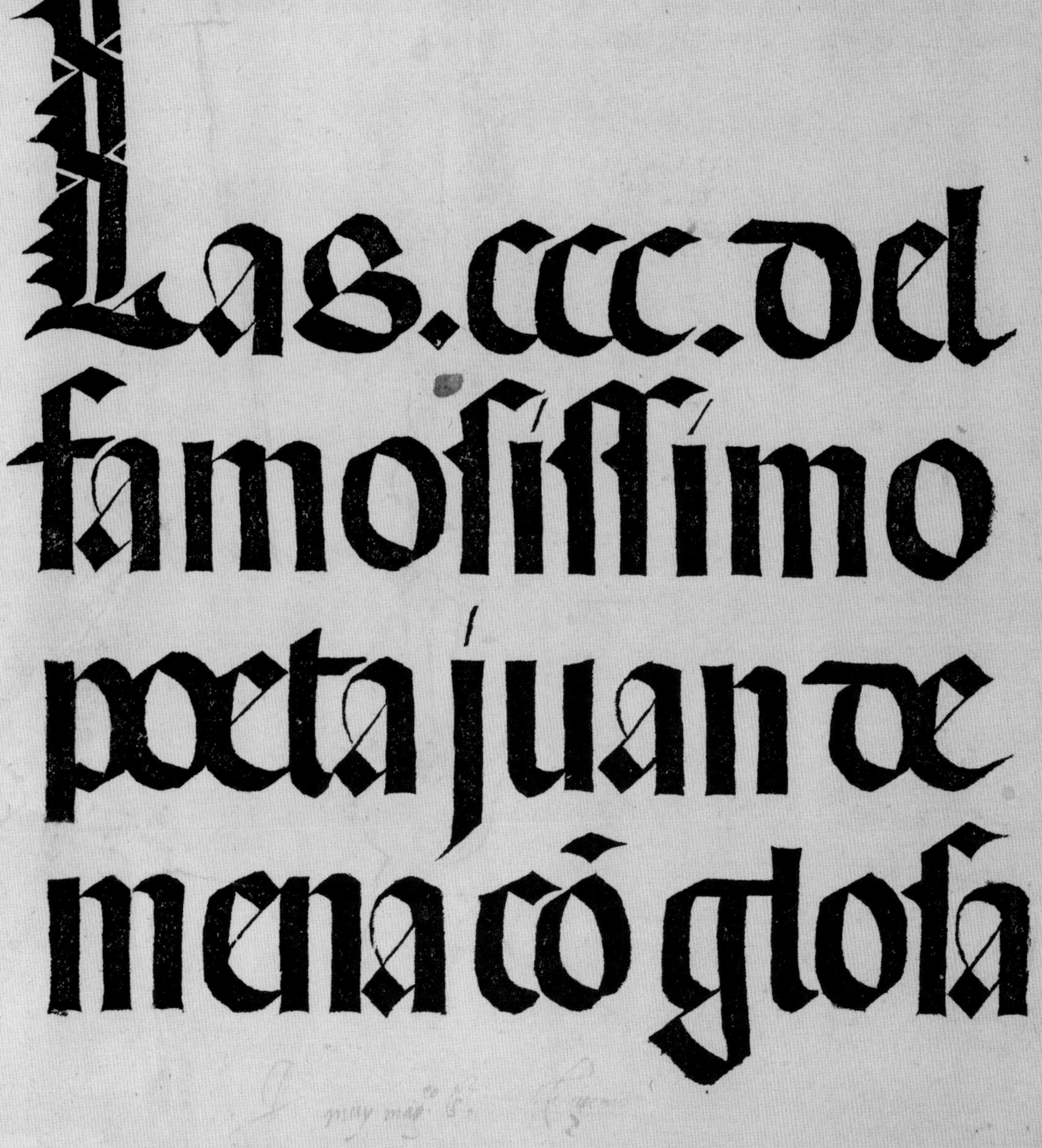

Las .ccc. del famosissimo poeta juan de mena cō glosa

2

1499

PICTURED:

1. and 2. Triumphal processions illustrating the *Hypnerotomachia Poliphili.*

Francesco Colonna (died 1527)
Hypnerotomachia Poliphili
Venice: Aldus Manutius, for Leonardus Crassus, December 1499

Carol Ann Duffy *is the Poet Laureate.*

HYPNEROTOMACHIA POLIPHILI

You swipe the screen and scan
the pages of the *Hypnerotomachia Poliphili,*
a dream within a dream; where, it seems,
even the future has already passed.
It truly is the world's most unreadable text:
'In this horrid and cuspidinous littoral
and most miserable site of the algent, fetorific lake
stood saevious Tisiphone, efferal and cruel,
with her viperine capillament...'

And yet,
that evening in the emptying Library, the human chain,
from Venice 1499 to here and now, joined
warm and open palms to yours, a living link
around the precious charm of a book.
Woodcutter to printer; ink's solemn vow to page;
word and image in their beautiful Renaissance dance.

How we know what we love-
what we make, or hold,
or pass on with
our hands.

**
*

EL TERTIO cæleste triumpho seguiua cum quatro uertibile rote di Chrysolitho æthiopico scintule doro flammigiante, Traiecta per el quale la seta del Asello gli maligni dæmonii fuga, Alla leua mano grato, cum tutto quello cħ di sopra di rote e dicto. Daposcia le assule sue in ambito per el modo compacte sopra narrato, erano di uirente Helitropia Cyprico, cum potere negli lumi cælesti, el suo gestāte çcela, & il diuinare dona, di sanguinee guttule punctulato.

Offeriua tale historiato insculpto la tabella dextra. Vno homo di regia maiestate īsigne, Oraua in uno sacro templo el diuo simulacro, quello che della formosissima fiola deueua seguire. Sentendo el patre la eiectione sua per ella del regno. Et ne per alcuno fusse pregna, Fece una munita structura di una excelsa torre, Et in quella cum solēne custodia la fece inclaustrare. Nella quale ella cessabonda assedēdo, cum excessiuo solatio, nel uirgineo sino gutte doro stillare uedeua.

*

tante nymphe hymni & cantici, & cum dulciſſimi moduli pſallẽte ꝑ tut
to adſonauano, cum cæleſte plauſo lætiſſimamente feſtigianti cum hila-
re cerimonie & cum delicato & uirginale tripudio ardeliamente, & alcune cum ſaltatione pyrrhica, & altiſone laude extollendo la diuina genitri
ce & il potente filiolo, cum feſtiui ſpectaculi cum maximo triumpho, &
ſuperba pompa paulatinamente pueniſſimo ad uno proſcenio, oue era
una conſpicua, & faberrima, & ſcitiſſima porta hiante, di materia, & di o-
peratura di uno mirabiliſſimo amphitheatro ſublime inſtructo di fabrica, pleno di artificio di ornamenti & arte non uiſo mai tale, Ne in Atella
ne in qualũque altro famoſo loco exquiſitiſſimamente fabrefacto & ꝑfe-
ctamente abſoluto di lunga narratione explicabile, & quaſi non cogitabi
le. Quale dire ſi potrebbe non humana, ma piu p̃ſto diuina operatione,
& oſtentamento maximo di ſtructura.

GIVNTI dunque cum ſolẽniſſimo gaudio, & incredibile lætitia, &
ſolatioſo dilecto per la triumphale uia cum diſtributa aſpergine indi &
quindi per alcune ſtrictiſſime auree fiſtulete, irrorante di odoratiſſime
aquule gli proceſſionarii, & tutta la triumphatrice turma roſidulamente
ꝑfuſa alla porta di lingreſſo, mirai che lera ſtupendo artificio. Laquale
conſtructa era di orientale litharmeno, nelquale infinite ſcintule, quale
ſcope diſperſe ſe cerniuano di fulgurãte oro. Et di queſto puro metallo e-
rano

2

rano dille exacte colũne le baſe,gli capituli. Il trabe . zophoro , coroni-ce, & faſtigio limine & ante, & omni altro opamento dilla recenſita materia uedeuaſe,renuẽte il duro & tenace chalybe & aſpernabile la toreumata antiquariamente uariata,gratioſo elegante & ſpectatiſſimo expreſſo , & ſtructura oltra modo magnifica. Laquale io penſo da gli terriculi nõ factibile,cũ ſummo ĩpendio & longanimitate,graue & diutia faticha,& cum nõ mediocre ingegnio,cura & induſtria,& diligentia , che ad tale oſtento fuſſe abſoluta & adfabrefacta era nella cluſura di tutto larco di ophitea petra,& le collaterale colũne ambe prophyrice. Poſcia laltre uariando, & ophitea una,& laltra ꝑphyrica. Le mediane ſupaſtante alle porphyrite,ãbe ophite,& le ſupernate quadrãgule mediane di porphyrite,& poſcia contrariãdo luna allaltra,& cuſi ꝑ il contrario mutamine erano capituli baſe & arule.

Dinanti laquale uno per lato,era uno ꝑtioſiſſimo uaſo,uno di ſaphyro,laltro di ſmaragdo,di maximo & obſtinato artificio faberrimamente dædale facti .Penſai degli uaſi allingreſſo dil tẽplo di Ioue in Athene collocati.

A queſta deſcripta porta mirabile dil triũphale & uolucre uehiculo il ſignore Arquite diſceſe. Lo ãphitheatro era di ĩcredibile inuiſitata & ĩaudita ſtructura. Impoche il pedamẽto elegante,& gli emuſicati concincti ,

PICTURED:

1. The Virgin's joy at Christ's birth.
2. The Mass of St Gregory.
3. St Jerome removing a thorn from the lion's foot.
4. A sorrowful pietà.
5. The opening woodcut of Mary, her crown pointed with red dots, suggesting a crown of roses.

Weaving a crown for the Virgin

Fraternitas rosaceae coronae ad honorem beatissimae Virginis Mariae
[Cologne: Johann Landen, about 1500]
Inc.5.A.4.30[736]

From obscure origins, rosary devotions swiftly rose to prominence in late fifteenth-century Europe. The rosary, a set of Hail Marys interspersed with Our Fathers and meditations on the lives of Mary and Jesus, received its name from the belief that each *Ave Maria* was a rose woven into a crown for Mary. Central to the devotion were rosary confraternities, the most famous founded at Cologne in 1475. As well as playing other important social roles, confraternities existed to help living and deceased members reduce their time in purgatory. The Cologne confraternity was sponsored by the Dominicans, popes, and Emperor Frederic III, and within seven years claimed 100,000 members. The confraternity was open to members across social boundaries, and the advent of print also facilitated the swift circulation of the rosary across Europe. In turn, rosary devotions, amenable to popular, short, and inexpensive publications, contributed to the success and innovation of printing.

The *Liber fraternitatis rosaceae coronae* ('Book of the Rosary Brotherhood'), probably written by a Cologne Dominican, is a short text publicizing and justifying the confraternity. It opens with Mary as Queen of Heaven, accompanied by the text 'it is impossible for a man to be damned, if Mary, the mother of grace, defends him'. Mary's crown has been pointed with red dots, suggesting a crown of roses. Blocks of mismatched border decoration surround the image, showing the pragmatic reuse of these blocks in early printing and their inspiration by manuscript decoration.

The *Liber* is divided into two books. The first outlines the purposes, origins and benefits of the devotion, concluding with the popular prayer *Ave rosa sine spinis* ('Hail rose without thorns'). Book Two commences with Marian miracles: a detractor of the confraternity dies suddenly, likened to those who dared touch the Ark of the Covenant with unclean hands. Mary, the new ark of Christ, likewise permits no reproach. Less threatening examples are the Virgin's liberation of demoniacs and resuscitation of the drowned. The book closes with two 'decades' of the rosary – meditations on Mary's life and Christ's passion which accompanied sets of ten Hail Marys – and four woodcuts: the Virgin's joy at Christ's birth; the miraculous Mass of St Gregory; St Jerome removing a thorn from a lion's foot and a sorrowful pietà. Through these images, a reader might meditate on the incarnation, crucifixion, and redemption while praying the rosary, hailing Mary as the 'rose without thorns'.

Miri Rubin *is Professor of Medieval and Early Modern History at Queen Mary University of London, and co-wrote this article with Dr Matthew Champion, who is Research Fellow at St Catharine's College, Cambridge.*

1

2

3

4

Incipit liber fraternitatis ro sacee corone ad honorem bea-tissime v̄ginis marie ⁊ ad salutē hoim editus ꝯtinens in se maximas vtilitates quā fraternitatē quicūqꝫ deuote seruauerit. impossibile est illum damnari quia maria mater gratie eum defendet.

1500

PICTURED:

1. Petrus de Montagnana in his study.
2. Urine consultation and the flask wheel.

A doctor's handbook for daily consultation

Johannes de Ketham (active 15th century)
Fasciculus medicinae
Venice: Johannes and Gregorius de Gregoriis, de Forlivio, 28 March 1500
Inc.3.B.3.45[1519]

The first printed edition of the *Fasciculus medicinae*, an edited compilation of short medical treatises drawn from a variety of authors, appeared in 1491, but this succinct, practical handbook, intended for daily consultation by doctors, surgeons and apothecaries, had been circulating widely in manuscript since the early 1400s. The printed edition followed the manuscript tradition by using illustrations on a grand scale, filling the whole page and giving a level of detail invaluable for medical practitioners. Previous printed works, such as blood-letting almanacs, were more sparsely illustrated, and the 1491 first edition of the *Fasciculus* was ground-breaking in the scale of its printed imagery.

It was published in Venice by the enterprising de'Gregori brothers. Recognizing that the large number of manuscript medical texts in circulation equated to a ready market for printed equivalents, they moved from producing legal works into the field of medical printing in 1489, and printed at least five editions of the *Fasciculus* between 1491 and 1501. The second edition of 1493/4 was in a smaller format, but introduced a remarkable new suite of images which were used in all subsequent editions including the one illustrated here.

The illustrations remain powerfully evocative, including the dissection of a cadaver, and a visit to a plague patient. Alongside these are depicted practical images familiar from the *Fasciculus*'s manuscript sources, and in daily use since medieval times: modern medics would recognize the importance of the analysis of urine, for example, depicted in the circle of flasks, though diagnosis is nowadays based on more than merely colour. Other figures, with annotations explaining the significance of various details, included the vein man, the wound man and the disease man, surrounded by an alphabetical list of potential complaints. The female figure is described as a pregnant woman, though the tiny foetus illustrated in the first edition is no longer present in the woodcut used for subsequent editions.

By the early seventeenth century this book was out of medical hands, belonging to the family of the collector Thomas Knyvett. A seventeenth-century hand, perhaps one of his descendants, has heavily annotated the chapter of the text on fertility and pregnancy, as well as some of the treatments for wounds, suggesting that the work was not merely owned, but closely read and used by lay readers for centuries after the medieval texts were first composed.

Leszek Borysiewicz *is Vice-Chancellor of the University of Cambridge, and was knighted in 2001 for services to medical education and research.*

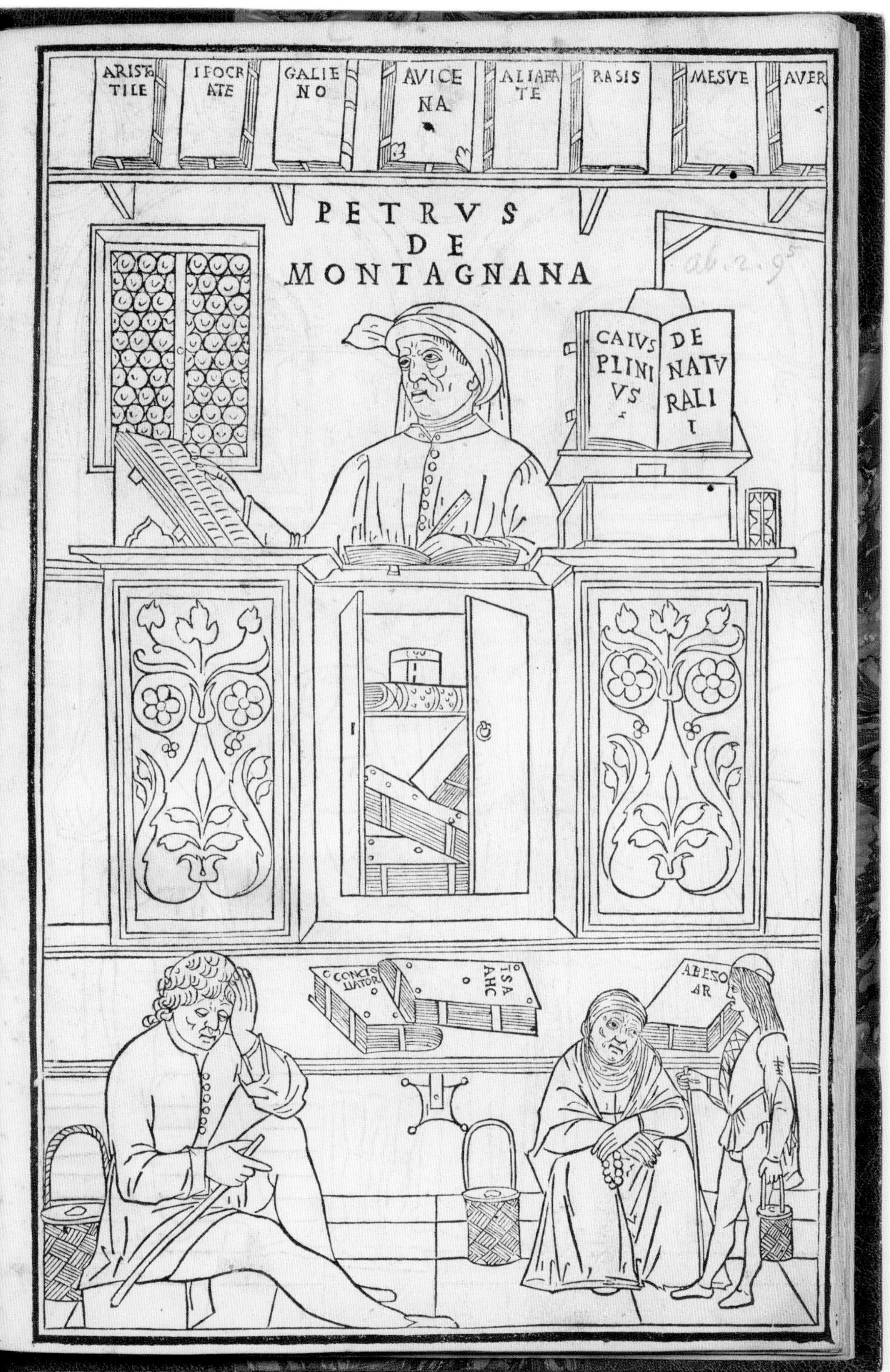

ARISTO TILE
IPOCR ATE
GALIE NO
AVICE NA
ALIABA TE
RASIS
MESVE
AVER
PETRVS DE MONTAGNANA
CAIVS PLINIVS
DE NATVRALI
CONCILIATOR
ISAAHC
ABEZOAR

1

2

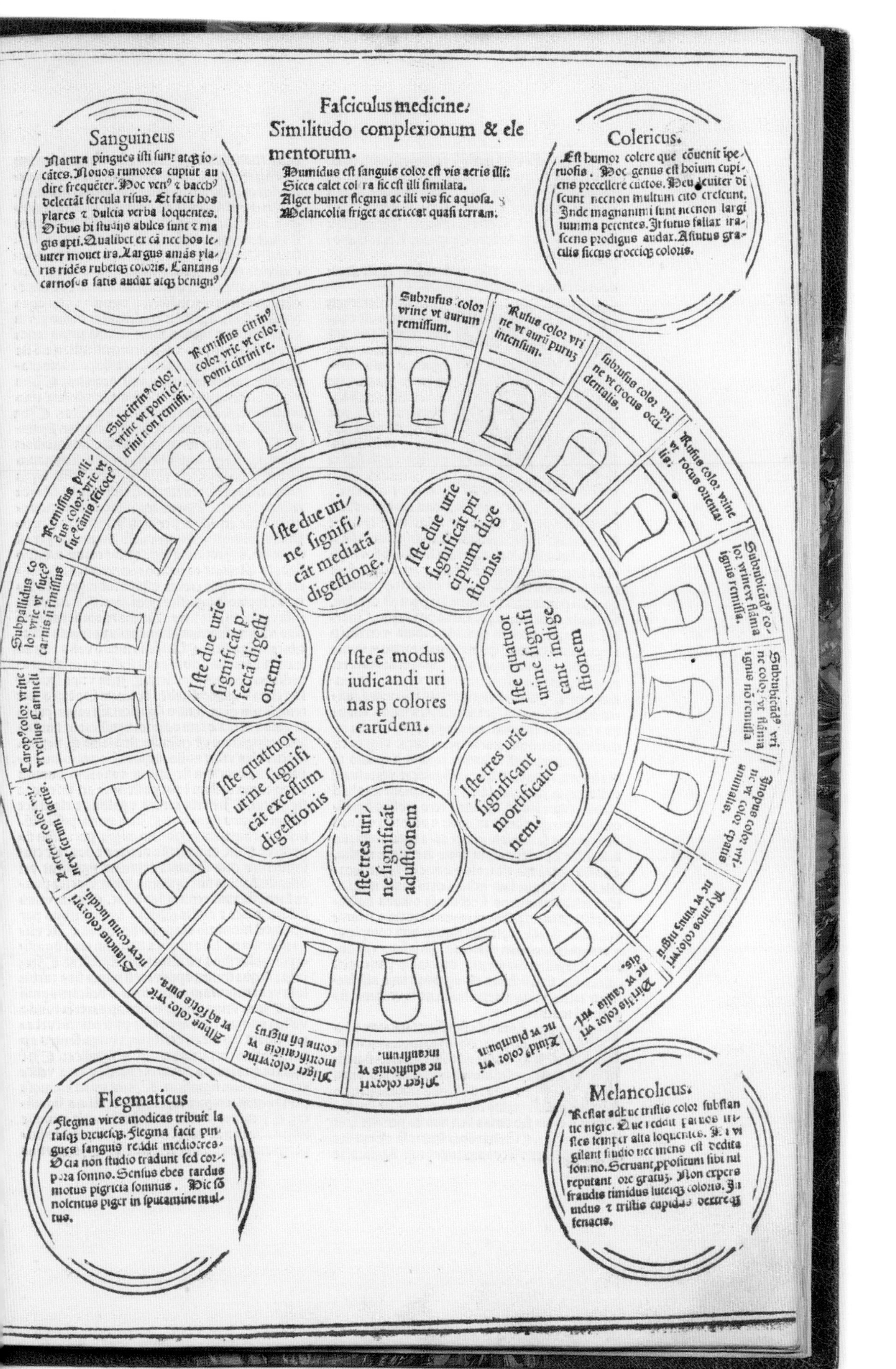

Fasciculus medicine.

Similitudo complexionum & elementorum.

Humidus est sanguis color est vis aeris illi:
Sicca calet col ra sic est illi similata.
Alget humet flegma ac illi vis sic aquosa.
Melancolia friget ac exiccat quasi terram.

Sanguineus

Natura pingues isti sunt atqz iocātes. Nouos rumores cupiūt audire frequēter. Hoc ven⁹ ꝛ bacch⁹ delectāt fercula risus. Et facit hos ylares ꝛ dulcia verba loquentes. Omibus hi studijs abiles sunt ꝛ magis apti. Qualibet ex cā nec hos leuiter mouet ira. Largus amās ylaris ridēs rubeiqz coloris. Cantans carnosus satis audax atqz benign⁹

Colericus.

Est humor colere que cōuenit ipetuosis. Hoc genus est hoium cupiens precellere cūctos. Hii leuiter discunt necnon multum cito crescunt. Inde magnanimi sunt necnon largi summa petentes. Irsutus fallax irascens prodigus audax. Astutus gracilis siccus croceiqz coloris.

Subrufus color vrine vt aurum remissum.

Rufus color vrine vt aurū purū intensum.

Subrufus color vrine vt crocus occidentalis.

Rufus color vrine vt crocus orientalis.

Subrubicūd⁹ color vrine vt flamma ignis remissa.

Subrubicūd⁹ vrine color vt flāma ignis nō remissa.

Inopus color vrine vt color epatis animalis.

Kyanos color vrine vt vinū nigrū.

Viridis color vrine vt caulis viridis.

Liuid⁹ color vrine vt plumbum.

Niger color vrine vt adustionis incaustum.

Niger color vrine mortificationis vt cornu hō nigrū.

Albus color vrine vt aq̄ fōtis pura.

Glaucus color vrine vt cornu lucidū.

Lacteus color vrine vt serum lactis.

Carop⁹ color vrine vt vellus Carmeli.

Subpallidus color vrine vt succ⁹ carnis n̄ remissus.

Remissus pallidus color vrine vt succ⁹ carnis decocte.

Subcitrin⁹ color vrine vt pomi citrini non remissi.

Remissus citrin⁹ color vrine vt color pomi citrini re.

Iste due urine significāt principium digestionis.

Iste quatuor urine significant indigestionem

Iste tres urie significant mortificationem.

Iste tres urine significāt adustionem

Iste quattuor urine significāt excessum digestionis

Iste due urie significāt pfectā digestionem.

Iste due urine significāt mediatā digestionē.

Iste ē modus iudicandi urinas p colores earūdem.

Flegmaticus

Flegma vires modicas tribuit latasqz breuesqz. Flegma facit pingues sanguis reddit mediocres. Ocia non studio tradunt sed corpora somno. Sensus ebes tardus motus pigricia somnus. Hic sō nolentus piger in sputamine multus.

Melancolicus.

Restat adhuc tristis color substantie nigre. Que reddit prauos tristes semper alta loquentes. Hi vigilant studio nec mens est dedita somno. Seruant ppositum sibi nil reputant ore gratum. Non expers fraudis timidus luteiqz coloris. Inuidus ꝛ tristis cupidus dextreqz tenacis.

The Dragon and the Beast of the Sea, from the *Blockbook Apocalypse*, Edition VI [Germany, about 1470, impression about 1478–1480]; Inc.3[4245].

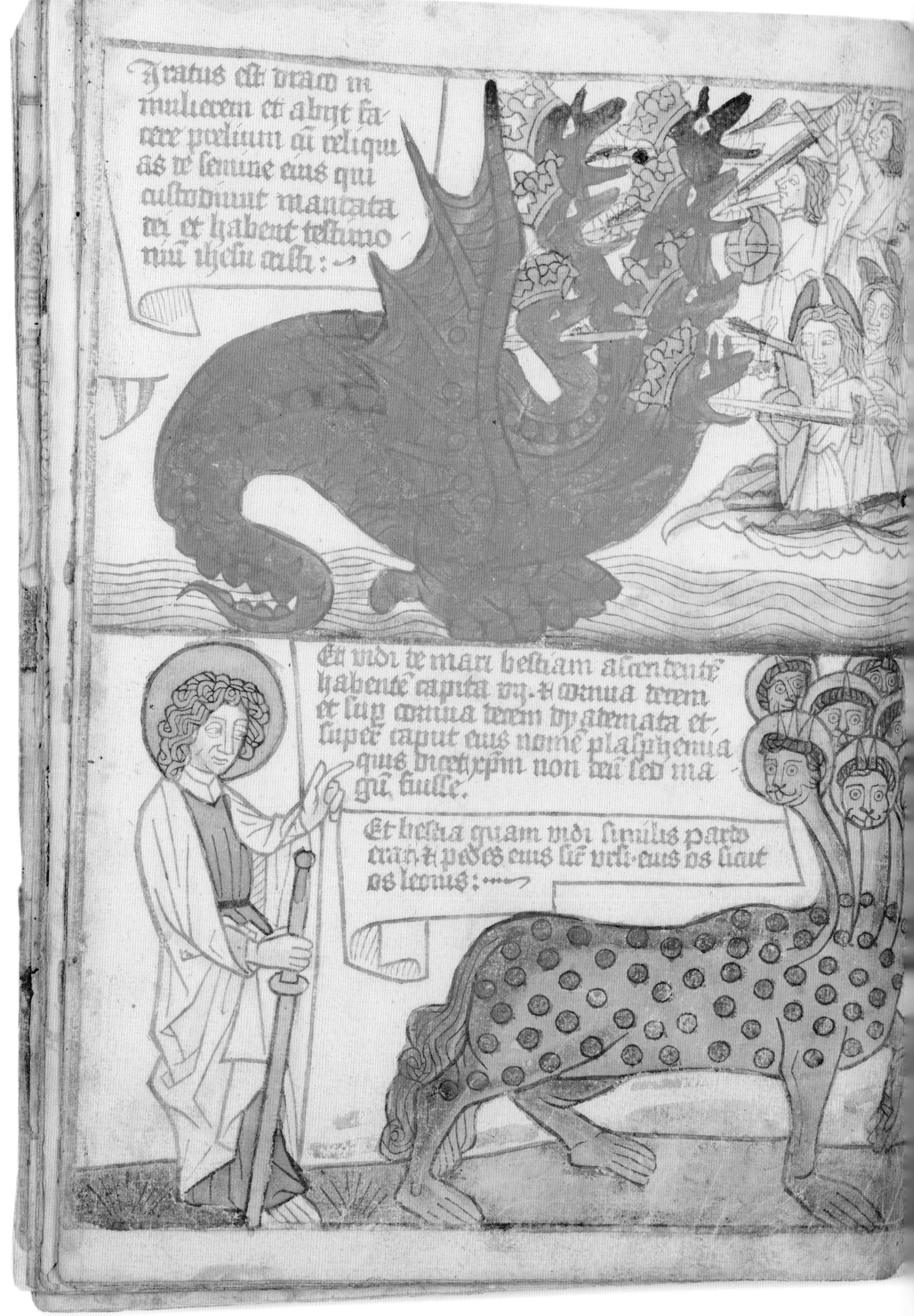

Concordance

Page	Classmark	Oates	ISTC	Page height
2	Inc.1.A.1.1[3671]	14	ib00526000	391/415 mm.
2	Inc.1.A.2.3[84]	110	ib00533000	395/397 mm.
6	Inc.0.A.1.2[6]	18	ic00699680	342x255 mm.
8	Inc.3.B.1.1[1122]	1356	il00001000	283 mm.
12	Inc.3.A.1.3b[13]	29	id00318500	205 mm.
14	Inc.1.B.3.1b[1330.1-2]	1608	il00238000	390 mm.
18	Inc.2.B.2.39[1320]	1600	ib00701000	338 mm.
22	Inc.2.B.3.3[1366]	1648	ic00542000	337 mm.
24	SSS.15.5	1647	id00204000	205 mm.
28	Inc.2.B.19.1[2158]	2593	iv00088000	333 mm.
32	Inc.2.A.6.2[777]	893	ic00237000	312 mm.
34	Inc.3.B.4.1[3782]	2235	id00022000	276 mm.
38	Inc.3.H.2.2[3472-3]	4039	ia00984000	298 mm.
40	Inc.3.F.3.2[3308]	3839	ic00413000	269 mm.
42	Inc.4.F.2.3[4152](1)	787	ic00740000	209 mm.
42	Inc.4.F.2.3[4152](2)	3792	ia01014450	209 mm.
44	Inc.5.B.21.1[4236]	2611	ip00676000	205 mm.
46	Inc.1.A.2.5[104]	132	ia01342000	389 mm.
46	Inc.2.A.2.15[181]	222	ij00477000	348 mm.
46	Inc.5.A.4.2[359]	432	it00313800	202 mm.
46	Inc.4.A.4.2[367]	442	ih00193500	188 mm.
46	Inc.5.A.4.2[387]	460	il00341000	205 mm.
46	Inc.3.A.4.26[721]	526	ic01018000	285 mm.
46	Inc.5.A.13.1[1011]	567	it00291000	203 mm.
46	Inc.2.A.4.15[574]	659	ib00539000	299 mm.
46	Inc.3.A.4.15[588]	673	ih00315000	282 mm.
46	Inc.3.A.4.17[611]	700	in00175000	285 mm.
46	Inc.3.E.4.1[2895]	3424	is00651000	292 mm.
46	Inc.3.E.4.1[2913]	3445	ia00234000	290 mm.
48	Inc.1.B.3.2[1360]	1640	ip00801000	389 mm.
50	Inc.5.J.1.1[3486]	4062	il00406100	205 mm.
50	Inc.5.J.1.1[3488]	4061	il00407100	205mm.
52	Inc.5.A.4.9[514]	596	ib00296700	212 mm.
54	Inc.5.B.3.2[4321]	1643.5	ib00915500	174 mm.
58	Inc.4.B.3.6d[1389]	1672	ij00402000	213 mm.
62	Inc.3[4245]	2	Not in ISTC	284 mm.
66	Inc.4.B.19.2[2161]	2596	ia00148000	217 mm.
70	MS.Add.5944(11)	9	Not in ISTC	118x80 mm.
70	Inc.4.E.1.6[2794]	3319	ig00422000	206 mm.
72	Inc.4.B.3.6d[1391]	1674	ib00566000	237 mm.
74	Inc.3.J.1.1[4434]	4084.5	iv00315000	288 mm.
76	SSS.19.16	3343	ih00429300	154 mm.

Concordance *continued*

Page	Classmark	Oates	ISTC	Page height
80	SSS.40.15	3391	id00159100	285 mm.
84	Inc.3.F.2.2[3178](1)	3707	ih00053000	280 mm.
84	Inc.3.F.2.2[3178](2)	3786	ib01347000	232 mm.
84	Inc.3.F.2.2[3178](3)	3731	il00343500	282 mm.
88	Inc.1.B.8.4[1933]	2334	id00029000	373 mm.
90	Inc.3.J.1.1[3506]	4094	ic00430500	273 mm.
92	Inc.5.A.14.2[1017]	1183	il00201500	195 mm.
94	Inc.3.J.1.1[3517]	4098	ib00902500	277 mm.
96	Inc.3.J.4.1[3636]	4214	ib01030000	285 mm.
100	Inc.4.F.6.2[3367]	3903	ir00136300	201 mm.
102	SSS.2.3	1864	is00005000	416 mm.
106	Inc.5.A.6.18[829]	955	it00361000	212 mm.
110	SSS.3.10-11	3007	ir00346000	374 mm.
114	Inc.5.F.6.3[3409](1)	3948	ij00055000	202 mm.
114	Inc.5.F.6.3[3409](2)	4112	Not in ISTC	140x92 mm.
116	SSS.15.17	3929	is00448600	212 mm.
118	Inc.5.D.1.19[2530]	3011	ih00369170	162 mm.
122	Inc.3.A.1.8[37]	55	ih00486000	292 mm.
126	Inc.4.J.1.2[3570]	4150	ih00420450	190 mm.
130	Inc.3.H.5.3[4138]	4048	ib00923200	271 mm.
132	Inc.4.B.2.27[1283]	1537	iv00124000	224 mm.
132	Inc.4.B.2.27[1283]	1547	iv00127000	224 mm.
136	Inc.0.A.7.2[888]	1026	is00307000	453 mm.
140	Inc.2.A.6.18[837]	964	im00653000	323 mm.
142	Inc.3.J.1.2[3534]	4118	ih00564000	278 mm.
144	Inc.Bdsides.0[4100]	4034	im00875300	430x275 mm.
146	Inc.4.B.3.134[4580]	2167.5	ib00304000	206 mm.
148	Inc.1.A.3.3[4187a]	10	Not in ISTC	262x187 mm.
148	Inc.1.A.3.3[4187b]	277	im00647000	346 mm.
150	Inc.3.J.1.2[3559]	4144	ib00143000	264 mm.
152	Inc.5.E.3.10[2890]	3419	ih00433250	165 mm.
154	SSS.15.12	2853	ib01090000	201 mm.
156	Inc.5.J.1.2[3556]	4140	im00162550	175 mm.
160	Inc.3.B.3.68[1602]	1907	is00518000	312 mm.
162	Inc.3.H.4.3b[4208]	4044	im00486000	278 mm.
164	Inc.3.B.3.134[1830]	2192	ic00767000	304 mm.
168	Inc.5.A.4.30[736]	844	if00306000	195 mm.
170	Inc.3.B.3.45[1519]	1819	ik00015000	311 mm.